Advances in Planetary Science – Vol. 6

CERES

AN ICE-RICH WORLD IN THE INNER SOLAR SYSTEM

Advances in Planetary Science

Print ISSN: 2529-8054
Online ISSN: 2529-8062

Series Editor: Wing-Huen Ip *(National Central University, Taiwan)*

The series on Advances in Planetary Science aims to provide readers with overviews on many exciting developments in planetary research and related studies of exoplanets and their habitability. Besides a running account of the most up-to-date research results, coverage will also be given to descriptions of milestones in space exploration in the recent past by leading experts in the field.

Published

Vol. 6 *Ceres: An Ice-Rich World in the Inner Solar System*
by Jian-Yang Li and Julie C Castillo-Rogez

Vol. 5 *Mars on Earth: A Study of the Qaidam Basin*
edited by Long Xiao

Vol. 4 *Planetary Habitability in Binary Systems*
by Elke Pilat-Lohinger, Siegfried Eggl and Ákos Bazsó

Vol. 3 *Planetary Habitability and Stellar Activity*
by Arnold Hanslmeier

Vol. 2 *Origin and Evolution of Comets: Ten Years after the Nice Model and One Year after Rosetta*
by Hans Rickman

Vol. 1 *Nuclear Planetary Science: Planetary Science Based on Gamma-Ray, Neutron and X-Ray Spectroscopy*
by Nobuyuki Hasebe, Kyeong Ja Kim, Eido Shibamura and Kunitomo Sakurai

Advances in Planetary Science – Vol. 6

CERES

AN ICE-RICH WORLD IN THE INNER SOLAR SYSTEM

Jian-Yang Li

Julie C Castillo-Rogez

JERSEY • LONDON • SINGAPORE • BEIJING • SHANGHAI • HONG KONG • TAIPEI • CHENNAI • TOKYO

Published by

World Scientific Publishing Co. Pte. Ltd.
5 Toh Tuck Link, Singapore 596224
USA office: 27 Warren Street, Suite 401-402, Hackensack, NJ 07601
UK office: 57 Shelton Street, Covent Garden, London WC2H 9HE

Library of Congress Cataloging-in-Publication Data
Names: Li, Jian-Yang, author. | Castillo-Rogez, Julie, author.
Title: Ceres : an ice-rich world in the inner solar system / Jian-Yang Li, Julie C. Castillo-Rogez.
Description: New Jersey : World Scientific, [2022] | Series: Advances in planetary science, 2529-8054 ; Vol. 6 | Includes bibliographical references and index.
Identifiers: LCCN 2021015354 | ISBN 9789811238147 (hardcover) | ISBN 9789811238154 (ebook for institutions) | ISBN 9789811238161 (ebook for individuals)
Subjects: LCSH: Ceres (Dwarf planet)
Classification: LCC QB705 .L55 2022 | DDC 523.44--dc23
LC record available at https://lccn.loc.gov/2021015354

British Library Cataloguing-in-Publication Data
A catalogue record for this book is available from the British Library.

For any available supplementary material, please visit
https://www.worldscientific.com/worldscibooks/10.1142/12310#t=suppl

Desk Editors: Aanand Jayaraman/Amanda Yun

Typeset by Stallion Press
Email: enquiries@stallionpress.com

Preface

Ceres is the first to be discovered and the largest object in the main asteroid belt between the orbits of Mars and Jupiter. It has been full of mysteries since the first day astronomers spotted it in the sky more than two hundred years ago. Although located in the middle of the main asteroid belt (semimajor axis 2.77 au) and orbiting the Sun in a nearly circular orbit (eccentricity 0.076) not far from the ecliptic plane (inclination 10.6°), Ceres contrasts with the main-belt asteroid population in many aspects. Per its large diameter (940 km, about twice the size of the next largest asteroid, 4 Vesta) and its near-hydrostatic shape, Ceres is the only dwarf planet in the inner solar system. Most importantly, Ceres's relatively low density indicates a water mass fraction of ~25%, which is more akin to bodies formed in the outer solar system. It has a remarkably uniform surface in terms of albedo and color, possibly related to some global-scale emplacement processes. Lastly, Ceres shows evidence for an evolved interior with geophysical evidence for layering like a planet, and an aqueously altered surface composition.

In 2001, the National Aeronautics and Space Administration (NASA) selected Dawn, the ninth mission in the agency's Discovery program, for flight. Dawn was launched in 2007 and achieved orbit insertion at Ceres in 2015 after a first rendezvous with asteroid 4 Vesta in 2011–2012. Dawn was the first mission to rendezvous with two large asteroids.

Dawn's three-and-a-half years of intensive investigations revolutionized our understanding of Ceres, revealed its possible origin from the outer solar system, and confirmed its kinship with the outer solar system icy objects with its high content in volatiles and the presence of ammonia and high carbon content. Ceres's surface geology and geomorphology are consistent with a water ice-rich crust similar to the outer solar system icy moons, but with more high-strength components such as salts and clathrate hydrates. Many geomorphologic features are potentially associated with cryovolcanic activity that involves deep brine reservoirs, potentially mobilized via impact-produced heating and fractures. The discovery of hydrated sodium chloride (hydrohalite) in the recent Occator crater suggests ongoing transfer from a deep brine reservoir, likely sourced near the crust-mantle boundary. Altogether, the Dawn data point to Ceres's astrobiological significance and suggest the dwarf planet may be a relict ocean world that once harbored a global ocean in its subsurface, similar to many outer solar system icy moons. Now in an advanced freezing stage, Ceres informs scientists on the long-term evolution of subsurface oceans. More generally, Ceres is the only large, water-rich body that has been characterized with such an extraordinary level of detail. As such, the Dawn results advance the relatively recent field of ocean world science, which likely applies to a large population of bodies in the outer solar system.

This book provides a review of the current state of knowledge about Ceres after the Dawn mission. After a brief introduction about the discovery of Ceres, which led to the discovery of the asteroid belt, in the first chapter, we review our knowledge of Ceres before Dawn's exploration in Chapter 2, and provide an overview of the Dawn mission in Chapter 3. In Chapter 4 through Chapter 8, we discuss the Dawn mission results, organized roughly in the order from the surface to the interior of Ceres, including surface composition, geology, expressions of water ice, interior structure, and recent activity. The astrobiological significance of Ceres is discussed in Chapter 9. The final chapter lays out outstanding questions that drive follow-on research and Earth-based observations and will shape future in situ missions to the dwarf planet.

The analyses and interpretations based on the Dawn mission data produced a large repository of published literature about Ceres. The study of Ceres using the Dawn data and other remote sensing observations, theoretical modeling, and laboratory experiments has been progressing full throttle during the development of this book and will last for many years to come. Although we strived to be as comprehensive as possible in our review, we acknowledge that we could not capture the results from the >200 research articles derived from the Dawn data while aiming at keeping this work accessible to the non-expert. Similarly, our knowledge base of Ceres will keep expanding, and our view of Ceres will likely evolve as new analyses become available. Nonetheless, we hope this book provides readers with a mostly complete snapshot of our current understanding of Ceres and conveys the significant contributions of the Dawn mission to planetary exploration.

Finally, we want to thank Prof. Wing-Huen Ip for his initiative and encouragement for this book, and Dr. Lucy McFadden for her useful feedback and help in copyediting. We are grateful to the entire Dawn mission science and operations teams and everyone who contributed to making the mission a great success.

Drs. Jian-Yang Li and Julie C. Castillo-Rogez
May 2021

About the Authors

Dr. Jian-Yang Li is a research scientist at the Planetary Science Institute, USA. His interest in Ceres started during his Ph.D. research when he produced the then-highest-resolution maps of Ceres from the Hubble Space Telescope images. These maps revealed a remarkably uniform surface and suggested the uniqueness of Ceres among asteroids. After obtaining his Ph.D. in Astronomy from the University of Maryland at College Park, USA, he was involved in the Dawn mission as an affiliate, participating scientist, and co-investigator. He was also involved in a number of small bodies exploration missions such as Deep Impact, Stardust-NExT, EPOXI, OSIRIS-REx, and DART.

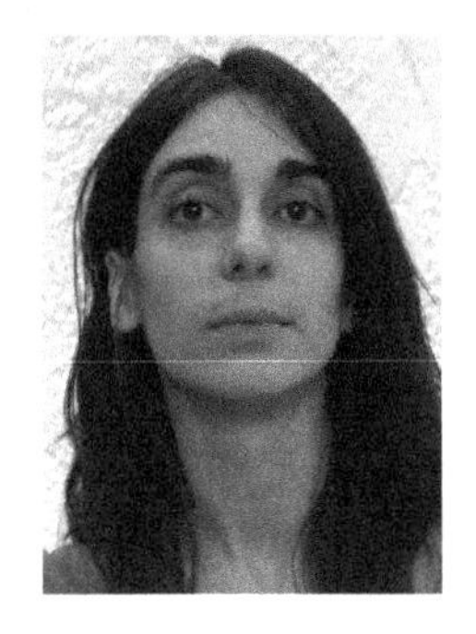

Dr. Julie C. Castillo-Rogez is a research scientist at the Jet Propulsion Laboratory, California Institute of Technology, USA. She holds a Ph.D. in Geophysics from Rennes University, France. She has been involved in the Dawn mission since 2014, first as an affiliate, then a co-investigator, project scientist, and deputy principal investigator. Dr. Castillo-Rogez was also an affiliate of the Cassini mission and is currently a co-investigator on the Europa Clipper mission and the science principal investigator for the Near-Earth Asteroid Scout CubeSat mission.

Contents

Chapter 1

Discovery of Ceres and the Asteroid Belt

Humans' view of the Solar System has been slowly expanding since the first day we looked up into the sky. The discovery of Ceres marked a significant milestone that opened a whole new territory of the solar system in front of us for the first time.

1.1 Discovery of Ceres

Astronomical research in the 18th century bloomed as a result of the development of astrometry and star catalogs, like those of John Flamsteed and James Bradley, which led to the discovery of phenomena such as the aberration of light in 1726 and the nutation of the Earth's axis in 1740. The stellar coordinates were measured as accurately and precisely as possible in order to determine proper motions and parallax of the stars. The development of celestial mechanics by Pierre Simon de Laplace of France enabled precise calculation of the positions of known planets and their moons, and inversely, to determine the orbits of Solar System objects from their observed positions in the sky. The first predicted return of Halley's Comet happened in 1758, proclaiming the success of modern physics and mathematics.

Prior to the discovery of Uranus in 1781 by William Herschel, the picture of the Solar System was simple: It had six planets from Mercury to Saturn, all of which were visible to unaided eyes, orbiting the Sun in nearly circular orbits close to the ecliptic plane, or zodiacal belt as called at the time. A few moons that orbited some planets, and comets that could appear far from the zodiacal belt and occasionally came near the Sun and became spectacular for a short period of time, were also known. Before the recognition of Uranus as the seventh planet by Herschel, it had actually been spotted by a few others many times, even possibly dating back to 128 BC by Hipparchus in his ancient star catalog. People just did not realize that there could be more objects in the Solar System other than the six planets, moons, and comets. The discovery of Uranus represented the first expansion of humans' view of the Solar System after thousands of years of staring at the sky, motivating astronomers to continue the search for more objects in the Solar System.

But, where could they be? Astronomers looked at the distribution of known planets. Their heliocentric distances, including that of the then-newly discovered Uranus, appeared to follow a simple numerical relationship, the so-called Titius–Bode law, except for a puzzling gap between Mars and Jupiter that should harbor a planet. Although we do not recognize any underlying physical reasons for the Titius–Bode law even today, this beautiful numerical relationship made some astronomers at the time strongly believe in the existence of a planet that they had to keep seeking for years. Such a deep belief led to the establishment of a scientific society of 24 observers, both professional and non-professional, in Lilienthal, Germany, in 1800 to conduct an observational campaign to hunt down the missing planet. Giuseppe Piazzi (Fig. 1.1), the head of the Palermo Astronomical Observatory in Sicily, was also sent an invitation letter to join the society, although, interestingly, he had already spotted Ceres before the letter arrived.

Piazzi was appointed the Chair of Astronomy in the newly established *Accademia dei Regj Studi di Palermo*, or Palermo Academy of Royal Studies, in 1786. Soon after his appointment, he started to build the Palermo Astronomical Observatory, with an ambitious program in mind to revise the existing star catalogs. To prepare the observatory, Piazzi took a long preparatory journey to France and England in 1787–1789, and visited the leading astronomers of the time, such as Jérôme de Lalande and Jean-Baptiste Delambre in Paris, and Nevil Maskelyne and William Herschel in London. He then managed to purchase valuable instruments and cutting-edge telescopes, such as the Ramsden Circle that was able to measure precise star positions, for his observatory.

Ceres was noticed for the first time by Piazzi on the night of January 1, 1801, in his routine work of revising the positions of stars. He described Ceres as follows: *Its light was a little faint and colored as Jupiter, but similar to many others that are usually classified in the eighth magnitude.*

Figure 1.1: Oil portrait of Giuseppe Piazzi painted by the Sicilian artist Giuseppe Velasco (1750–1827), a friend of Piazzi around 1803. Piazzi is pointing at Ceres. From the Palermo Astronomical Observatory collection.

After continuous observations through January 4, he was convinced that *it had moved according to the same law followed in the previous days.* Being extremely cautious, Piazzi did not associate his newly discovered object to the missing planet, but instead announced it as a comet to the press without providing any data. However, he knew it was not a comet, as he wrote in a letter to his friend Barnaba Oriani in late January: *I have presented this star as a comet, but owing to its lack of nebulosity, and to its motion being so slow and rather uniform, I feel in the heart that it could be something better than a comet, perhaps. However, I should be very careful in passing this conjecture to the public. When I have a greater number of observations, I will try to calculate its elements.* However, by late February, Piazzi was no longer able to observe this object because it was lost in the glare of the Sun, before anyone else had a chance to observe it.

Since the news of this newly discovered "comet", in March and April, both Lalande's student and Bode calculated the orbit of this newly discovered object using Piazzi's data, and found that the observations were not consistent with the orbit of a comet, but rather fitted a circular orbit better. After estimating this object's distance to the Sun to be between Mars and Jupiter, Bode was convinced that it was the missing planet, and broke the news to the public. In the meantime, Oriani, after roughly calculating the orbit from all of Piazzi's data, broke the news to Baron von Zach, Secretary of the Lilienthal Society, asking him to publish the news on his well-known astronomical monthly journal, the *Monatliche Correspondenz*, as soon as possible, and then immediately informed Piazzi about his results and actions.

By late July 1801, everybody knew the discovery of the "missing planet" between Mars and Jupiter. Piazzi finally released his observations from January 1 to February 11 to the public. He also officially gave the "new star" the name of *Ceres Ferdinandea*. Piazzi's choice of the name was his homage to Sicily and its king: Ceres, the goddess of harvest and agriculture in Roman mythology, was the patron deity of the island. Bode later welcomed this name in his letter to Piazzi, *You have discovered it in Taurus, and it was re-observed in Virgo, Ceres of the old times. These two constellations are the symbol of Agriculture. This occurrence is quite unique.*

However, the discovery could not be considered confirmed until Ceres was recovered after it came out of the glare of the Sun the next year. The recovery was hindered by the difficulty in precisely calculating its ephemeris and predicting its position from Piazzi's data, which only covered a very short arc of about 9° along Ceres's orbit around the Sun. Without a predicted position, astronomers would have to reobserve tens of thousands of stars in the zodiac belt, at least to the eighth magnitude, hoping to spot Ceres again from its motion against the star background.

It was the genius mathematician Carl Friedrich Gauss, aged 24 at the time, who solved the problem. By that time, Gauss had just developed the method of least squares, which made it possible to determine the orbit of a planetary object without making *a priori* assumption about its eccentricity as was previously done in calculating comets' and Uranus's orbits. After he read the news and saw the calculations of others, Gauss immediately realized that this was the right chance for him to check out his new method. He derived an orbit that placed the position of Ceres agreeing almost perfectly with all of Piazzi's data, although his predicted position of Ceres was some 6°–7° different from others' calculations. On the night of December 7, 1801, von Zach was the first to observe Ceres again near the position predicted by Gauss. Then, Olbers observed it on January 1,

1802, followed by Bode on January 15 and later by others. Piazzi himself finally reobserved Ceres on February 23 after losing it for a year. The discovery of the "missing planet" was finally confirmed.

1.2 Discovery of the Asteroid Belt

Just a few months after the recovery of Ceres, on March 28, 1802, Olbers in Bremen discovered another object, later named Pallas, that displayed a similar feature as Ceres. The orbit of Pallas is also between Mars and Jupiter, but with higher eccentricity and inclination than those of Ceres. Therefore, just shortly after the celebration of the discovery of the missing planet, astronomers found themselves in a dilemma of having not only one, but two planets at the same location in the Solar System.

William Herschel's amazing intuition made him the first to recognize that a new class of objects in the Solar System was emerging, based on only two objects of the class that we now know contains millions of members. After comparing the nature of Ceres and Pallas to that of planets and comets, he announced his suggestion of this new class of objects and gave them the name "asteroids" in his article published in *Philosophical Transactions of the Royal Society* (Herschel, 1802) for the stellar appearance bodies, and even accurately predicted their dynamic characteristics: *Asteroids are small celestial bodies that move in orbits around the sun having low or high eccentricity; the planes of their orbits can be tilted to any angle with respect to the ecliptic. Their motion can be direct or retrograde, they may or may not have substantial atmosphere, tiny halo discs or nuclei.* He argued, *Moreover, if we called it planet, it would not fill the space between Mars and Jupiter with the dignity required by that position.*

Interestingly, even Piazzi himself did not realize the significance of his own discovery, thinking that Herschel was trying to diminish the value of his finding, reacting to Herschel's article, *Be they called planetoids or cometoids then, but never asteroids. [...] If an Asteroid Ceres must be called, so must also be called Uranus.* This was perhaps the first "Great Planet Debate" that occurred among astronomers, to be repeated 200 years later on the nature of Pluto.

Despite the unwillingness of Piazzi and the debate among astronomers, the discovery of Juno and Vesta, in 1804 and 1807, respectively, confirmed the validity of Herschel's view. The hunt for new asteroids surged around the mid-19th century after a long hiatus, following the discovery of Vesta, with 33 new asteroids discovered just in the decade of 1845–1855. By the end of the 19th century, 452 asteroids were known. As of 2017, nearly half a million numbered asteroids have been discovered, and many more unnumbered asteroids have been reported. Their orbits spread almost everywhere in the solar system, although a large population reside between the orbits of Mars and Jupiter.

What is the origin of asteroids? Olbers (1805) first postulated that they are fragments of a broken planet between Mars and Jupiter, where there should have been a planet based on Titius–Bode's law. Such a view of collisional break up in asteroids was supported by the recognition of groups of asteroids that share similar orbital elements by Hirayama (1918), later termed "asteroid families". Kuiper (1950) examined various possible mechanisms to form asteroids from broken up planets, and recognized that asteroid families could form by secondary collisions between asteroids. On the contrary, Kuiper regarded the largest asteroids, such as Ceres, as the original objects directly condensed from the solar nebula. The formation of the largest asteroids together with planets was supported by Alfvén (1964), who noticed that the rotational period of large asteroids does not systematically vary with their size, and is comparable with that of planets, and argued that the same formational process must be responsible for forming planets and large asteroids.

It has been widely accepted by now that large asteroids, perhaps 100 kilometers in diameter or larger, are likely primordial and formed by directly accreting materials condensed from the solar nebula during planetary formation, while smaller asteroids are dominated by multigeneration collisional fragmentations of large asteroids over time (e.g., Bottke *et al.*, 2015). In this picture, Ceres, Vesta, Pallas, Hygiea, etc., represent those originally formed planetesimals that have undergone limited heating that caused complete or partial melting and differentiation in their interior. They not only preserve the original composition of objects formed in the early solar system but also contain clues about the geophysical and geochemical processes that the full-sized planets in the solar system have once undergone. Small asteroids, on the contrary, are fragments that sample the compositions and conditions of their parent asteroids from the surface to the interior.

In the meantime, the connection between meteorites and asteroids was slowly but firmly established by the 1960s (e.g., Anders, 1964). Meteorites are solid pieces of stone or metal or mixtures of both that originate in outer space and survive the passage through the Earth's atmosphere before landing on Earth's surface. Their origin was also mysterious in the early times, when scientists only knew about the six major planets, their then-known moons, comets, and a few hundred asteroids in the beginning of the 20th century.

On the other hand, scientists can take the meteorite pieces to the laboratory for careful examinations about their composition, mineralogy, and petrology to infer their environment and the conditions that they underwent, such as melting and cooling history, and pressure. This information provides constraints to the size and thermal evolutionary history of the objects from where meteorites originate. The dynamic properties of meteorites before they entered the Earth's atmosphere, and their chemical and isotopic properties suggested that the most likely parent bodies are located in the Mars-crossing orbits. Therefore, meteoroids, which are meteorites in orbit around the Sun before they hit the Earth, are like small asteroids but of even smaller fragments produced by asteroidal collisions.

Laboratory analyses of meteorite samples showed a large diversity in mineralogy, petrology, and isotopic properties. Some appear to have been heated and undergone differentiation and fractionation processes, while others just show very limited processing by heating or aqueous alteration (the alteration in the presence of water). Therefore, their parent bodies in general must have undergone both minimum thermal and/or aqueous alteration processes, and preserved the original composition and conditions when they had just formed from the solar nebula. Some of them record the processes that occurred right after their formation.

By the mid-20th century, scientists finally recognized that asteroids and their natural samples, meteorites, preserve the signatures of the formation and early evolutionary processes of planetary bodies in the solar system that have been long erased in the planets, which have undergone global, full-scale differentiation and complex evolution. This is just like fossils preserving the clues of early formation and evolution of life that no longer exist today.

The discovery of Ceres led to the discovery of a whole new territory in the solar system that contains millions of small asteroids, which were later connected to meteorites. These discoveries ultimately opened the path that allows us to travel back in time to take a peek at the birth of our planetary system. However, Ceres, as the largest and the first to be discovered of this new population, still remained enigmatic after more than 200 years. The numerous discoveries made by NASA's Dawn spacecraft while in orbit around Ceres from 2015 to 2018 started to reveal the nature of Ceres, and ultimately changed our view of this exciting small world.

References

Alfvén, H. (1964). On the origin of the asteroids. *Icarus*, **3**, 52–56.

Anders, E. (1964). Origin, age, and composition of meteorites. *Space Sci. Rev.*, **3**, 583–714.

Bottke, W. F., Brož, M., O'Brien, D. P., Bagatin, A., Morbidelli, A. and Marchi, S. (2015). The collisional evolution of the main asteroid belt. In: *Asteroids IV*, Michel, P., DeMeo, F. E. and Bottke, W. F. (eds.), University of Arizona Press, Tucson, 701–724.

Herschel, W. (1802). Observations on the two lately discovered celestial bodies. *Philos. Trans. R. Soc. London*, **92**, 213–232.

Hirayama, K. (1918). Groups of asteroids probably of common origin. *Astron. J.*, **31**, 185–188.

Kuiper, G. P. (1950). On the origin of asteroids. *Astron. J.*, **55**, 164.

Olbers, W. (1805, April 4). Letter to Gauss. Göttingen Archives.

Chapter 2

Pre-Dawn Exploration

The study of Ceres has a long history. Early observations before the 1970s were focused on astrometry, photometry, and polarimetry that helped determine its basic properties such as orbit, albedo, size, and color. The understanding of its composition greatly benefited from the development of modern spectroscopic observations of asteroids since the 1970s. Theoretical modeling has allowed us to gain some knowledge about its interior and evolutionary history based on its shape since the start of this century. In this chapter, we provide a comprehensive review of the state of knowledge about Ceres prior to the arrival of NASA's Dawn mission in 2015.

2.1 Overview

Pre-Dawn observations of Ceres focused on determining the bulk physical properties, surface composition, and surface heterogeneity. Based on the bulk properties and theoretical modeling, the interior structure and clues about its formation and evolution were derived. The basic techniques for remote observations of Ceres include astrometry, photometry and polarimetry, reflectance spectroscopy, thermal observations, and high-resolution imaging from the ground and near-Earth space.

The earliest report of Ceres's bulk properties probably dated back to Herschel (1802), who, shortly after its discovery, stated that Ceres was "ruddy" more so than Pallas. Not until nearly 100 years later, through a micrometrical measurement of Ceres's angular size, did people recognize that the albedo of Ceres was comparable to that of Mercury

(Barnard, 1895). The early observations of the brightness of asteroids with visual estimates, and photometric and photographic techniques before and at the beginning of the 20th century revealed the change of brightness with respect to phase angle (the angle subtended by the Sun and observer as seen from an asteroid) and with respect to time. The former, termed phase function, had been established by Müller and Parkhurst (e.g., Parkhurst, 1901), and as we understand it now is affected by surface physical properties. The latter, termed light curve, was slowly recognized as being due primarily to the changing aspects of irregularly shaped asteroids with rotation. This forms the basis of determining basic physical properties, such as rotational period, pole, and shape of asteroids from photometric observations. Harwood (1924) summarized these early observations of more than 70 asteroids including Ceres. However, the accuracy of the photometric data was rarely sufficient to establish the period of the light curves for Ceres. Calder (1936) started photoelectric observations of Ceres, significantly improving the photometric accuracy, establishing the modern era of determining the bulk properties of asteroids from photometric observations. In the meantime, spectroscopic observations of asteroids, as pioneered by Bobrovnikoff in the 1920s (e.g., Bobrovnikoff, 1929; Johnson, 1939; Watson, 1940), provided clues about the surface compositions of asteroids.

The observing campaign of asteroids using modern techniques started in the 1950s, when Groeneveld and Kuiper (1954) initialized a photometric campaign with photoelectric techniques, resulting in the first high-quality light curve of Ceres (Ahmad, 1954). Sporadic photometric light curves of Ceres were obtained (Gehrels and Owings, 1962; Chang *et al.*, 1981; Taylor *et al.*, 1976) before the first, dedicated worldwide photometric campaign of Ceres was organized at the 1975–1976 apparition (Tedesco *et al.*, 1983). The campaign provided accurate measurements of albedo, phase function, surface color and color variations, and rotational period, forming the basis of many later observations and analyses.

High-resolution imaging of Ceres was first made possible by the Hubble Space Telescope (HST) (Merline *et al.*, 1996; Parker *et al.*, 2002; Thomas *et al.*, 2005), later joined by the adaptive optics (AO) technique using ground-based telescopes (Carry *et al.*, 2008; Drummond *et al.*, 2014). The HST imaging observations in the 2003–2004 apparition represented a major milestone that significantly improved the density determination of Ceres, revolutionized our understanding about its interior structure (Thomas *et al.*, 2005) and evolution (McCord and Sotin, 2005), and provided the first high-resolution mapping of its surface (Li *et al.*, 2006).

Spectroscopic study of asteroids was pioneered by McCord and Gaffey (1974) who established the connection between the spectra of asteroids and those of meteorites measured in the laboratory. However, no meteoritic groups have been identified to match the spectrum of Ceres due to spectral mismatches in the 3 μm region (Burbine, 1998), hindering our understanding of Ceres's surface composition. The spectrum of Ceres in the visible and near-infrared spectral range has been repeatedly observed, but an unambiguous interpretation has never been reached (Lebofsky, 1978, 1981; King *et al.*, 1992; Vernazza *et al.*, 2005; Rivkin *et al.*, 2006; Milliken and Rivkin 2009). In the meantime, observations have been expanding the spectral range toward UV and mid-infrared.

Other observations of Ceres include the determination of its mass from the dynamic interactions between Ceres and other asteroids based on precise astrometric measurements, determination of its surface properties from radar observations, and the search for a water exosphere (A'Hearn and Feldman, 1992; Küppers *et al.*, 2014; Rousselot *et al.*, 2011). In this section, we provide a review of the determinations of Ceres's fundamental properties based on remote observations from the ground and near-Earth space and theoretical modeling before Dawn arrived at Ceres in early 2015. The knowledge gained during and after the Dawn mission is reviewed in Chapters 4–9 that follow.

2.2 Bulk Properties

2.2.1 *Early Photometry*

Intense photometric campaigns of Ceres were performed during three apparitions: 1953–1954 (Ahmad, 1954; Groeneveld and Kuiper, 1954; Gehrels and Owings, 1962), 1975–1976 (Tedesco *et al.*, 1983; Taylor *et al.*, 1976; Schober, 1976), and 1985–1986 (Lagerkvist and Magnusson, 1990; Lagerkvist *et al.*, 1988, 1989; Hollis and Toone, 1985; Hollis, 1988). From these data, light curve and phase function at multiple colors were derived, from which the basic properties of Ceres were inferred.

Light curve is primarily affected by the rotation and shape, as well as from surface albedo heterogeneities. The light curves of Ceres from three different ecliptic longitudes (34°, 66°, and 114°) all showed a similarly

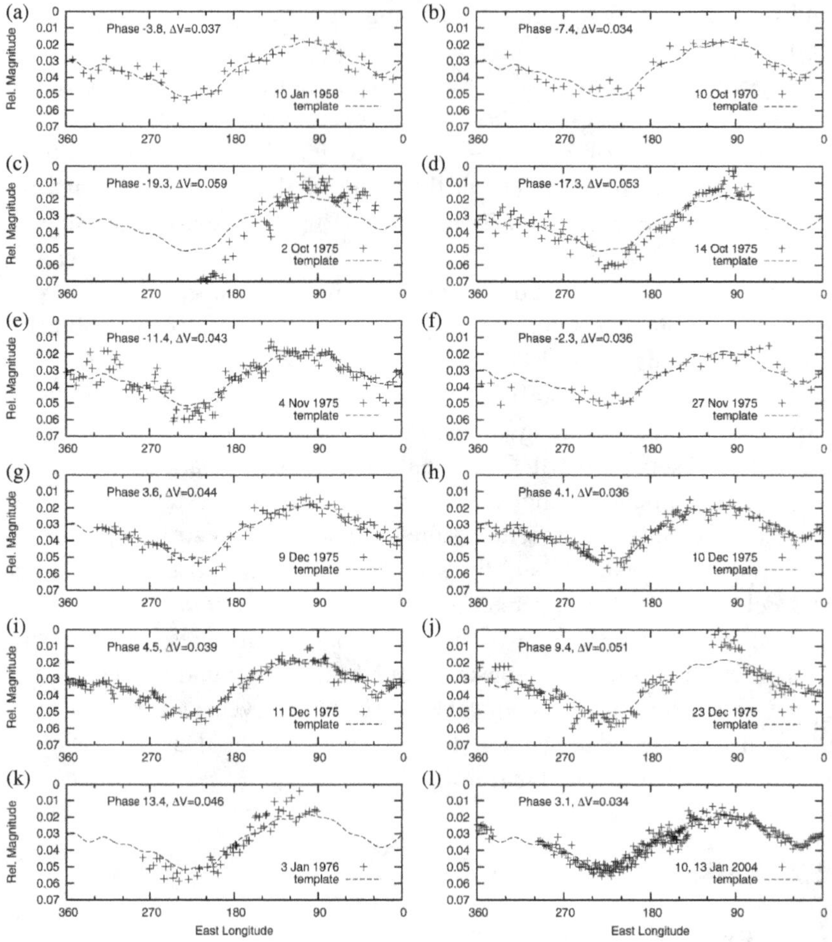

Figure 2.1: Light curves of Ceres from various apparitions. Reprinted from Chamberlain *et al*. (2007). Copyright with permission from Elsevier.

small amplitude of 0.04 mag (Fig. 2.1), suggesting either low obliquity (angle between rotational pole and orbital pole) or a rotationally symmetric shape, or both (Tedesco *et al*., 1983). The rotational period of Ceres was derived from the photometric light curve to be 9.075 ± 0.001 hours (Tedesco *et al*., 1983), which was later improved by combining all light curves acquired over more than 50 years to be 9.074170 ± 0.000002 hours (Chamberlain *et al*., 2007). The small rotational variations of Ceres's light curve, color (Tedesco *et al*., 1983), and polarization

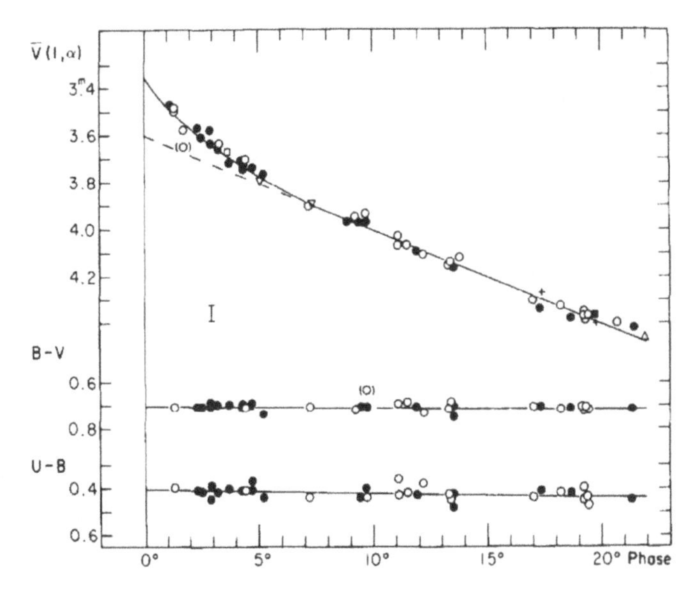

Figure 2.2: Phase function of Ceres from 1975–1976. Open symbols are pre-opposition and solid symbols post-opposition. The dashed line is a linear fit to data at phase angles ≥ 7°. The curved line is the "empirical opposition effect" model defined by Gehrels and Tedesco (1979). Reprinted from Tedesco *et al.* (1983). Copyright with permission from Elsevier.

(Zellner *et al.*, 1974; Zellner and Gradie, 1976) were strong indications for a relatively uniform surface of Ceres compared to the Moon and terrestrial planets.

The phase functions of Ceres (Fig. 2.2) from different apparitions show similar shapes at the range of phase angles accessible from the ground for main-belt asteroids, and are linear between 7° and 22°. Phase angle dependence of the broadband colors of Ceres is weak (Fig. 2.2). The linear slope of Ceres's phase function is 0.040 ± 0.001 mag/deg, and the mean absolute magnitude (the magnitude at 0° phase angle and 1-au observer distance and heliocentric distance) in V-band is 3.61 ± 0.03. The U–B and B–V color indexes at 0° phase angle are +0.41 ± 0.01 and +0.70 ± 0.01, respectively. A moderate opposition surge (nonlinear increase of brightness toward 0° phase angle) has an amplitude of about 0.25 mag within 7° phase angle. The best-fit phase function parameters in the IAU HG photometric system (Bowell *et al.*, 1989) for Ceres were H = 3.36 mag and G = 0.12 (Lagerkvist and

Magnusson, 1990; Lagerkvist *et al.*, 1988, 1989). The geometric albedo of Ceres was then derived to be about 0.090 ± 0.003 (Li *et al.*, 2006), using the size determined from Hubble Space Telescope data (Thomas *et al.*, 2005). The Bond albedo, which quantifies the flux scattered by Ceres's surface into space as a fraction of the total solar flux received at Ceres, is about 0.03.

The polarization phase function of Ceres has a minimum of −1.7% at about 8° phase angle (Fig. 2.3), coinciding with where the opposition surge starts to appear. The polarization inverses to positive beyond about 18° phase angle, which is termed inversion angle (Tedesco *et al.*, 2002; Cellino *et al.*, 2005; Muinonen *et al.*, 2002). No rotational variation of polarization was detected, but polarization at small phase angles of <10° shows slightly less negative polarization with increasing wavelength, a behavior typical for dark C-type asteroids (Belskaya *et al.*, 2009). Lupishko *et al.* (1992) reported that the plane of negative polarization of Ceres increases monotonically with wavelength, and interpreted this

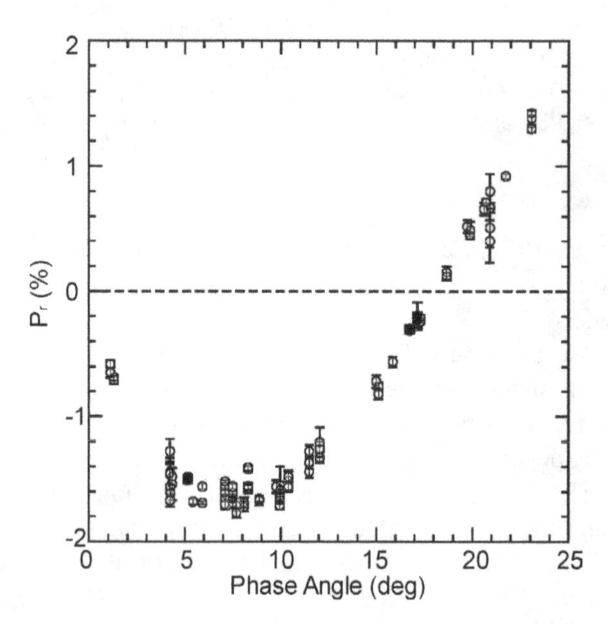

Figure 2.3: Polarimetric phase function of Ceres with the data available in the literature marked by different symbols. From Cellino *et al.* (2006), Albedo and size of (99942) Apophis from polarimetric observations. Proceedings of the International Astronomical Union, 2(S236), 451–454. Copyright © International Astronomical Union 2007, reprinted by permission.

"peculiar behavior" as caused by a gas–dust shell or gas emission, although the observations have never been confirmed. Using the general relationship between polarimetric slope and albedo for asteroids, an albedo of 0.077 ± 0.006 was derived (Rivkin *et al.*, 2011).

High-resolution imaging from the ground using AO and from HST provides detailed information about the size, shape, and rotational pole of Ceres. The first reliable determination of the rotational pole orientation of Ceres was derived from AO images obtained with the 3.6 m European Southern Observatory (ESO) telescope (La Silla, Chile) at near-infrared wavelengths in the K, L', and M bands (Saint-Pé *et al.*, 1993). The pole orientation at RA = 300 ± 5° and Dec = +53 ± 15° suggested a low obliquity, as indicated by the previous photometric observations. The mean radius of Ceres was measured to be 484 ± 20 km. No albedo variations were detected. Later AO observations at 0.85 μm wavelength with a 1.5 m telescope (Starfire Optical Range of the United States Air Force Phillips Laboratory) resulted in two pole solutions: one at RA = 280° and Dec = +56° (radius 4°) is consistent with the previous determination, while the other, which points to the southern sky, is inconsistent with the prograde rotation of Ceres. Later high-resolution imaging acquired in 2003–2004 from HST at a pixel size of about 30 km directly tracked the rotation of Ceres through its surface features, and resulted in a pole solution of RA = 291° and Dec = 59°, with an uncertainty circle of 5° in radius (Thomas *et al.*, 2005). The inferred obliquity was about 3°.

2.2.2 *Size and Shape*

The size of Ceres was one of its first properties to be measured. Barnard (1895) estimated its angular size through micrometrical measurement to be 780 km in diameter, which was about 15% smaller than the size measured by the Dawn mission. A stellar occultation of Ceres in 1984 suggested that it has an oblate spheroidal shape with an equatorial radius of 479.6 ± 2.4 and polar radius of 453.4 ± 4.5 km (Millis *et al.*, 1987). This is a much more accurate measurement than before. Later AO observations revised the mean radius to 484 ± 20 km (Saint-Pé *et al.*, 1993), and a triaxial ellipsoidal shape of radii (509 ± 5, 473 ± 7, 444 ± 5) km (Drummond *et al.*, 1998). The HST imaging in the ultraviolet (UV) yielded elliptical semimajor axes of 484.8 ± 5.1 km and 466.4 ± 5.9 km (Parker *et al.*, 2002). The best pre-Dawn shape and size measurement of Ceres came from the 2003–2004 HST observations in the UV to visible wavelengths, suggesting an oblate spheroid of mean equatorial radius 487.3 ± 1.8 km and polar radius 454.7 ± 1.6 km (Thomas *et al*., 2005).

2.2.3 *Surface Features*

Merline *et al*. (1996) reported albedo patterns on the surface of Ceres for the first time using HST at a pixel scale of 53 km at the asteroid. Parker *et al*. (2002) identified a prominent dark albedo feature of about 250 km in diameter on Ceres from their HST images in the UV, and proposed the name "Piazzi". No other significant features could be identified from their images. The 2003–2004 HST images revealed a surface rich in features, although subtle in terms of albedo and color variations, at wavelengths of 535, 335, and 223 nm (Fig. 2.4) (Thomas *et al*., 2005; Li *et al*., 2006). The albedo ranges ±6% peak to peak, with a full width at half max (FWHM) of about 4% at a resolution of 30 km, consistent with the light curve amplitude. Li *et al*. (2006) identified six bright features and five dark features, ranging in diameter from about 100 to about 600 km. All these features were later confirmed to correspond to specific geological features on Ceres based on Dawn data (Schröder *et al*., 2017). The different albedo distributions at different wavelengths reflect color variations. The maps in the near infrared at J-, H-, and K-bands derived from the AO imaging with the Keck telescope resulted in similar albedo features and distribution at a scale of two hundred kilometers and larger on an overall uniform surface (Carry *et al*., 2008).

The albedo and color of Ceres's surface are much more uniform in the UV to near-IR wavelengths compared to other asteroids or satellites at similar spatial resolution, including Gaspra (Helfenstein *et al*., 1994), Ida (Helfenstein *et al*., 1996), Eros (Murchie *et al*., 2002; Li *et al*., 2004), Phobos (Simonelli *et al*., 1998), and Deimos (Thomas *et al*., 1996), which typically have albedo variations twice that observed for Ceres. Many factors affect the albedo and color variation in these wavelengths, including composition, particle sizes, and regolith maturity. Because the interior of Ceres is likely differentiated (Thomas *et al*., 2005; McCord and Sotin, 2005), the remarkably uniform surface of Ceres strongly suggests that its surface never experienced any giant impacts like the one that formed the large Rheasilvia impact basin near the south pole of Vesta (e.g., Thomas *et al*., 1997; Asphaug, 1997) or that

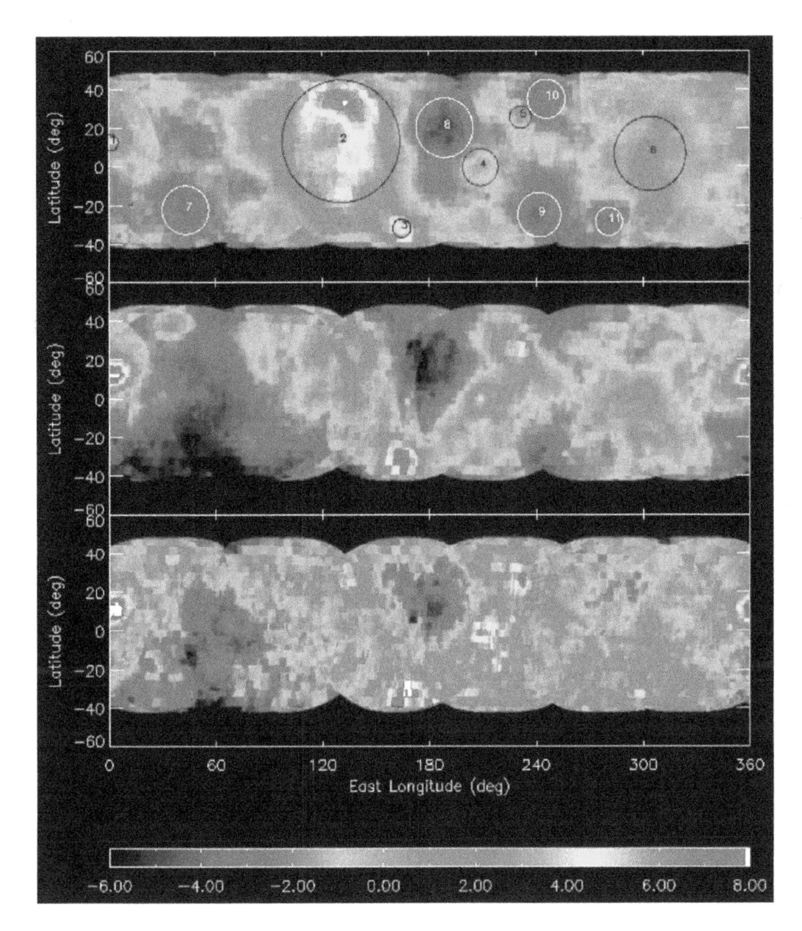

Figure 2.4: Surface albedo maps of Ceres at 535 nm, 335 nm, and 223 nm, produced from HST images. Reprinted from Li *et al.* (2006). Copyright with permission from Elsevier.

resurfacing events have erased any significant variation that might have resulted from large impacts.

2.2.4 *Thermal Properties*

Brown *et al.* (1982) and Lebofsky *et al.* (1986) obtained 10 μm and 20 μm radiometric observations of Ceres, respectively, which were later used by Spencer (1990), coupled with the diameter measured from stellar occultation observations (Millis *et al.*, 1987), to derive a thermal inertia of 15 $J/(m^2 s^{0.5} K)$ (thermal inertia units, hereafter "tiu"). Lebofsky *et al.* (1986) also presented a thermal phase curve of Ceres at phase angles from −20.6° to +17.9° (negative phase angle means pre-opposition, and positive post-opposition), and described the asymmetric thermal phase curve as consistent with the prograde rotation of Ceres. Saint-Pé *et al.* (1993) derived a value of 38 ± 14 tiu based on their ground-based AO observations in M-band (3.55–4.15 μm). A more comprehensive thermophysical modeling based on the thermal flux of Ceres in 7–2000 μm collected by a series of telescopes (including the Infrared Astronomical Satellites (IRAS), James Clark Maxwell Telescope (JCMT), the United Kingdom Infrared Telescope (UKIRT), NASA Infrared Telescope Facility (IRTF), and Infrared Space Observatory (ISO)), resulted in a consistently low thermal inertia of about 10 tiu (Müller and Lagerros, 1998). Low thermal inertia results in little delay for temperature to peak with respect to local noon, as well as a shallow thermal skin depth that is in the order of millimeters for diurnal temperature variations and a few decimeters for seasonal temperature variations. A layer of loose, fine-grained dust cover on the surface of Ceres is commonly adopted to explain the low thermal inertia of Ceres (e.g., Delbo *et al.* (2015)).

Observations in radio wavelengths from sub-millimeters to decimeters are affected not only by thermal emission from the surface of Ceres but also by that from the relatively cold subsurface due to the strong thermal gradient resulting from the low thermal inertia, making them more complicated to model and interpret than those at shorter wavelengths. The contribution of subsurface thermal emission follows radiative transfer theories (e.g., Hapke, 2012) and depends on the dielectric properties of surface and subsurface materials. In particular, the real part of the complex dielectric constant determines the refractive index and therefore changes the direction of emission when it crosses the boundaries of layers with different refractive indexes and the surface. The loss tangent, which is the ratio of the imaginary part to the real part of the dielectric constant, determines how strongly the emission is absorbed when penetrating through the subsurface medium. Microwave measurements of the Moon showed that the electrical absorption length is about 7 wavelengths in the millimeter wavelengths, and 10–15 wavelengths in the centimeter wavelengths (e.g., Gary and Keihm, 1978). For comparison, Rosetta/MIRO observations of Comet 67P/Churyumov-Gerasimenko suggested an electrical absorption length of 39 millimeter at a wavelength of 1.5 millimeter and 10 millimeters at a wavelength of

0.5 millimeter (Schloerb *et al.*, 2015). Therefore, observations at longer wavelengths effectively probe into the subsurface. Modeling the thermal emission in the radio wavelengths could therefore constrain both the thermal inertia and the dielectric properties of the top surface regolith (e.g, Li *et al.*, 2020).

Because the subsurface temperature usually decreases with depth in the daytime, the observed brightness temperature of asteroids, including Ceres, usually decreases with increasing wavelength in the millimeter to decimeter wavelengths (Webster *et al.*, 1988; Webster and Johnston, 1989). If we define the ratio of the observed thermal flux to the expected thermal flux based on the surface temperature as effective emissivity, then the observed effective emissivity in the radio wavelengths is in general less than one, typically ranging between 0.6 and 0.8 for main-belt asteroids (e.g., Keihm *et al.*, 2013). Redman *et al.* (1998) performed a detailed analysis of the different spectral energy distributions (SEDs) of a number of asteroids, including Ceres, from thermal infrared to decimeter wavelengths, and showed that those SEDs are related to the mineralogical composition of asteroid surfaces. Meanwhile, Keihm *et al.*, (2013) further performed a detailed self-consistent thermophysical and radiative transfer model to reconcile the SEDs of four large asteroids from thermal infrared to decimeter wavelengths, and found that a thermal inertia of 80 tiu fits the data the best for Ceres, although a thermal inertia as high as 200 tiu cannot be ruled out. The modeling of ALMA thermal observations of Ceres in the mm wavelength also suggested a thermal inertia between 40 and 160 tiu (Li *et al.*, 2020). These results probably indicate some vertical variations in the thermal inertia and/or the dielectric properties in the top millimeters to decimeters of Ceres's regolith.

Depending on the wavelength, the light curve of Ceres in thermal wavelengths could be affected by both the spatial distribution of thermal properties and dielectric properties of the top layer of the regolith in various depths. Inconsistent results have been reported for the rotational light curve of Ceres in radio wavelengths. Altenhoff *et al.* (1996), Moullet *et al.* (2010), and Li *et al.* (2020) all reported an amplitude of about 3% at 250–265 GHz frequency. The 50% peak-to-peak amplitude at 345 GHz reported by Chamberlain *et al.* (2009) might be less likely given the noisy data of their observations. Given the low Bond albedo of Ceres of about 3%, and the small albedo variations in the reflected light, Li *et al.* (2020) interpreted the thermal light curve amplitude as dominated by the spatial variations in the physical properties (e.g., grain size, porosity) or rock composition (ammoniated phyllosilicate) of Ceres's regolith at millimeter depth.

2.2.5 *Mass*

The purpose of mass measurement in understanding Ceres is to calculate its bulk density and density distribution. For a large object that should have minimal internal porosity, these properties reflect its composition and internal structure when combined with the shape, and therefore its geophysical evolution. Large asteroids introduce non-negligible and, sometimes, strong gravitational perturbations on the orbits of a great number of other objects, including both asteroids and planets, providing a means to measure their masses. Table 2.1 lists the historical measurements of the mass of Ceres. Early determinations made use of the fact that the orbital periods of Ceres and Pallas closely match a 1:1 commensurability, causing observable effects in the mean longitudes of each object. With an increasing number of close encounters between Ceres and other asteroids observed, the mass determination of Ceres has been slowly improved over time. The precise astrometry of asteroids from space-based observations, such as Hipparcos and later Gaia, as well as the precise location of Mars based on radio link between Earth and Mars landers and rovers (e.g., Mars Pathfinder) helped to shrink the uncertainty of the measurement. The precision of mass measurement for Ceres significantly benefited from the advancement in computational capabilities in the late 1990s and into the 21st century that enabled including hundreds to thousands of asteroids with precise orbital determinations in dynamical model fitting.

2.3 Surface Composition and Taxonomy

After the first description of Ceres's color by Herschel (1802), attempts to quantitatively study the reflectance spectra of Ceres and other asteroids started in the late 1920s and 1930s with both microphotometric tracings of photographic spectra in comparison with G-type solar analog stars (Bobrovnikoff, 1929; Johnson, 1939) and wideband photographic colorimetry (Watson, 1940). Sandakova (1962) performed the then largest survey of asteroid color indices. Photoelectric programs that started in the 1950s (Kitamura, 1959; Gehrels, 1970) provided much more reliable measurements of the colors of asteroids. Chapman *et al.* (1971) provided a detailed review of the early work on the spectroscopic observations of Ceres.

The first reliable spectral information of Ceres became available in the early 1970s (Chapman *et al.*, 1973), which led to the recognition that its surface was dark and spectrally neutral. That observation also showed

Table 2.1: Historical measurements of the mass of Ceres.

Mass ($\times 10^{-10}$ solar mass)	Method	References
6.7 ± 0.4	Pallas	Schubart (1970)
5.9 ± 0.3	Pallas	Schubart (1974)
5.2 ± 0.3	Pallas	Landgraf (1988)
5.0 ± 0.2	Mars	Standish and Hellings (1989)
4.7 ± 0.3	(203) Pompeja	Goffin (1991)
4.796 ± 0.085	(203) Pompeja, (348) May	Sitarski and Todorovic-Juchniewicz (1992)
4.622 ± 0.071	(197) Arete, (203) Pompeja, (348) May, (486) Cremona	Sitarski and Todorovic-Juchniewicz (1995)
4.35 ± 0.05	—	Hilton (1997)
5.0 ± 0.2	Pallas	Viateau and Rapaport (1995)
4.785 ± 0.039	4 asteroids from Hipparcos	Viateau and Rapaport (1997)
4.759 ± 0.023	9 asteroids	Viateau and Rapaport (1998)
4.70 ± 0.04	25 asteroids	Michalak (2000)
4.81 ± 0.01	DE403, DE405	Pitjeva (2001)
4.749 ± 0.020	Mars	Pitjeva (2004)
4.753 ± 0.007	301 asteroids and planets	Pitjeva (2005)
4.699 ± 0.028	Mars	Konopliv *et al.* (2006)
4.736 ± 0.026	(5303) Parijskij, (7298) 1992 WM5	Kovačević and Kuzmanovski (2007)
4.500 ± 0.004	Gaia data of 20,000 asteroids	Mouret *et al.* (2007)
4.755 ± 0.008	300 asteroids, planets	Baer and Chesley (2008)
4.746 ± 0.006	300 asteroids, planets	Fienga *et al.* (2008)
4.757 ± 0.007	Thousands of asteroids	Baer *et al.* (2011)
4.54 ± 0.07	21 asteroids	Kovačević and Andjelka (2012)

no match to the spectra of any meteorites, a result that still remains true today. The detection of weak and complex absorption features in the 3 μm region in Ceres's spectrum (Lebofsky *et al.*, 1981) resulted in non-unique interpretations. Mid-infrared spectroscopic data of Ceres were mostly collected around 2000 and later from both ground (Cohen *et al.*, 1998; Lim *et al.*, 2005; Takahashi *et al.*, 2011) and the Infrared Space

Observatory (ISO) (Dotto *et al.*, 2000). The UV observations of Ceres were first performed by the International Ultraviolet Explorer (IUE) in the 1980s (Butterworth and Meadows, 1985), followed by the HST observations (Li *et al.*, 2009; Hendrix *et al.*, 2016).

2.3.1 *Visible and Near-Infrared* (0.4–2.5 μm)

The visible and near-infrared region is the most readily observed for asteroids because of the abundant solar flux available and the high transparency of the terrestrial atmosphere. The spectrum of Ceres in this region is mostly free of diagnostic features (Fig. 2.5), with a nearly neutral slope and a decrease in reflectance at wavelengths shorter than 0.4 μm that is much stronger and more abrupt than other asteroid spectral types. This strong UV absorption edge is an intervalence charge-transfer band due to iron oxides (Fe^{2+}–Fe^{3+}), and is one of the defining features of C-class and related subclass asteroids in the Tholen taxonomy (Tholen, 1984). The very broad absorption band centered near 1.2 μm has never

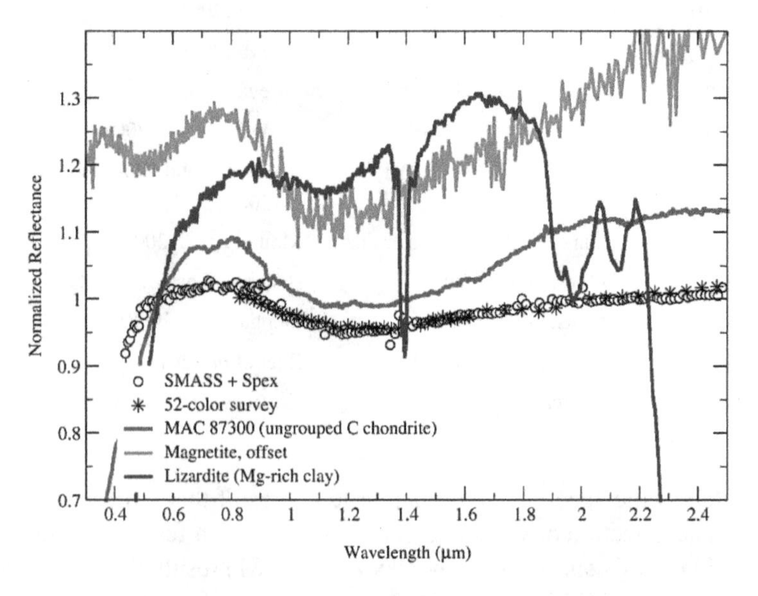

Figure 2.5: Ceres's spectrum in the visible and near-infrared spectral range, in comparison with the spectra of a carbonaceous meteorite and minerals measured in the laboratory. Reprinted from Rivkin *et al.* (2011). Copyright with permission from Springer.

been specifically addressed, although Larson *et al.* (1979) implied it was due to magnetite as shown in some carbonaceous chondrites. This feature could also be due to other minerals, such as plagioclase feldspar, although magnetite is more consistent with our understanding of Ceres's history and low albedo.

Vilas *et al.* (1993) and Fornasier *et al.* (1999) reported a subtle absorption near 0.6 μm in Ceres's spectrum, and suggested that charge transfer in aqueous alteration products may be responsible for this feature, like the 0.7 μm absorption feature often observed in some carbonaceous chondrites and other asteroids. However, this feature was not observed by Bus and Binzel (2002). Some inconsistencies in the spectral slopes of Ceres's spectrum also exist in the literature.

2.3.2 *Ultraviolet (UV)* (<0.4 *μm*)

Observations in the UV wavelengths (<0.4 μm) are possible only from above the atmosphere due to the strong UV absorption of O_3 in the upper atmosphere. Early observations of Ceres in the UV with the International Ultraviolet Explorer (IUE) showed a possible broad feature at the 200–300 nm spectral range (Roettger and Buratti, 1994). Broadband photometry with the HST was overall consistent with the IUE data, and suggested a possible reflectance peak at about 150 nm (Parker *et al.*, 2002; Li *et al.*, 2009). Later observations with the HST Space Telescope Imaging Spectrograph (STIS) in the spectral range of 115 nm to 570 nm (Fig. 2.6) confirmed the reflectance maximum at about 150 nm that is consistent with graphitized carbon (Hendrix *et al.*, 2016), although the feature is not as strong as suggested by previous observations. The UV reflectance drop at wavelengths shorter than 0.4 μm is interpreted as the presence of sulfur or sulfur dioxide frost.

Furthermore, Ceres shows both rotational variations and latitudinal variations in its UV spectrum (Hendrix *et al.*, 2016). The HST/STIS observations were conducted at two sub-Earth longitudinal zones of 335°–360° (prime meridian) and 213°–240° (western hemisphere). The two hemispheres of Ceres show similar spectral characteristics at wavelengths shorter than 200 nm, but the prime meridian zone appears brighter than the western hemisphere zone in 200–570 nm. If the UV absorption peak at about 150 nm is interpreted as graphitized carbon, then the rotational variations might indicate stronger contribution of carbon in the western hemisphere zone. In the latitudinal direction along the prime

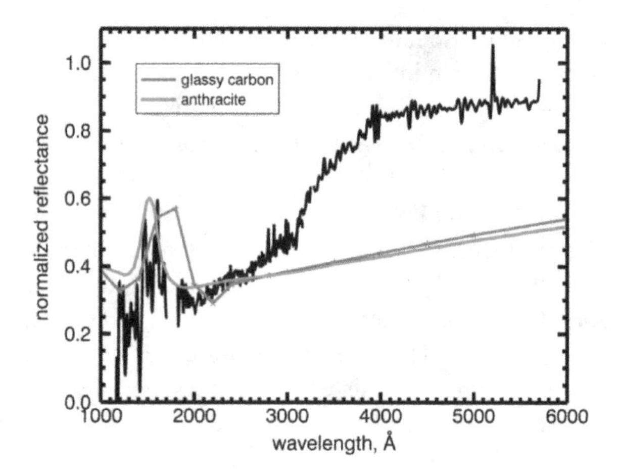

Figure 2.6: UV spectrum of Ceres from 100 nm to 570 nm, showing a UV reflectance drop-off starting from 400 nm, a minimum at about 200 nm, and a maximum at about 150 nm. Reprinted from Hendrix *et al.* (2016). Copyright with permission from Wiley-VCH Verlag GmbH & Co. KGaA.

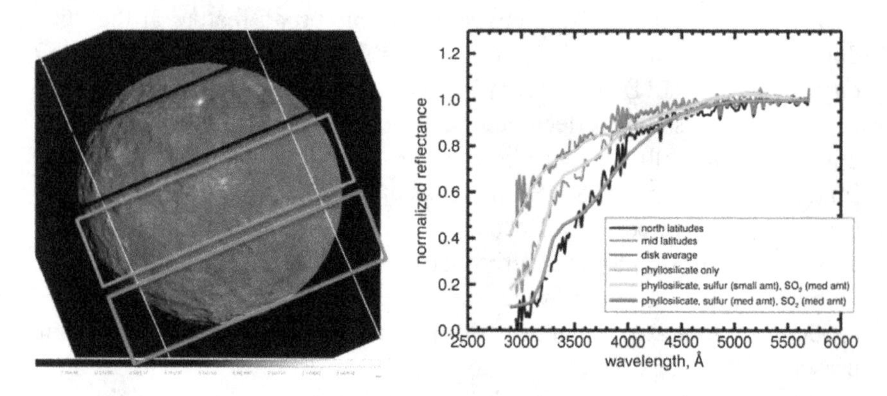

Figure 2.7: UV-vis spectrum of Ceres (right panel) extracted in three latitudinal zones centered at a sub-Earth longitude of near 0° (left panel) with corresponding color boxes. Reprinted from Hendrix *et al.* (2016). Copyright with permission from Wiley-VCH Verlag GmbH & Co. KGaA.

meridian zone, the northern mid-latitude region shows stronger UV reflectance drop-off than the southern mid-latitude region, with the equatorial region in between (Fig. 2.7). This might indicate higher abundance of sulfur/SO_2 in the northern hemisphere than in the southern hemisphere.

2.3.3 3 μm Region (2.5–5 μm)

The 2.5–5 μm region is certainly one of the most important spectral regions in remote sensing observations of asteroids, because it contains a number of vibrational absorptions due to the most widespread volatiles and mineralogical constituents in the solar system, such as water, hydroxyl, carbonates, carbon dioxide, ammonia and other volatiles, and organics. All these species could be present on the surface of asteroids and carry significant scientific values in revealing the composition, formation environment, and evolutionary history of the host asteroids. Despite the challenges in observing the 3 μm region from the ground due to the interference of water and methane in the terrestrial atmosphere, this region has been observed for Ceres ever since the emergence of spectroscopic studies of asteroids for nearly 40 years, providing the bulk of the quantitative information of Ceres's surface composition.

The features of Ceres's spectrum in this spectral range include the narrow absorption band centered at about 3.06 μm, and sets of overlapping bands in 3.3–3.4 μm and 3.8–3.9 μm (Fig. 2.8). Scientists have never agreed

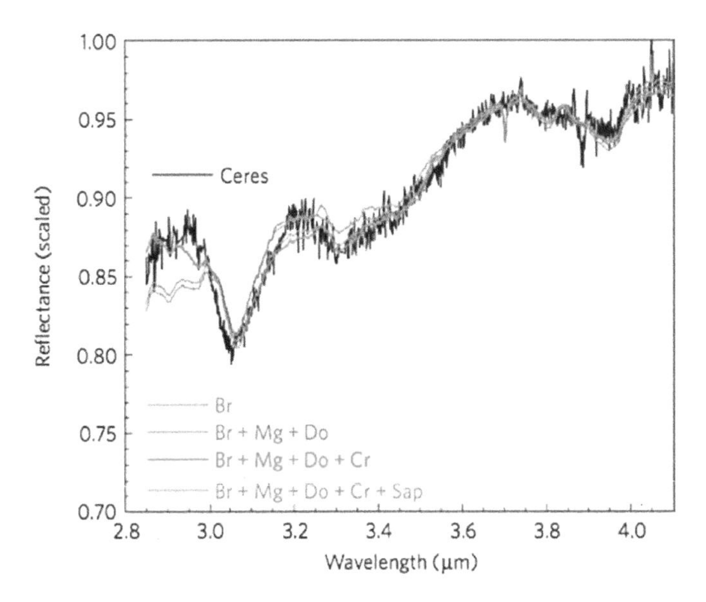

Figure 2.8: Near-infrared spectrum of Ceres in the 2.8–4.0 μm region, compared with various modeled spectra as marked in the plot. Reprinted from Rivkin *et al.* (2011). Copyright with permission from Springer.

on the interpretations of the 3 μm feature based on ground-based data. It was originally explained as a very thin water ice frost (Lebofsky *et al.*, 1981), but later reinterpreted as due to NH_4-bearing phyllosilicates (King *et al.*, 1992). Vernazza *et al.* (2005) proposed a mixture of irradiated organics and crystalline water ice as another possibility. With their newly obtained high-quality data, Rivkin *et al.* (2006) reinterpret the same feature as an iron-rich clay (the serpentine cronstedtite) and the 3.3–3.4 and 3.8–3.9 μm bands as due to carbonates. Milliken and Rivkin (2009), using the same dataset, showed that brucite ($Mg(OH)_2$) could be a potentially better explanation for the 3.06 μm band.

Interestingly, water ice and organic materials are not unambiguously observed on Ceres from the ground in this spectral region, despite their strong absorption and the likely presence of water in the interior of Ceres (Thomas *et al.*, 2005) and organics in potential carbonaceous chondrite analogues. This could be due to the low abundances of these species on Ceres's surface.

2.3.4 *Mid-Infrared* (5–13 *μm*)

The spectral features in the mid-infrared (MIR) wavelength region are due primarily to vibrational and lattice modes of molecules, but their wavelength and strength are strongly affected by surface properties such as grain size, porosity, ambient pressure, temperature (see review by Reddy *et al.*, 2015 and references therein). Silicate minerals display a series of bands at about 8.5 to 12 μm (e.g., Lyon, 1964; Hunt, 1982; Salisbury *et al.*, 1991) due to Si-O asymmetric stretching, and a second series of bands at 16.5 to 25 μm associated with Si-O-Si bending. Crystalline silicate minerals have strong diagnostic absorption features between 9 and 12 μm as well as several other minor bands at longer wavelengths, and the wavelength locations of the bands depend on the Fe/(Fe+Mg) content (Koike *et al.*, 2003, 2006; Chihara *et al.*, 2002). Amorphous olivines and pyroxenes have broad absorption features near 10 μm with a weaker band near 20 μm (e.g., Day, 1981; Koike and Hasegawa, 1987; Scott and Duley, 1996; Brucato *et al.*, 1999). McAdam *et al.* (2015) established a connection between the shape and wavelengths of the silicate features in 8−25 μm and the aqueous alterations' status in CM and CI meteorites based on laboratory work. Therefore, the MIR wavelength region can be highly complementary to the VNIR wavelength region in determining the surface mineralogy of Ceres.

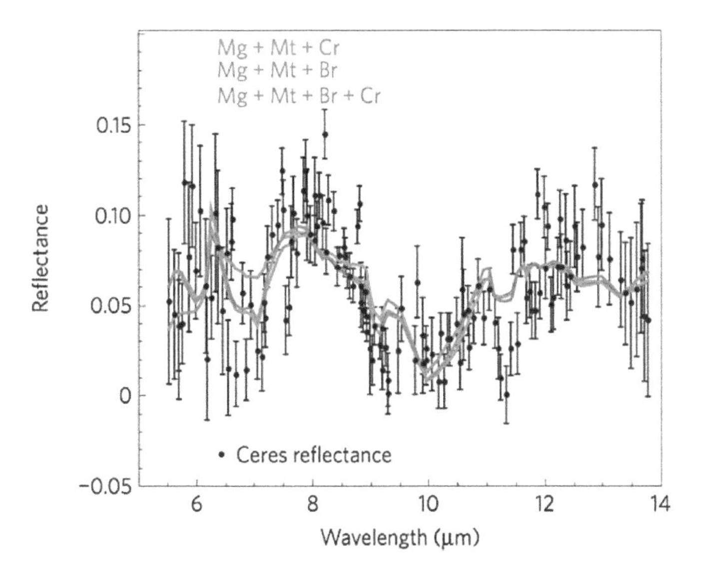

Figure 2.9: Ceres's spectrum in the mid-infrared from 5 μm to 14 μm in comparison with various model spectra. Reprinted from Rivkin *et al.* (2011). Copyright with permission from Springer.

Ceres displays about a 10% contrast in its MIR reflectance spectrum in the 6–14 μm region (Fig. 2.9) (Cohen *et al.*, 1998), the strongest among all 29 asteroids included in the ground-based MIR survey by Lim *et al.* (2005), highlighting the unusual properties of Ceres's surface. The most prominent MIR spectral feature of Ceres is the broad silicate absorption centered at 10 μm. Other features include a narrow absorption at 6.6 μm, and possible absorption features at 9 μm and 11.4 μm. The 9 μm feature is close to a telluric absorption near 8.5 μm, and appears very noisy in the Cohen *et al.* ground-based data and very weak in the Dotto *et al.* (2000) ISO data, and did not show up in later observations (Lim *et al.*, 2005; Takahashi *et al.*, 2011). Similarly, the 11.4 μm feature was not repeatedly observed by later ground-based observations. Although the sub-Earth longitudes of these observations were all different (Table 2.2), the presence or lack of the 8 μm and 11.4 μm features do not appear to be correlated with longitude (Fig. 2.10).

Similar to the 3 μm feature, the modeling of the MIR features of Ceres has also been difficult and the results highly uncertain. The spectral contrast of powdered Murchison meteorites is too low in the MIR

Table 2.2: Mid-IR (8–13 μm) spectral observations.

Instrument	Date	UT	9 μm feature?	11.4 μm feature?	Sub-Earth Lon	Sub-Earth Lat	Phase	References
KAO (HIFOGS)	1993-11-09	4:13:12–5:32:24	Yes	Weak	5.7–313	3.6	8.1	Cohen *et al.* (1998)
KAO (HIFOGS)	1995-05-05	3:21–4:15	Yes	Strong	324–289	−6.7	23.2	Cohen *et al.* (1998)
ISO (PHT-S)	1997-05-14	10:53:43– 10:54:47	Weak	None	157	1.7	19.4	Dotto *et al.* (2000)
Palomar (SC-10)	2002-09-21	7:52:19– 8:31:55	None	None	178–151	6.6	7.2	Lim *et al.* (2005)
Palomar (SC-10)	2002-09-22	8:07:02– 8:18:47	None	None	295–287	6.6	6.9	Lim *et al.* (2005)
UKIRT/Michelle	2004-04-18	8:15–8:27	None	None	334–326	−7.2	22.8	Takahashi *et al.* (2011)

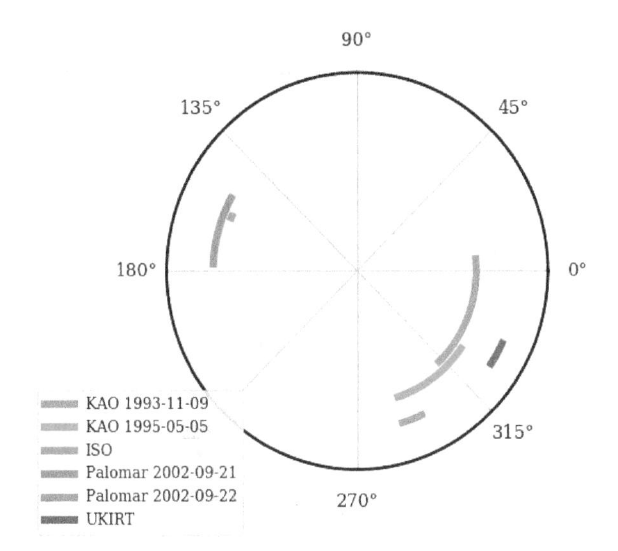

Figure 2.10: The true anomaly of Ceres during the observations in the mid-infrared reported in Table 2.2.

compared with Ceres, and its 9 μm emissivity maximum was at a slightly shorter wavelength than that observed for Ceres (Cohen *et al.*, 1998). Ammoniated saponite, as suggested by King *et al.* (1992) based on NIR modeling results, produced a poor match throughout the 8–11 μm region (Milliken and Rivkin, 2009). A better fit was found to the 11.4 μm feature by including dolomite (a carbonate mineral) in the model (Rivkin *et al.*, 2006), or using assemblages of magnesite, brucite, and magnetite that produced the then-best spectral match in the 3 μm region (Fig. 2.9) (Milliken and Rivkin, 2009). Therefore, the MIR spectrum of Ceres is consistent with the presence of carbonates, with Mg-bearing carbonates resulting in a better match than Fe- or Ca-carbonates.

2.4 Internal Evolution Modeling

When the Dawn mission was selected in 2001, Ceres was understood to be a pristine planetesimal, a fossil from the early solar system (Russell *et al.*, 2004). However, scientists working on the icy moons of giant planets pointed out that Ceres's large size and water content should drive its internal evolution, given its high water content of ~25% inferred from its density (McCord and Sotin, 2005). At the time, the thinking was that Ceres accreted with other large C-type asteroids, within a few million years after the formation of calcium aluminum inclusions (CAIs), which were considered to be the first solids condensed in the solar system. Hence, Ceres likely experienced heating from aluminum-26, which is a short-lived radioisotope with a half-life of 0.717 million years. Aluminum-26 is believed to be responsible for the rapid melting of volatiles in carbonaceous chondrite parent bodies, leading to the aqueous alteration of their refractory component and the production of, e.g., phyllosilicates and carbonates (Schramm *et al.*, 1970). McCord and Sotin (2005) demonstrated that, considering its large size, and per analog with icy moons, Ceres should have differentiated into an ice-rich crust and a rocky mantle. At the time, uncertainties in Ceres's geophysical properties led to a range of possible interior structures depending on Ceres's evolution (Fig. 2.11). First, it was unclear whether Ceres would be able to preserve a primitive, undifferentiated crust or if that top layer would actually founder. Castillo-Rogez and McCord (2010) pointed out that the latter scenario was the most likely because accretional heat and the high impact rate in Ceres's early history would lead to a thin and broken crust, a hypothesis supported by Neveu and Desch (2015). Another unknown that remained until Dawn obtained gravity data of Ceres was the prospect of the metallic core separating. This could be possible if Ceres's mantle temperature exceeded the melting temperatures of hydrated silicates (>1000 K). Lastly, under Ceres's low gravity conditions, it is possible that the volatiles and silicates would not cleanly separate, potentially preserving a mixed layer. This possibility was explored in greater detail by Bland and Travis's (2017) "mudball" model.

Follow-on work by Castillo-Rogez and McCord (2010) refined some aspects of the McCord and Sotin (2005) models by elaborating on the role of salts in driving some aspects of Ceres's evolution. They showed that brines (salts in solution) could remain throughout Ceres's history due to the combination of Ceres's relatively warm surface temperature and the brine's low eutectic temperature (Fig. 2.12). Concentrated salt mixtures may decrease the solution's melting point by more than 80 K (see, e.g., Wynn-Williams *et al.*, 2001).

Based on geophysical constraints available at the time, mostly shape data derived from large telescopes (Section 2.2), Castillo-Rogez and McCord (2010) concluded that Ceres's interior should be partially differentiated (Fig. 2.13). Other studies of that period showed that available

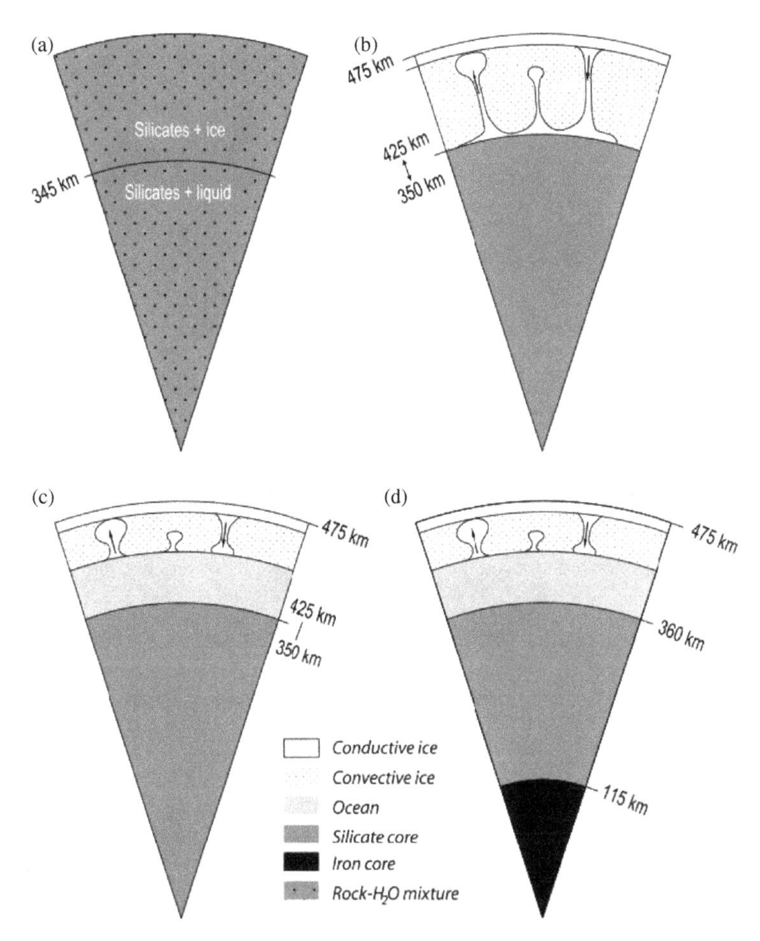

Figure 2.11: Different internal structures covering the range of possible interiors for Ceres, based on uncertainties on its formation and evolution prior to the Dawn observations. (a) Undifferentiated model in the unlikely case that Ceres's heat budget was significantly less than predicted by cosmochemical models. (b) and (c) two types of partially differentiated models in which the rocky phase separated from the volatiles and settled into a mantle. In these models, heating in the mantle was limited so that the silicates remained mostly hydrated throughout Ceres's evolution. In (c), a mixture of ice and rock may remain because Ceres's low gravity and cold surface temperature prevented clean separation of the two materials. (d) Advanced differentiation due to heating of the rocky mantle, leading to the separation of a metallic core. Reprinted from McCord and Sotin (2005). Copyright with permission from Wiley-VCH Verlag GmbH & Co. KGaA.

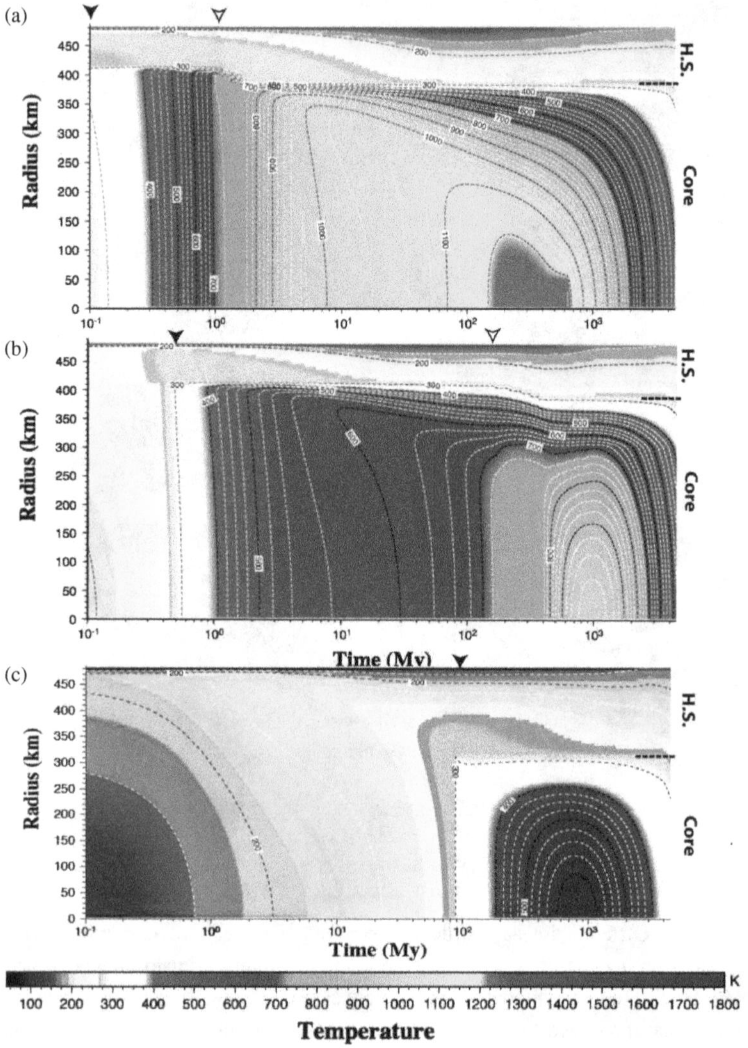

Figure 2.12: Evolution models of Ceres for three different times of formation after CAIs, (a) less than 3 m.y. after the formation of CAIs, leading to the partial differentiation of a metallic core at a temperature >1200 K; (b) 3 to 4 m.y., leading to partial differentiation with the separation of a rocky mantle from the volatile phase and whose temperature may reach the dehydration temperature of phyllosilicates at about 750–800 K; (c) >5 m.y., leading to the preservation of a ~100-km-thick pristine crust overlaying an ice-rich layer and a small rocky mantle. H.S refers to the hydrosphere (including remnant outer ice/rock layer in the bottom model); "core" here refers to the rocky mantle. Arrows point to the beginning of volatile melting and internal differentiation (black) and silicate dehydration (white). Reprinted from Castillo-Rogez and McCord (2010). Copyright with permission from Elsevier.

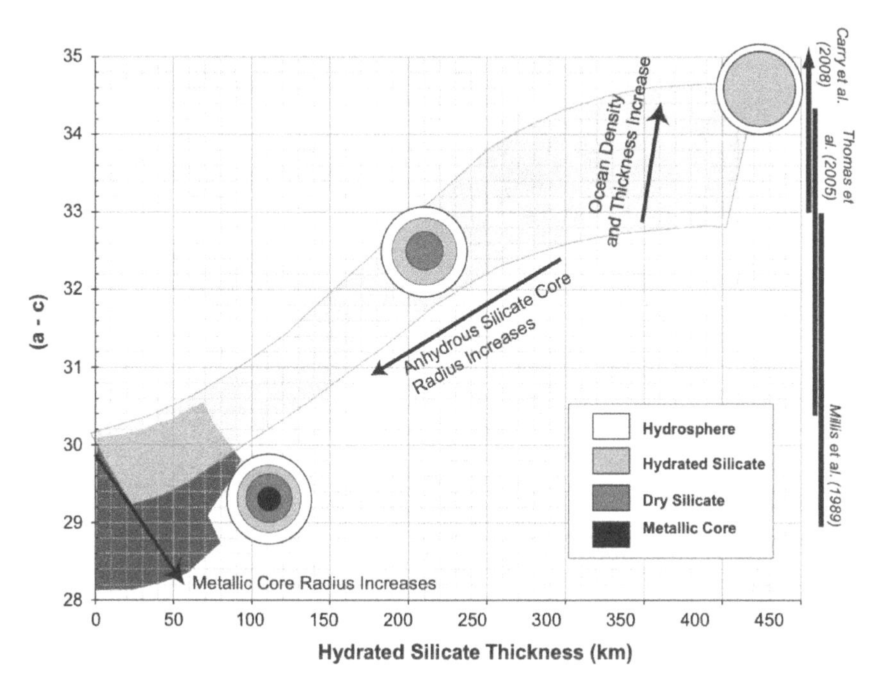

Figure 2.13: Internal structure models compared against pre-Dawn shape data. This figure shows that Ceres is likely partially differentiated (i.e., without a metallic core). Reprinted from Castillo-Rogez and McCord (2010). Copyright with permission from Elsevier.

shape data could alternatively be explained by a porosity gradient (Zolotov 2009). In that model, Ceres accreted from carbonaceous material after aluminum-26 was mostly decayed (about 10 million years after CAIs) and porosity compaction was responsible for the density gradient. However, Castillo-Rogez (2011) modeled the thermal evolution for this model and showed that the low thermal conductivity of a porous mixture of hydrated silicate, salts, and organic matter would lead to melting of the silicates and organics early in Ceres's history. Water released as a consequence of this phase of thermal metamorphism would lead to the formation of a water- and salt-rich crust.

Neveu *et al.* (2015) further refined the understanding of Ceres's mantle evolution by accounting for a more complex chemistry of the rock (e.g., salts) and processes observed in terrestrial environments such as rock cracking and salt precipitation (Fig. 2.14). These processes can lead to the consolidation of the rock by cementation, which in turn increases the overall thermal conductivity of the mantle.

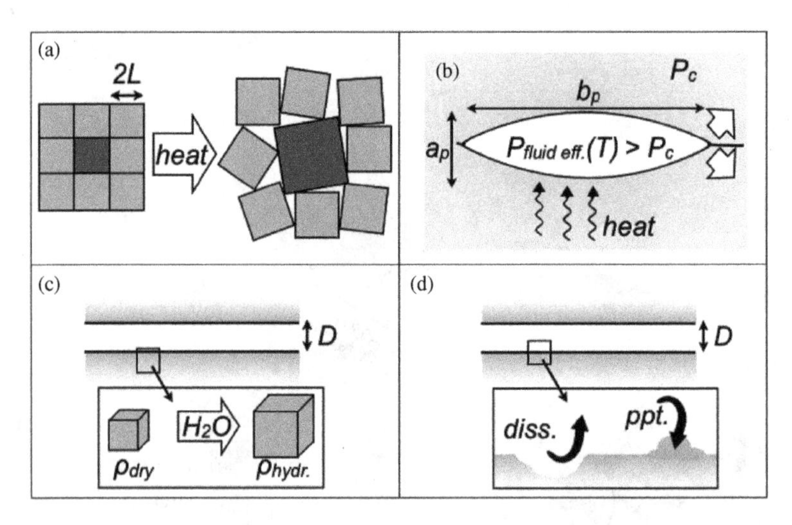

Figure 2.14: Example of processes that may affect the evolution of a rocky mantle in a mid-sized, i.e., low-gravity, body. (a) Change in mineral volume as a consequence of internal heating; (b) local precipitation of saturated salts in pores, which may act as a cement and increase mantle strength; (c) rock hydration as a result of aqueous alteration, which also leads to volume change; (d) local transport of elements during aqueous alteration and their redistribution. Reprinted from Neveu *et al.* (2015). Copyright with permission from Wiley-VCH Verlag GmbH & Co. KGaA.

2.5 Volatiles

A'Hearn and Feldman (1992) first reported a detection of the emission line from OH at the wavelength of 309 nm at 2-sigma above the noise level off the north limb of Ceres using the IUE data. Another observation off the south limb of Ceres with the same instrumental setting one year earlier, on the contrary, showed no evidence of this emission line. Interpreting the putative OH as the photodissociation product of water vapor, and assuming a spherical distribution of quasi-bound water exosphere around Ceres, they calculated a production rate of ~1.4×10^{26} molecules/sec for the positive detection and an upper limit of ~5.3×10^{25} molecules/sec for the negative detection.

The amount of OH detected by A'Hearn and Feldman (1992) is nonetheless consistent with the possible existence of a seasonal polar cap on Ceres discussed by Fanale and Salvail (1989) based on thermal models of Ceres. The possibility of a water exosphere prompted continuous observing efforts, but the combination of the low amount of water and the high brightness of Ceres itself makes it a difficult task. Ground-based

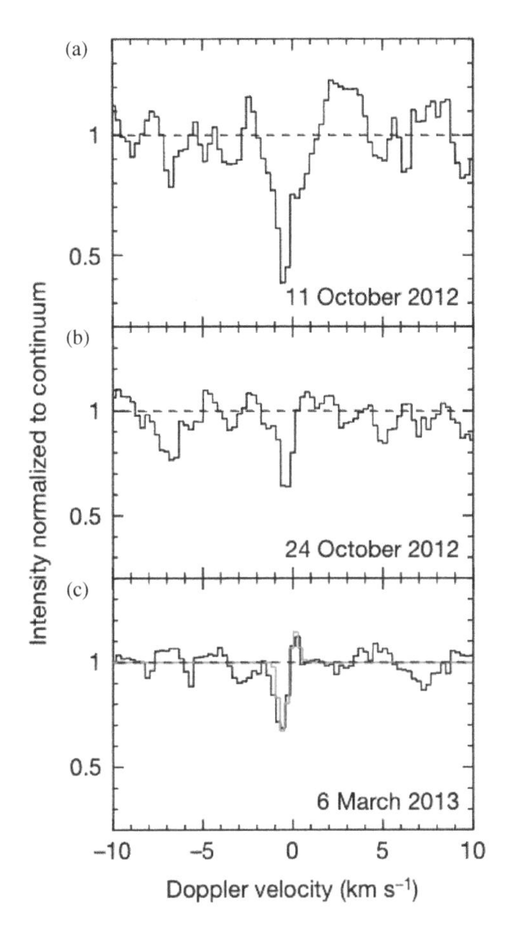

Figure 2.15: Detection of H_2O vapor around Ceres by HSO. The black lines are observed spectra from three dates, and the red line is a model spectra for the last observation assuming two active spots of 60 km in diameter. Reprinted from Küppers *et al.* (2014). Copyright with permission from Springer Nature.

observing efforts in 2007 and 2009 targeted to the same OH emission line returned negative results with an upper limit production rate of $\sim 7 \times 10^{25}$ molecules/sec (Rousselot *et al.*, 2011).

A breakthrough was made with the spaceborne Herschel Space Observatory (HSO), which is a 3.5-meter-diameter telescope operating in the far infrared wavelengths of 55–700 μm. Küppers *et al.* (2014) reported a definitive detection of water vapor spectral absorption in the background thermal emission from Ceres in three epochs in 2012 to 2013 (Fig. 2.15). In one epoch that covered a full rotation of Ceres, the strength

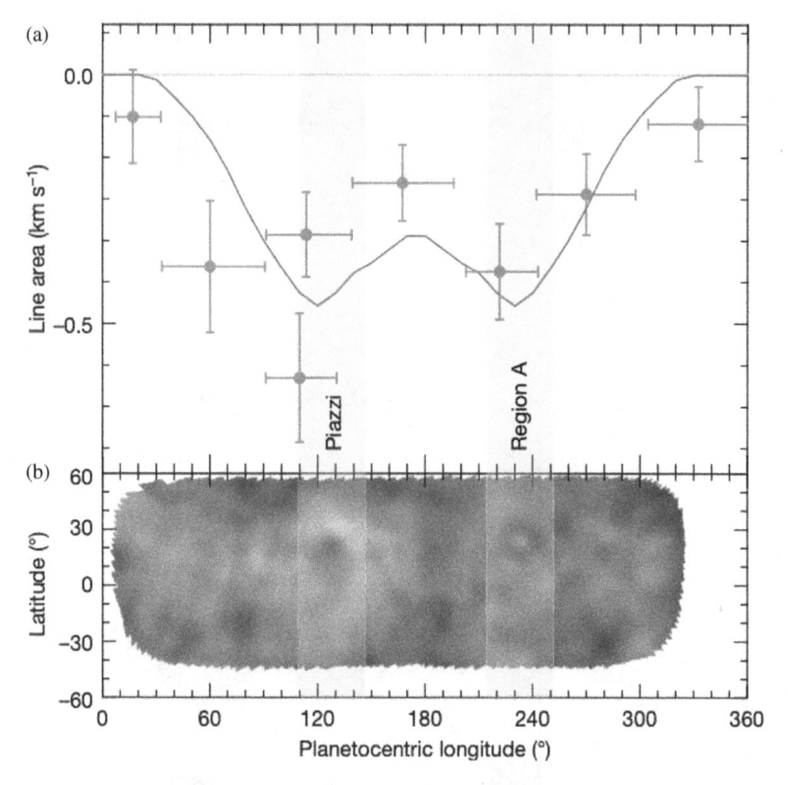

Figure 2.16: Rotational variations of water vapor line strength by HSO. Upper panel shows the observed line area for the water spectral absorption feature (red symbols with error bars), and the model (blue line). Lower panel is the albedo map of Ceres in the near infrared from Carry *et al.* (2008). Shaded regions mark the longitudinal zones of the strongest water vapor emission. Reprinted from Küppers *et al.* (2014). Copyright with permission from Springer Nature.

of absorption appeared to vary with rotation, showing two maxima centered at longitudes of ~120° and ~240° (Fig. 2.16). Because the absorption line was optically thick, the measurement of the column density of water molecules, as well as the calculation of water production rate, involved complicated modeling under many assumptions and poorly constrained parameters, and is therefore highly uncertain. Nonetheless, Küppers *et al.*, (2014) estimated a water production rate of ~2×10^{26} molecules/sec, or 6 kg/sec. This low production rate, if directly sublimated from ice exposed on the surface of Ceres, would just require a total area of the order of 1 km^2 covered by pure water ice.

Searches of water around Ceres continued from the ground and near-Earth space after the exciting detection by HSO. However, no detection has been made ever since. Roth *et al.* (2016) observed the OI 130.4 nm emission line with the Cosmic Origin Spectrograph (COS) onboard the HST on August 26, 2015. The OI line can be produced by photoelectron excitation of H_2O (Feldman *et al.*, 2015). The observed spectrum is consistent with no OI line around Ceres, corresponding to an upper-limit column density of $8.2 \pm 13.4 \times 10^{10}$ cm^{-2}, and a production rate of 4×10^{26} s^{-1} if one assumes a spherically asymmetric water vapor production. Further analysis of the same set of data, as well as new HST/COS data collected in October 2016 targeted to the atomic species of oxygen and sulfur, led to a similar upper-limit production rate estimate for water, and non-existence of SO_2 on Ceres's sunlit surface, inconsistent with the results from the UV observations of Ceres (Hendrix *et al.*, 2016).

Theoretical modeling predicted that water ice could survive the age of the solar system when buried a few meters beneath a dusty surface on main-belt asteroids (Schörghofer, 2008). For the thermal conditions on Ceres, water ice could be stable on the surface at latitudes higher than ~40°–60°, depending on the thermal inertia and roughness (Titus, 2015). If buried ice exists within the thermal skin depth, then the latitudinal boundary of stable surface ice could move toward higher latitudes due to the increased subsurface temperature caused by the higher thermal inertia of water ice. With a rough topography on Ceres due to cratering and other geological features, about 0.4% of Ceres's surface could host stable water ice, and other volatiles such as CH_3OH, NH_3, SO_2, and CO_2 could be cold trapped in smaller abundance as well (Hayne and Aharonson, 2015). The low obliquity of Ceres is an important factor for the stability of volatiles on the surface in the polar regions. A small enhancement of ice in Ceres's northern hemisphere could exist owing to the direction of its pole tilt and the timing of the perihelion. Therefore, if water plumes emerge from low latitudes, a mechanism is required to recharge subsurface ice tables.

In the subsurface, water ice could exist at depths of only 10–100 m near the equator and less than 1 to 10 m at latitudes greater than 40° (Fanale and Salvail, 1989). The subsurface water could lead to a global water supply rate of 30 to 300 g/s, implying a global water production rate of the order of 10^{24} molecules/s, compared to the typical values of comets between 10^{28}–10^{29} molecules/s near their perihelia.

Theoretical modeling also suggested that water molecules in Ceres's exosphere could be cold trapped and form an optically thin polar cap. Such a polar cap could cause a significant short-term increase to the water production rate if activated (Tu *et al.*, 2014; Schörghofer *et al.*, 2017). Because of Ceres's low gravity, the tenuous exosphere dissipates rapidly once the source has faded. Other factors that could cause water outgassing, including chemical sputtering via solar wind and meteoroid impact, are probably inadequate to maintain a water exosphere on Ceres (Tu *et al.*, 2014). All the theoretical modeling efforts seem to be consistent with the low production rate of water from Ceres and the transient nature of water vapor production as suggested by observations. However, the sources and mechanisms for Ceres's outgassing are undertermined.

2.6 Summary: State of Knowledge and Open Questions Prior to Dawn's Arrival

Due to its large size and significance as a mission target, as well as its classification as a dwarf planet, Ceres benefited from many observations prior to Dawn's arrival in 2015. By then, its global physical properties were mostly understood, which helped the planning of the Dawn operations. Ceres was expected to be at least partially differentiated into a rocky mantle and icy crust, similar to large icy moons. That differentiation phase involved the aqueous alteration of the rock and could explain the pervasive hydrated material and carbonates found across Ceres's surface by ground-based telescopes. By 2010, Ceres was identified as an astrobiological target because of its large water content and the prospect that its interior could preserve brines until present.

Key knowledge gaps prior to Dawn's arrival dealt with Ceres's thermal evolution, the origin of outgassing activity, and the extent of chemical fractionation, all of which determine Ceres's habitability potential. Salts and organic compounds were suspected to be present and to play a role in Ceres's evolution, but that aspect was not approached in detail in the absence of actual detection of these compounds. The status and history of water on Ceres carry significant implications for understanding the cosmochemistry of the solar system, astrobiology, and potential in situ resource utilization. The relevant questions include the following: What is the vertical and lateral distribution of water on Ceres? What is the phase partitioning of water on Ceres? How was water transported between the subsurface and interior? What are the mechanisms driving water loss from Ceres? How did water affect Ceres's geochemical evolution? Has Ceres been habitable in the past and does it still have global or localized habitable sites at present? All of these questions would be tackled by detailed in situ observations by the Dawn mission.

Before the arrival of the Dawn mission, the close connection between Ceres and water was slowly strengthened by remote sensing observations and theoretical modeling. The potentially significant role that water must have played in the history of Ceres and its current state was being recognized. The connection between Ceres and the outer solar system icy bodies started to emerge.

References

A'Hearn, M. F. and Feldman, P. D. (1992). Water vaporization on Ceres. *Icarus*, **98**, 54–60.

Ahmad, I. I. (1954). Photometric studies of asteroids. IV. The light-curves of Ceres, Hebe, Flora, and Kalliope. *Astrophys. J.*, **120**, 551–559.

Altenhoff, W. J., *et al.* (1996). Precise flux density determination of 1 Ceres with the Heinrich-Hertz-Telescope at 250GHz. *Astron. Astrophys.*, **309**, 953–956.

Asphaug, E. (1997). Impact origin of the Vesta family. *Meteorit. Planet. Sci.*, **32**, 965–980.

Baer, J. and Chesley, S. R. (2008). Astrometric masses of 21 asteroids, and an integrated asteroid ephemeris. *Celest. Mech. Dyn. Astron.*, **100**, 27–42.

Baer, J., Chesley, S. R. and Matson, R. D. (2011). Astrometric masses of 26 asteroids and observations on asteroid porosity. *Astron. J.*, **141**, 143 (12 pp.).

Barnard, E. E. (1895). Micrometrical determinations of the diameters of the minor planets Ceres (1), Pallas (2), Juno (3), and Vesta (4), made with the Filar Micrometer of the 36-inch equatorial of the Lick Observatory; and on the albedos of those planets. *Mon. N. R. Astron. Soc.*, **56**, 55–63.

Belskaya, I. N., *et al.* (2009). Polarimetry of main belt asteroids: Wavelength dependence. *Icarus*, **199**, 97–105.

Bland, P. A. and Travis, B. J. (2017). Giant convecting mud balls of the early solar system. *Sci. Adv.*, **3**, e1602514.

Bowell, E., *et al.* (1989). Application of photometric models to asteroids. In: *Asteroids II*, University of Arizona Press, Tucson, 524–556.

Bobrovnikoff, N. T. (1929). The spectra of minor planets. *Lick Observatory Bulletin No. 407*, Berkeley, University of California Press, 18–27.

Brown, R. H., *et al.* (1982). Calibration of the radiometric asteroid scale using occultation diameters. *Icarus*, **52**, 188–195.

Brucato, J. R., Colangeli, L., Mennella, V., Palumbo, P. and Bussoletti, E. (1999). Mid-infrared spectral evolution of thermally annealed amorphous pyroxene. *Astron. Astrophys*, **348**, 1012–1019.

Burbine, T. H. (1998). Could G-class asteroids be the planet bodies of the CM chondrites. *Meteorit. Planet. Sci.*, **33**, 253–258.

Bus, S. J. and Binzel, R. P. (2002). Phase II of the small main-belt asteroid spectroscopic survey: A feature-based taxonomy. *Icarus*, **158**, 146–177.

Butterworth, P. S. and Meadows, A. J. (1985). Ultraviolet reflectance properties of asteroids. *Icarus*, **62**, 305–318.

Calder, W. A. (1936). Photoelectric photometry of asteroids. *Harvard College Observatory Bulletin*, **904**, 11–18.

Carry, B., *et al.* (2008). Near-infrared mapping and physical properties of the dwarf planet Ceres. *Astron. Astrophys.*, **478**, 235–244.

Castillo-Rogez, J. C. (2011). Ceres—Neither a porous nor salty ball. *Icarus*, **215**, 599–602.

Castillo-Rogez, J. C. and McCord, T. B. (2010). Ceres' evolution and present state constrained by shape data. *Icarus*, **205**, 443–459.

Cellino, A., *et al.* (2005). Asteroid polarimetric observations using the Torino UBVRI photopolarimeter. *Icarus*, **179**, 304–324.

Cellino, A., Delbò, M. and Tedesco, E. F. (2006). Albedo and size of (99942) Apophis from polarimetric observations. *Proceedings IAU Symposium*, **236**, 451–454.

Chamberlain, M. A., Sykes, M. V. and Esquerdo, G. A. (2007). Ceres lightcurve analysis—Period determination. *Icarus*, **188**, 451–456.

Chamberlain, M. A., Lovell, A. J. and Sykes, M. V. (2009). Submillimeter photometry and lightcurves of Ceres and other large asteroids. *Icarus*, **202**, 487–501.

Chang, Y. C., Zhou, X.-H., Yang, X.-Y., Zhang, Y.-Y., Li, X.-Q. and Wu, Z.-X. (1981). Lightcurves of variable asteroids. IV. *Acta Astron. Sin.*, **22**, 169–173.

Chapman, C. R., Johnson, T. V. and McCord, T. B. (1971). A review of spectrophotometric studies of asteroids. NASA Special Publication, **267**, 51.

Chapman, C. R., McCord, T. B. and Johnson, T. V. (1973). Asteroid spectral reflectivities. *Astron. J.*, **78**, 126–140.

Chihara, H., Koike, C., Tsuchiyama, A., Tachibana, S. and Sakamoto, D. (2002). Compositional dependence of infrared absorption spectra of crystalline silicates. I. Mg-Fe pyroxenes. *Astron. Astrophys.*, **391**, 267–273.

Cohen, M., *et al.* (1998). Spectral irradiance calibration in the infrared. VIII. 5–14 micron spectroscopy of the asteroids Ceres, Vesta, and Pallas. *Astron. J.*, **115**, 1671–1679.

Day, K. L. (1981). Infrared extinction of amorphous iron silicates. *Astrophys. J.*, **246**, 110–112.

Delbo, M., Mueller, M., Emery, J. P., Rozitis, B., Capria, M.T. (2015). Asteroid thermophysical modeling. In: Asteroids IV (Michel, P., et al., eds.), pp. 107–128, Univ. Arizona, Tucson.

Dotto, E., *et al.* (2000). ISO results on bright main belt asteroids: PHT-S observations. *Astron. Astrophys.*, **358**, 1133–1141.

Drummond, J. D., Fugate, R. Q., Christou, J. C. and Hege, E. K. (1998). Full adaptive optics images of asteroids Ceres and Vesta: Rotational poles and triaxial ellipsoid dimensions. *Icarus*, **132**, 80–99.

Drummond, J. D., *et al.* (2014). Dwarf planet Ceres: Ellipsoid dimensions and rotational pole from Keck and VLT adaptive optics images. *Icarus*, **236**, 28–37.

Fanale, F. P. and Salvail, J. R. (1989). The water regime of asteroid (1) Ceres. *Icarus*, **82**, 97–110.

Feldman, P. D., *et al.* (2015). Measurements of the near-nucleus coma of comet 67P/Churyumov-Gerasimenko with the Alice far-ultraviolet spectrograph on Rosetta. *Astron. Astrophys.*, **583**, A8 (8 pp.).

Fienga, A., Manche, H., Laskar, J. and Gastineau, M. (2008). INPOP06: A new numerical planetary ephemeris. *Astron. Astrophys.*, **477**, 315–327.

Fornasier, S., Lazzarin, M., Barbieri, C. and Barucci, M. A. (1999). Spectroscopic comparison of aqueous altered asteroids with CM2 carbonaceous chondrite meteorites. *Astron. Astrophys. Suppl.*, **135**, 65–73.

Gary, B. L. and Keihm, S. J. (1978). Interpretation of ground-based microwave measurements of the Moon using a detailed regolith properties model. Lunar and Planetary Science Conference IX, pp. 371–373.

Gehrels, T. and Owings, D. (1962). Photometric studies of asteroids. IX. Additional light-curves. *Astrophys. J.*, **135**, 906–924.

Gehrels, T. (1970). Photometry of asteroids. In: A. Dollfus (ed.) *Surfaces and Interiors of Planets and Satellites*, 317–375.

Gehrels, T. and Tedesco, E. F. (1979). Minor planets and related objects. XXVIII. Asteroid magnitudes and phase relations. *Astron. J.*, **84**, 1079–1087.

Goffin, E. (1991). The orbit of 203 Pompeja and the mass of Ceres. *Astron. Astrophys.*, **249**, 563–568.

Groeneveld, I. and Kuiper, G. P. (1954). Photometric studies of asteroids. II. *Astrophys. J.*, **120**, 529–546.

Hapke, B. (2012). Theory of reflectance and emittance spectroscopy (2nd Ed). Cambridge University Press.

Harwood, M. (1924). Variations in the light of asteroids. Harvard College Observatory Circular **269**, 1–15.

Hayne, P. O. and Aharonson, O. (2015). Thermal stability of ice on Ceres with rough topography. *J. Geophys. Res. Planet.*, **120**, 1567–1584.

Helfenstein, P., *et al.* (1994). Galileo photometry of asteroid 951 Gaspra. *Icarus,* **107**, 37–60.

Helfenstein, P., *et al*. (1996). Galileo photometry of asteroid 243 Ida. *Icarus,* **120**, 48–65.

Hendrix, A. R., Vilas, F. and Li, J.-Y. (2016). Ceres: Sulfur deposits and graphitized carbon. *Geophys. Res. Lett*., **43**, 8920–8927.

Herschel, W. (1802). Observations on the two lately discovered celestial bodies. *Philos. Trans. R. Soc*. London, **92**, 213–232.

Hilton, J. L. (1997). New masses and densities for 1 Ceres, 2 Pallas, and 4 Vesta. 191st AAS Meeting, id.71.06. Bulletin of the AAS 29, 1318.

Hollis, A. J. and Toone, J. (1985). The photometric properties of 1 Ceres — Observations in 1980–1981. *J. British Astron. Assoc*. **96**, 18.

Hollis, A. J. (1988). Photometric properties of the minor planets: Observations of (1) Ceres in 1972, 1977, 1982, 1984 and 1985. *J. British Astron. Assoc*., **98**, 351–354.

Hunt, G. R. (1982). Spectroscopies properties of rocks and minerals. In: Carmichael, R. S. (ed.), *Handbook of Physical Properties of Rocks*, vol. 1, CRC press, Boca Raton, FL.

Johnson, W. A. (1939). Spectrophotometric study of three asteroids. Harvard College Observatory bulletin No. 911, 13–16.

Keihm, S., *et al*. (2013). Reconciling main belt asteroid spectral flux density measurements with a self-consistent thermophysical model. *Icarus*, **226**, 1086–1102.

King, T. V. V., Clark, R. N., Calvin, W. M., Sherman, D. M. and Brown, R. H. (1992). Evidence of ammonium-bearing minerals on Ceres. *Science*, 255, 1551–1553.

Kitamura, M. (1959). Photoelectric study of colors of asteroids and meteorites. *Publ. Astron. Soc. Japan*, **11**, 79–89.

Koike, C. and Hasegawa, H. (1987). Mid-infrared extinction coefficients of amorphous silicates. *Astrophys. Space Sci*., **134**, 361–379.

Koike, C., *et al*. (2003). Compositional dependence of infrared absorption spectra of crystalline silicate. II. Natural and synthetic olivines. *Astron. Astrophys*., **399**, 1101–1107.

Koike, C., *et al*. (2006). Temperature effects on the mid- and far-infrared spectra of olivine particles. *Astron. Astrophys*., **449**, 583–596.

Konopliv, A. S., *et al*. (2006). A global solution for the Mars static and seasonal gravity, Mars orientation, Phobos and Deimos masses, and Mars ephemeris. *Icarus,* **182**, 23–50.

Kovačević, A. and Kuzmanoski, M. (2007). A new determination of the mass of (1) Ceres. *Earth Moon Planet*, **100**, 117–123.

Kovačević, A. and Andjelka, B. (2012). Determination of the mass of Ceres based on the most gravitationally efficient close encounters. *Mon. N. R. Astron. Soc*., **419**, 2725–2736.

Küppers, M., *et al*. (2014). Localized sources of water vapour on the dwarf planet (1) Ceres. *Nature*, **505**, 525–527.

Lagerkvist, C.-I. and Magnusson, P. (1990). Analysis of asteroid lightcurves. II. Phase curves in a generalized HG-system. *Astron. Astrophys. Suppl. Ser.*, **86**, 119–165.
Lagerkvist, C.-I., Magnusson, P., Williams, I. P., Buontempo, M. E. and Gibbs, P. (1988). Physical studies of asteroids. XVII. Phase relations and composite lightcurves obtained with the Carlsberg Meridian Circle. *Astron. Astrophys. Suppl. Ser.*, **73**, 395–405.
Lagerkvist, C.-I., Magnusson, P., Williams, I. P., Buontempo, M. E., Gibbs, P. and Morrison, L. V. (1989). Physical studies of asteroids. XIX. Phase relations and composite lightcurves obtained with the Carlsberg Meridian Circle. *Astron. Astrophys. Suppl. Ser.*, **78**, 519–532.
Landgraf, W. (1988). The mass of Ceres. *Astron. Astrophys.*, **191**, 161–166.
Larson, H. P., Feierberg, M. A., Fink, U. and Smith, H. A. (1979). Remote spectroscopic identification of carbonaceous chondrite mineralogies: Applications to Ceres and Pallas. *Icarus*, **39**, 257–271.
Lebofsky, L. A. (1978). Asteroid 1 Ceres: Evidence for water of hydration. *Mon. N. R. Astron. Soc.*, **182**, 17–21.
Lebofsky, L. A., Feierberg, M. A., Tokunaga, A. T., Larson, H. P. and Johnson, J. R. (1981). The 1.7- to 4.2-μm spectrum of asteroid 1 Ceres: Evidence for structural water in clay minerals. *Icarus,* **48**, 453–459.
Lebofsky, L. A., *et al.* (1986). A refined "standard" thermal model for asteroids based on observations of 1 Ceres and 2 Pallas. *Icarus*, **68**, 239–251.
Li, J.-Y., A'Hearn, M. F. and McFadden, L. A. (2004). Photometric analysis of Eros from NEAR data. *Icarus*, **172**, 415–431.
Li, J.-Y., *et al.* (2006). Photometric analysis of 1 Ceres and surface mapping from HST observations. Icarus, **182**, 143–160.
Li, J.-Y., *et al.* (2009). UV absorption features of asteroid 1 Ceres. 40th Lunar and Planetary Science Conference XL, id.2101.
Li, J.-Y., *et al.* (2020). Disk-integrated thermal properties of Ceres measured at millimeter wavelengths. *Astron. J.*, **159**, 215 (9 pp.).
Lim, L. F., *et al.* (2005). Thermal infrared (8–13 μm) spectra of 29 asteroids: The Cornell mid-infrared asteroid spectroscopy (MIDAS) survey. *Icarus*, **173**, 385–408.
Lupishko, D. F., Efimov, Yu.S. and Shackhovskoj, N. M. (1992). Ceres' peculiar polarization. Bulletin of the Astronomical Society, Vol. 24, No. 2, p. 874.
Lyon, R. J. P. (1964). Analysis of rocks by spectral infrared emission (8 to 25 microns). *Econ. Geol.*, **60**, 717–736.
McAdam, M. M., Sunshine, J. M., Howard, K. T. and McCoy, T. M. (2015). Aqueous alteration on asteroids: Linking the mineralogy and spectroscopy of CM and CI chondrites. *Icarus*, **245**, 320–332.
McCord, T. B. and Gaffey, M. J. (1974). Asteroids: Surface composition from reflection spectroscopy. *Science*, **186**, 352–355.

McCord, T. B. and Sotin, C. (2005). Ceres: Evolution and current state. *J. Geophys. Res.*, **110**, E05009.

Merline, W. J., Stern, S. A., Binzel, R. P., Festou, M. C., Flynn, B. C. and Lebofsky, L. A. (1996). HST imaging of 1 Ceres. American Astronomical Society, DPS meeting #28, id.10.25; Bulletin of the American Astronomical Society, Vol. 28, p. 1101.

Michalak, G. (2000). Determination of asteroid masses I. (1) Ceres, (2) Pallas and (4) Vesta. *Astron. Astrophys.*, **360**, 363–374.

Milliken, R. E. and Rivkin, A. S. (2009). Brucite and carbonate assemblages from altered olivine-rich materials on Ceres. *Nature Geosci.*, **2**, 258–261.

Millis, R. L., *et al.* (1987). The size, shape, density, and albedo of Ceres from its occultation of BD+8°471. *Icarus*, **72**, 507–518.

Muinonen, K., Piironen, J., Shkuratov, Yu.G., Ovcharenko, A. and Clark, B. E. (2002). Asteroid photometric and polarimetric phase effects. In: *Asteroids III*, Bottke, W. F. Jr., *et al.* (eds.), University of Arizona Press, Tucson, 123–138.

Müller, T. G. and Lagerros, J. S. V. (1998). Asteroids as far-infrared photometric standards for ISOPHOT. *Astron. Astrophys.*, **338**, 340–352.

Moullet, A., Gurwell, M. and Carry, B. (2010). Thermal rotational lightcurve of dwarf-planet (1) Ceres at 235 GHz with the Submillimeter Array. *Astron. Astrophys.*, **516**, L10 (4 pp.).

Mouret, S., Hestroffer, D. and Mignard, F. (2007). Asteroid masses and improvement with Gaia. *Astron. Astrophys.*, **472**, 1017–1027.

Murchie, S., *et al.* (2002). Color variations on Eros from NEAR multispectral imaging. *Icarus,* **155**, 145–168.

Neveu, M. and Desch, S. J. (2015). Geochemistry, thermal evolution, and cryovolcanism on Ceres with a muddy ice mantle. *Geophys. Res. Lett.*, **42**, 10,197–10,206.

Neveu, M., Desch, S. J. and Castillo-Rogez, J. C. (2015). Core cracking and hydrothermal circulation can profoundly affect Ceres' geophysical evolution. *J. Geophys. Res. Planet.*, **120**, 123–154.

Parker, J.Wm., *et al.* (2002). Analysis of the first disk-resolved images of Ceres from ultraviolet observations with the Hubble Space Telescope. *Astron. J.*, **123**, 549–557.

Parkhurst, H. M. (1901). Photometric observations of (433) Eros. *Astron. J.*, 21, 148–149.

Pitjeva, E. V. (2001). Progress in the determination of some astronomical constants from radiometric observations of planets and spacecraft. *Astron. Astrophys.*, **371**, 760–765.

Pitjeva, E. V. (2004). Estimations of masses of the largest asteroids and the main asteroid belt from ranging to planets, Mars orbiters and landers. 35th COSPAR Scientific Assembly, p. 2014.

Pitjeva, E. V. (2005). High-precision ephemerides of planets — EPM and determination of some astronomical constants. *Solar System Res.*, **39**, 176–186.

Reddy, V., *et al.* (2015). Mineralogy and surface composition of asteroids. In: Michel, P., DeMeo, F. E. and Bottle, W. F. (eds.), *Asteroids IV*, University of Arizona Press, Tucson, 43–63.

Redman, R. O., Feldman, P. A. and Matthews, H. E. (1998). High-quality photometry of asteroids at millimeter and submillimeter wavelengths. *Astron. J.*, **116**, 1478–1490.

Rivkin, A. S., Volquardsen, E. L. and Clark, B. E. (2006). The surface composition of Ceres: Discovery of carbonates and iron-rich clays. *Icarus*, **185**, 563–567.

Rivkin, A. S., *et al.* (2011). The surface composition of Ceres. *Space Sci. Rev.* **163**, 95–116.

Roettger, E. E. and Buratti, B. J. (1994). Ultraviolet spectra and geometric albedos of 45 asteroids. *Icarus*, **112**, 496–512.

Roth, L., *et al.* (2016). Constraints on an exosphere at Ceres from Hubble Space Telescope observations. *Geophys. Res. Lett.*, **43**, 2465–2472.

Rousselot, P., *et al.* (2011). A search for water vaporization on Ceres. *Astron. J.*, **142**, 125 (6 pp.).

Russell, C. T., *et al.* (2004). Dawn: A journey in space and time. *Planet. Space Sci.*, **52,** 465–489.

Saint-Pé, O., Combes, M. and Rigaut, F. (1993). Ceres surface properties by high-resolution imaging from Earth. *Icarus,* **105**, 271–281.

Salisbury, J. W., D'Aria, D. M. and Jarosewich, E. (1991). Midinfrared (2.5–13.5 μm) reflectance spectra of powdered stony meteorites. *Icarus*, **92**, 280–297.

Sandakova, E. V. (1962). O Pokazatelyakh Tsveta Malykh planet. *Publ. Astron. Observ. Kiev*, **10**, 3–15.

Schloerb, F. P., *et al.* (2015). MIRO observations of subsurface temperatures of the nucleus of 67P/Churyumov-Gerasimenko. *Astron. Astrophys.*, **583**, A29 (11 pp.).

Schröder, S. E., *et al.*, (2017). Resolved spectrophotometric properties of the Ceres surface from Dawn Framing Camera images. *Icarus*, **288**, 201–225.

Schober, H. J., (1976). Photoelectric photometry of 1 Ceres during the Ceres-campaign 1975. Mitteilungen der Astronomischen Gesellschaft, Vol. 40, p. 207.

Schörghofer, N. (2008). The lifetime of ice on main belt asteroids. *Astrophys. J.*, **682**, 697–705.

Schörghofer, N., *et al.* (2017). The putative cerean exosphere. *Astrophys. J.*, **850**, 85 (7 pp.).

Schramm, D. N., Tera, F. and Wasserburg, G. J. (1970). The isotopic abundance of 26Mg and limits on 26Al in the early solar system. *Earth and Planet. Sci. Lett.,* **10**, 44–59.

Schubart, J. (1970). The mass of Ceres. *IAU Circ.*, **2268**, #1.

Schubart, J. (1974). The masses of the first two asteroids. *Astron. Astrophys.*, **30**, 289–292.

Scott, A. and Duley, W. W. (1996). Ultraviolet and infrared refractive indices of amorphous silicates. *Astrophys. J. Suppl.*, **105**, 401–405.

Simonelli, D. P., *et al.* (1998). Photometric properties of Phobos surface materials from Viking images. *Icarus,* **131**, 52–77.

Sitarski, G. and Todorovic-Juchniewicz, B. (1992). Determination of the mass of (1) Ceres from perturbations on (203) Pompeja and (348) May. *Acta Astron.*, **42**, 139–144.

Sitarski, G. and Todorovic-Juchniewicz, B. (1995). Determination of masses of Ceres and Vesta from their perturbations on four asteroids. *Acta. Astron.*, **45**, 673–677.

Spencer, J. R. (1990). A rough-surface thermophysical model for airless planets. *Icarus,* **83**, 27–38.

Standish, E. M. and Hellings, R. W. (1989). A determination of the masses of Ceres, Pallas, and Vesta from their perturbations upon the orbit of Mars. *Icarus,* **80**, 326–333.

Takahashi, J., Itoh, Y. and Takahashi, S. (2011). Mid-infrared spectroscopy of 11 main-belt asteroids. *Publ. Astron. Soc. Jap.*, **63**, 499–511.

Taylor, R. C., Gehrels, T. and Capen, R. C. (1976). Minor planets and related objects. XXI. Photometry of eight asteroids. *Astron. J.*, **81**, 778–786.

Tedesco, E. F., *et al.* (1983). Worldwide photometry and lightcurve observations of 1 Ceres during the 1975–1976 apparition. *Icarus,* **54**, 23–29.

Tedesco, E. F., Noah, P. V., Noah, M. and Price, S. D. (2002). The supplemental IRAS minor planet survey. *Astron. J.*, **123**, 1056–1085.

Tholen, D. J. (1984). Asteroid taxonomy from cluster analysis of photometry. Thesis (Ph.D.), The University of Arizona, 1984.

Thomas, P. C., Adinolfi, D., Helfenstein, P., Simonelli, D. and Veverka, J. (1996). The surface of Deimos: Contribution of materials and processes to its unique appearance. *Icarus,* **123**, 536–556.

Thomas, P. C., *et al.* (1997). Impact excavation on asteroid 4 Vesta: Hubble Space Telescope results. *Science,* **277**, 1492–1495.

Thomas, P. C., *et al.* (2005). Differentiation of the asteroid Ceres as revealed by its shape. *Nature,* **437**, 224–226.

Titus, T. N. (2015). Ceres: Predictions for near-surface water ice stability and implications for plume generating processes. *Geophys. Res. Lett.*, **42**, 2130–2136.

Tu, L., Ip, W.-H. and Wang, Y.-C. (2014). A sublimation-driven exospheric model of Ceres. *Planet. Space Sci.*, **104**, 157–162.

Vernazza, P., *et al.* (2005). Analysis of near-IR spectra of 1 Ceres and 4 Vesta, targets of the Dawn mission. *Astron. Astrophys.*, **436**, 1113–1121.

Viateau, B. and Rapaport, M. (1995). The orbit of (2) Pallas. *Astron. Astrophys. Suppl.*, **111**, 305.

Viateau, B. and Rapaport, M. (1997). Improvement of the orbits of asteroids and the mass of (1) Ceres. Proc. ESA Symposium "Hipparcos — Venice '97", ESA SP-402, 9–94.
Viateau, B. and Rapaport, M. (1998). The mass of (1) Ceres from its gravitational perturbations on the orbits of 9 asteroids. *Astron. Astrophys.*, **334**, 729–235.
Vilas, F., Larson, S. M., Hatch, E. C. and Jarvis, K. S. (1993). CCD reflectance spectra of selected asteroids. II. Low-albedo asteroid spectra and data extraction techniques. *Icarus,* **105**, 67–78.
Watson, F. G. (1940). Colar and magnitudes of asteroids. Harvard College Observatory Bulletin No. 913, 3–4.
Webster, W. J., *et al.* (1988). The microwave spectrum of the asteroid Ceres. *Astron. J.,* **95**, 1263–1268.
Webster, W. J., Jr. and Johnston, K. J. (1989). On the wavelength dependence of apparent emissivity of asteroid microwave emissions: Ceres and Vesta. *Publ. Astron. Soc. Pacif.*, **101**, 122–125.
Wynn-Williams, D. D., Cabrol, N. A., Grin, E. A., Haberle, R. M. and Stoker, C. R. (2001). Brines in seepage channels as eluants for subsurface relict biomolecules on Mars? *Astrobiology,* **1**, 165–184.
Zellner, B., Gehrels, T. and Gradie, J. (1974). Minor planets and related objects. XVI. Polarimetric diameters. *Astron. J.*, **79**, 1100–1110.
Zellner, B. and Gradie, J. (1976). Minor planets and related objects. XX. Polarimetric evidence for the albedos and compositions of 94 asteroids. *Astron. J.*, **81**, 262–280.
Zolotov, M. Yu. (2009). On the composition and differentiation of Ceres. *Icarus,* **204**, 183–193.

Chapter 3

Dawn Mission Overview

Dawn is one of NASA's Discovery Class missions, which are focused, low cost, and quick in development. Dawn carries three scientific instruments, a visible camera, a visible and near-infrared mapping spectrometer, and a gamma ray and neutron detector, plus a gravity science investigation utilizing the spacecraft's two-way radio communication system. Dawn is the first science mission that leverages the high fuel efficiency of ion propulsion systems to journey to the main asteroid belt, the first to orbit two targets with a single launch, and the first to orbit a dwarf planet.

The detailed history of Dawn is described by Russell and Raymond (2011). The original mission concept was conceived in the 1990s with different targets and technical details, and, after many years of iterations in both the targets and mission scenario, Dawn was finally selected in 2001. The development of the mission leading to the final launch in 2007 was full of bumps, but the exploration phases at Vesta and then Ceres were a great success full of eye-opening surprises and exciting results. The discoveries from the Dawn mission at Vesta and especially at Ceres permanently changed our views of these two objects, significantly advancing our understanding of the early evolution of terrestrial planets and icy bodies, and broadly impacted many fields in planetary science research.

This chapter will provide an overview of the Dawn mission, including its scientific drivers and goals, implementation, scientific payload, science operations, and overall mission timeline.

3.1 Scientific Goals and Measurement Objectives

The overarching goal of the Dawn mission was to understand the processes occurring in the early solar system when planets were formed and evolved. The two targets of the Dawn mission, (4) Vesta and (1) Ceres, are the two most massive objects residing in the main asteroid belt (Fig. 3.1).

Unlike asteroids of diameter <100 km, which are almost exclusively multigenerational, cascade-collisional fragments of larger precursors, the large asteroids (>100 km) in the asteroid belt have escaped collisional destruction. Their smaller size compared to full-sized planets (Fig. 3.2) implies faster cooling and limited full scale thermal evolution. Therefore, these large asteroids are considered protoplanets in that they inform on the internal structure, physical properties, and chemical composition of the early-stage evolution of full-sized planets, and their surfaces and shallow subsurfaces preserved the signatures of their early environments.

Figure 3.1: Comparison of Ceres, Vesta, and other asteroids visited by spacecraft missions. Credit: Marc Rayman, JPL/Caltech.

Figure 3.2: Sizes of Ceres and Vesta in comparison with Mars, Mercury, and the Moon. Credit: NASA/JPL-Caltech/UCLA.

From a large class of meteorites called the howardite, eucrite, and diogenite (HED) meteorites that are generally considered to originate from Vesta (McCord *et al.*, 1970), we know that the protoplanet has undergone magmatic differentiation and began to solidify as early as about two million years after the first condensation of solids in the solar nebula (McSween and Huss, 2010). On the other hand, no meteorite is known to be directly derived from Ceres, yet the knowledge prior to the Dawn mission suggests that Ceres is rich in water and could be partially differentiated (McCord *et al.*, 2011). Therefore, Vesta and Ceres represent the very early stage of planetary evolution of the two classes of planets in the solar system, terrestrial planets in the inner solar system and large icy bodies in the outer solar system, respectively. Hence, through exploring these two targets by the same suite of instruments in a single mission,

Dawn has essentially been investigating objects representing the dawn of the solar system, hence the name of the mission.

Dawn's scientific objectives for both targets included the following (Russell *et al*., 2011): (1) to characterize the surface and probe the internal structure; (2) to create a detailed shape model and map the geologic units on the surface; and (3) to determine the time of formation and the evolutionary processes. In order to achieve these science objectives, a set of measurement objectives was derived. These defined the Level 1 requirements listed below that were the basic requirements used to define mission success criteria.

List of Level 1 requirements:

1. Determine the bulk density to 1%.
2. Determine the orientation of the spin axis to within 0.5°.
3. Obtain images of 80% of the surface with a resolution of 100 m/pixel at Vesta and 200 m/pixel at Ceres in the clear and three color filters.
4. Obtain a topographic map of 80% of the surface with a horizontal resolution of 100 m at Vesta and 200 m at Ceres and a vertical resolution of 10 m at Vesta and 20 m at Ceres.
5. Obtain 10,000 spectral frames at wavelengths of 0.25–5.0 μm with a spectral resolution of 10 nm to measure and map the mineral composition. At least half of these frames will be at a spatial resolution of ≤200 m at Vesta and ≤400 m at Ceres with the rest at a spatial resolution of ≤800 m at Vesta and ≤1600 m at Ceres.
6. Measure and map the abundance of the major rock-forming elements to 20% precision and a spatial resolution of ~1.5 times the mapping altitude over the entire surface to ~1 m depth.
7. Determine the gravity field with a half-wavelength resolution of 90 km.

3.2 Spacecraft and Payloads

3.2.1 *Dawn Spacecraft*

Dawn was the first NASA science mission that took advantage of the high-efficiency ion propulsion system (IPS). The technology was successfully proven by NASA's Deep Space 1 technology demonstration mission. The design of the spacecraft (Fig. 3.3(a)) was driven by the propulsive requirements of the ion engines, the science data volume requirements, as well as

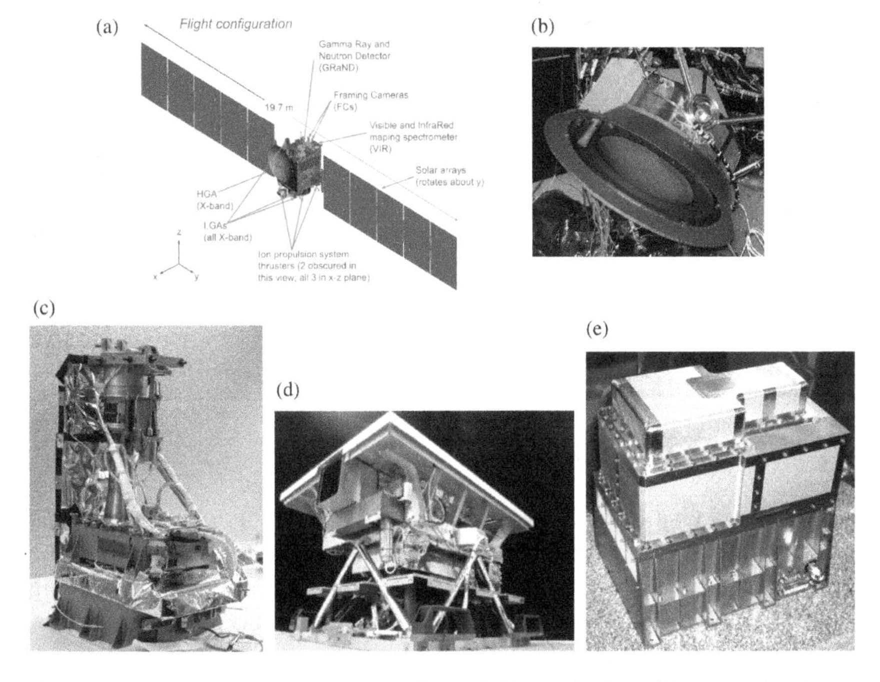

Figure 3.3: (a) Dawn spacecraft (Konopliv *et al.*, 2011). (b) One of the Dawn ion thrusters (Brophy, 2011). (c) Dawn Framing Camera (Sierks *et al.*, 2011). (d) Dawn Visible and infrared mapping spectrometer (De Sanctis *et al.*, 2011). (e) Dawn Gamma ray and neutron detector (Prettyman *et al.*, 2011). Not to scale.

reliability and robustness critical for the long duration of the mission (Thomas *et al.*, 2011).

The IPS was essential to enable such a long (planned duration 9 years) journey to the main asteroid belt and orbit two targets within the budget cap of the Discovery Mission (Fig. 3.3(b)). Over the 11 years of interplanetary travel and exploration of Vesta and Ceres, Dawn's IPS thrust for a total of 5.9 years, providing a cumulative velocity increment of ~11 km/s, which is similar to the velocity increment obtained from its launch vehicle (Brophy, 2011). The IPS system onboard the Dawn spacecraft was a fully redundant and fault-tolerant system that was composed of three 30-cm-diameter xenon ion thrusters and two Power Processor Units, as well as two Digital Control and Interface Units and three 2-axis thruster gimbal assemblies, one for each thruster. The Dawn IPS performed almost flawlessly over the course of the mission.

In order to provide sufficient power to the IPS, as well as the science payload, the Dawn spacecraft was equipped with a pair of solar panels that were about 16 m long combined and were capable of providing ~620 W power at the heliocentric distance of Ceres (2.8–2.9 au), where the solar flux is only about 1/8 of that near the Earth. The spacecraft carried a total of about 425 kg of xenon propellant used by the ion engines. The 1.5-meter-diameter high-gain antenna satisfied the downlink rate of 60 kbps required to transmit science data to the ground, and the onboard storage volume of 2.5 Gbits provided enough temporary storage for the data collected between successive downlinks.

3.2.2 *Framing Camera*

The Framing Camera (FC) was both a mission critical optical navigation system and a science instrument. The primary scientific objectives of the FC were to determine the physical properties of the targets, including rotational state, global shape, and surface geomorphology, and to contribute to the mapping of mineralogy and chemical composition through multicolor imaging, as well as the determination of the interior structure (Sierks *et al*., 2011). The FC was also the primary instrument used to produce high-resolution digital terrain models for both targets (Raymond *et al*., 2011). During approach and proximity operations, the FC performed searches for possible dust and satellite companions in the vicinity of both targets.

The FC was contributed by the Max Planck Institute for Solar System Studies in Katlenburg-Lindau (later moved to Göttingen), Germany. Fig. 3.3(c) shows the flight version of the FC. The camera system had two redundant cameras, termed FC1 and FC2. During the whole mission, FC2 was the primary camera that collected the majority of the science data, while FC1 was kept as backup because of the excessive residual charge on its CCD after readout, affecting the image quality and calibration (Schröder *et al*., 2013). Both cameras were equipped with one broadband panchromatic filter and seven narrow band color filters that covered from 440 nm to 980 nm wavelengths (Fig. 3.4). The basic characteristics of the optical system are summarized in Table 3.1. More details on the FC can be found in Sierks *et al*. (2011). The calibration of FC images is described in Schröder *et al*. (2013, 2014).

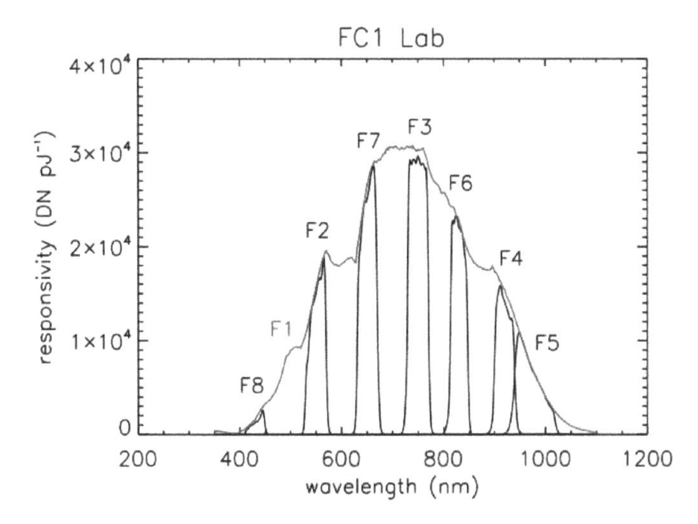

Figure 3.4: Framing Camera filter throughput. Reprinted from Space Science Review vol. 163, Sierks *et al.*, The Dawn Framing Camera, pp. 263–327, Copyright with permission from Springer.

3.2.3 *VIR Spectrometer*

The Dawn visible and infrared spectrometer (VIR) was a hyperspectral spectrometer with imaging capability. Its scientific objective was to determine the mineralogy of surface materials in geological context through the diagnostic absorption features of common rock-forming minerals expected on Vesta and Ceres. VIR was provided by the Italian Space Agency (ASI) and the Italian National Institute for Astrophysics (INAF) in Rome. It was derived from the previous VIRTIS-M instrument aboard the Rosetta and Venus Express missions. Its key parameters are listed in Table 3.1. The diagnostic features of minerals expected on the two objects covered by the VIR include the 1 μm and 2 μm mafic bands of pyroxene and olivine, the 3 μm water region of the hydration band, the 1.5, 2.0, and 3.0 bands of water ice, the 3.9 μm carbonate band, and the 3.2–3.6 μm C–H stretching bands of organic materials.

The VIR instrument (Fig. 3.3(d)) is equipped with a long slit on the focal plane of the optics and a grating behind the slit to enable spectral mapping of the scene with high spectral and spatial

Table 3.1: Key parameters of FC and VIR.

Parameter	FC	VIR-VIS	VIR-IR
Focal length	150 mm	152 mm	
F-number	7.5	5.6	3.2
Frame size	1024 × 1024	432 × 256 (band × sample)	
Field of View	5.5° × 5.5°	3.67° × 3.67°	
iFOV	93.7 μrad	250 μrad	
Spectral range	0.4 – 1.05 μm	0.25 – 1.05 μm	1.0 – 5.0 μm
Spectral resolution	—	1.8 nm/band	9.8 nm/band

resolutions. The spectrometer can be operated in both scanning mode utilizing the internal scanning mirror and push broom mode using the spacecraft motion for 2D mapping of the scene. Both modes have been used during the Dawn science operations while allowing the spacecraft to keep the instrument pointed nearly perpendicular to the local surface and the solar panels toward the Sun at the same time. A detailed review of the VIR instrument is provided by De Sanctis *et al.* (2011).

3.2.4 *Gamma Ray and Neutron Detector*

The Gamma Ray and Neutron Detector (GRaND) measured elemental abundances in the top meter of the regolith by the element's characteristic gamma ray emissions and neutron radiation activated by high-energy cosmic rays. The measurement objective of GRaND was to map the surface elemental composition at regional scales. It was targeted at the constituent elements of silicate and oxide minerals, ices, and the products of volcanic exposure for Vesta and aqueous alteration for Ceres.

The GRaND instrument (Fig. 3.3(e)) was built by the Los Alamos National Laboratory and operated by the Planetary Science Institute in the United States. The energy ranges of the various detectors in GRaND are listed in Table 3.2. The accuracy and spatial resolution of GRaND measurements depend on the total integration time and orbital altitude. For the details of this instrument, readers are referred to the review by Prettyman *et al.* (2011).

Table 3.2: Key characteristics for GRaND.

Sensor	**Energy Range (MeV)**	**keV per Channel**
±Z phos.	0–2.55	10
±Y BLP	0–2.55	10
BGO	0–10	10
CZT	0–3	2

Source: Prettyman *et al.* (2011).

3.2.5 *Radio Science*

The gravity investigation of Dawn is summarized by Konopliv *et al.* (2011). The objective of the Dawn gravity investigation was to achieve a half-wavelength surface resolution better than 90 km and 300 km in the measurement of the gravity fields of Vesta and Ceres, respectively, using high-precision X-band Doppler tracking and landmark tracking from optical images. The gravity field precision was specified to somewhere between harmonic degrees 15 and 25 for Vesta and about degree 10 for Ceres. Combined with the shape model, the gravity field measurement allowed for the determination of the interior structures of both targets. The spin pole of both objects was also determined to high-precision. Similar to the GRaND measurements, the precision yielded by the gravity experiment also increases with the duration of data collection and the proximity of the spacecraft to the surface.

3.3 Science Operations

Dawn was launched on September 27, 2007, from the Kennedy Space Center in Florida, USA. Its interplanetary trajectory throughout the mission is shown in Fig. 3.5. After a year and a half of cruising, it flew past Mars for a gravity assist to boost its velocity. Dawn arrived at Vesta in July 2011, stayed for slightly more than a year until September 2012. The journey from Vesta to Ceres took about two and a half years. Dawn arrived at Ceres in March 2015 and stayed in orbit around Ceres until the end of the mission in October 2018.

The mission operations served the objective of mapping the entire surfaces of the two targets with the three instruments and gravity science. All three instruments were coaligned on the mounting deck with the same

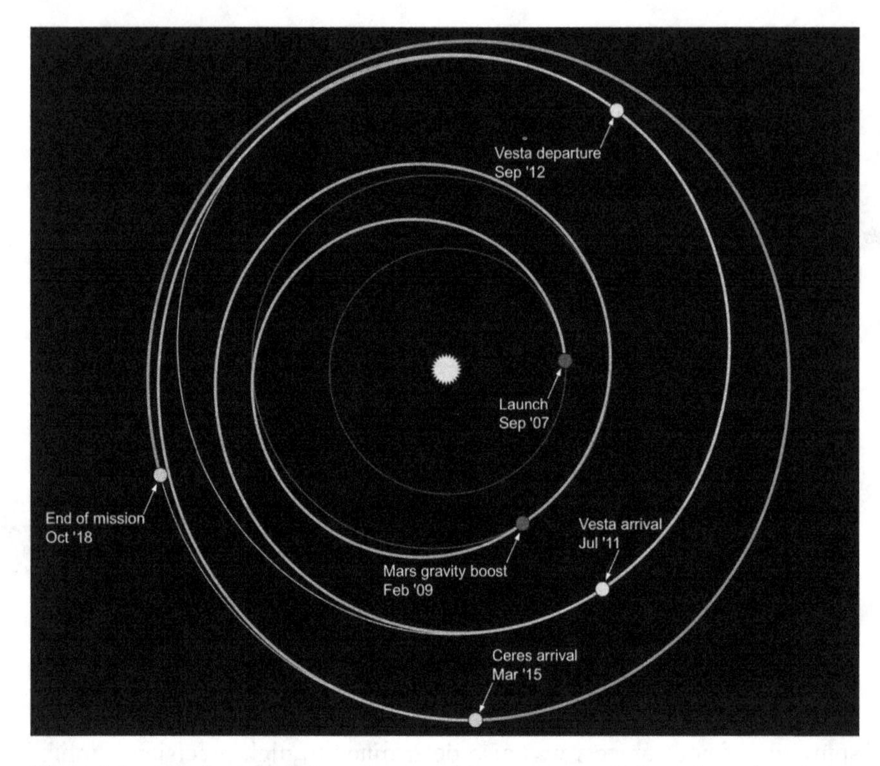

Figure 3.5: The interplanetary trajectory of Dawn spacecraft throughout the mission. Credit: NASA/JPL-Caltech.

pointing to allow them to work at the same time. The science sequences during the primary mission were similar for the two targets, both consisting of four phases, the Approach phase, Survey Orbit, High-Altitude Mapping Orbit (HAMO), and Low-Altitude Mapping Orbit (LAMO), with successively lower orbital altitudes (see Fig. 3.6 in the case of Ceres). At the end of the primary investigation of each target, extended mission phases were appended. For Ceres, the LAMO was first extended as XMO1 (eXtended Mission Orbit), and then the XMO2 orbit at the HAMO altitude. It was followed by the XMO3 at much higher altitude than Survey, both to allow GRaND to collect background measurements to improve the data analysis and in preparation for the elliptic XMO4. During XMO4, the spacecraft passed right between Ceres and the Sun near the periapse in order to observe Ceres at nearly 0° phase angle. Finally, after an extended phase of operational planning (XMO5), the

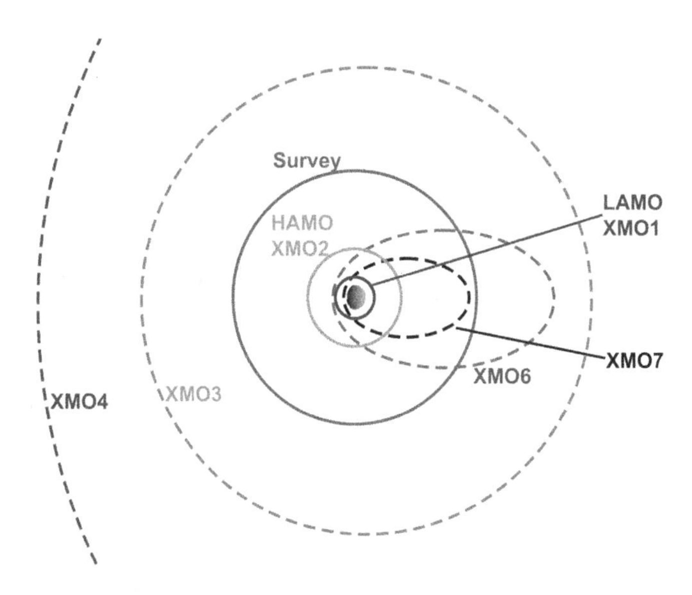

Figure 3.6: Science orbits of Dawn around Ceres. Solid lines are the orbits during the primary mission (Survey, HAMO, LAMO), and dashed lines are the orbits during the extended mission (XMO1–XMO7). XMO5 is not shown because no science investigation was planned during this phase. The orbital sizes and the size of Ceres are roughly proportional, although the orientations of the periapsis of elliptical orbits are just representative.

spacecraft was sent to two elliptic orbits with the periapse altitudes comparable to LAMO altitude in XMO6, and then about ten times lower than the LAMO altitude in XMO7. These mission phases and the orbital parameters of Dawn are summarized in Table 3.3.

Each mission phase served specific objectives and was driven by one science investigation. Approach started when the target was barely resolved in the camera, and ended when the spacecraft was in a circular orbit of radius about 30 times the radius of the target. The spacecraft was captured into orbit around the target during this phase. The objectives of Approach included the following: (1) to determine the size, bulk shape and the rotational pole and period of the target; (2) to survey the major geologic units and landmarks; and (3) to search for potential hazards such as satellites and dust in the vicinity of the target. Both the FC and the VIR were collecting science data during Approach, while GRaND stayed on but not expecting any signature of the target due to the large distance to the surface.

Table 3.3: Summary of Dawn science acquisition phases at Ceres. Gaps between phases represent transfers from one orbit to the next. Dates are provided in Coordinated Universal Time (UTC). XMO5 is not included because no science investigation was planned for this phase.

Phase	Start (UTC)	End (UTC)	Altitude (km)	FC Pixel Scale (m/pix)
Approach	2014-12-27	2015-05-09	Varies	Varies
Survey	2015-06-04	2015-07-01	4,400	410
HAMO	2015-08-16	2015-10-23	1,480	140
LAMO	2015-12-16	2016-06-19	375	35
XMO1	2016-06-19	2016-09-02	375	35
XMO2	2016-10-07	2016-11-04	1,480	140
XMO3	2016-12-10	2017-02-23	7,530–9,030	704–842
XMO4	2017-04-28	2017-06-03	13,000–52,800	1,900, 4,000
XMO6	2018-05-15	2018-05-31	440–4,700	41–440
XMO7	2018-06-09	2018-10-31	35–4,000	3.8–375

The objective of the Survey phase was to perform a global survey of the target with the camera and VIR. The driving instrument during this phase was VIR because it has a much smaller FOV than the FC, and the altitude of this orbit allowed VIR to cover the whole surface for mineralogical mapping. The survey orbit had an altitude about ten times Ceres's radius. The FOV of the FC covered about half the diameter of the target.

The HAMO orbit served as the primary mission phase to map the geomorphology of the whole surface of Ceres, as well as deriving a global digital terrain model. The driving instrument was the FC. The VIR spectrometer kept collecting data during this phase at a higher spatial resolution than during the Survey phase, but left gaps in between the ground tracks. The GRaND started to receive signals above the noise level, but not sensitive enough to provide useful results. The altitude of the HAMO orbit was about three times the target radius.

LAMO was the lowest circular orbit originally planned at Ceres, and was driven by the GRaND and gravity science for complete elemental composition mapping and high-precision gravity measurements. The FC and the VIR collected data at much higher spatial resolution, but only covered small patches along the spacecraft ground tracks. These imaging and spectral data provide details about geological and mineralogical evolution processes.

At Ceres, the extended mission phase XMO1 was designed to boost the signal-to-noise ratio in the GRaND measurements in order to enhance the science returns from elemental abundance mapping. The other extended phases XMO2 to XMO7 at Ceres were primarily focused on a few regions identified to be of high science value, such as the Juling crater where varying amount of water ice deposit was noticed (Raponi *et al.*, 2018) and the enigmatic bright spots, the Cerealia Facula inside Occator crater. The final orbit XMO7 put the periapses right above the Cerealia Facula at a mere 35 km altitude, resulting in images of resolutions as good as 3.8 m/pixel (Castillo-Rogez and Rayman, 2020).

The end of the mission was determined by the availability of hydrazine fuel. Dawn was originally equipped with four reaction wheels, one of which for redundancy, for 3-axis spacecraft attitude stability. Hydrazine was used as ancillary attitude control and backup. However, two wheels failed by the time Dawn reached Ceres. A hybrid attitude control mode had since been developed and implemented to use hydrazine to assist the two working wheels. The lifespan of the mission had been dictated by how fast hydrazine was consumed since then. By late April in 2017, during the XMO4 phase, the third wheel failed, leaving the spacecraft completely dependent on hydrazine for attitude control. When all hydrazine was depleted, the spacecraft lost its ability to keep the solar panels toward the Sun and its antenna toward the Earth, and became silent at the end of October 2018 in the XMO7 orbit around Ceres. After that point, the Dawn mission had far exceeded all of its goals and was successfully concluded.

3.4 Summary of Key Results

The Dawn observations of Ceres not only confirmed the pre-Dawn understanding that Ceres is water-rich and has undergone global aqueous alteration and partial differentiation with tremendous additional details, but also made striking discoveries about brine-driven geologic activity and deep brine reservoirs, thus putting Ceres into the group of ocean worlds together with outer solar system icy bodies. Furthermore, Dawn revealed many remarkable geological features (Fig. 3.7). In this section, we provide a brief summary of the fundamental properties of Ceres (Table 3.4) as well as the most interesting findings derived from the Dawn mission.

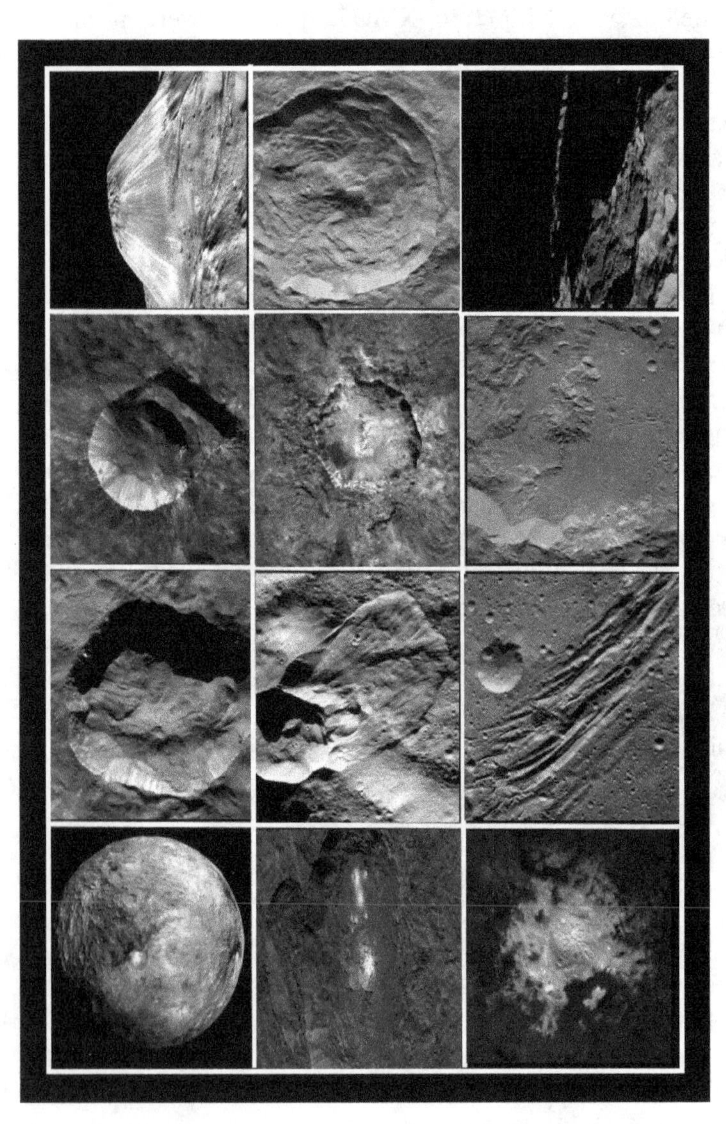

Figure 3.7: Collage of Features on Ceres https://photojournal.jpl.nasa.gov/catalog/PIA22090 This collage shows some of the most interesting geological sites that NASA's Dawn spacecraft has revealed at dwarf planet Ceres. Images were acquired with the spacecraft's framing camera during various phases of the mission: Survey orbit at a distance of about 4,400 kilometers; high-altitude mapping orbit (HAMO) at a distance of 1,470 kilometers from Ceres; and low-altitude mapping orbit (LAMO) at an altitude of 385 kilometers.

Table 3.4: Fundamental bulk properties of Ceres obtained by Dawn.

Volume	$(434.0 \pm 1.5) \times 10^6$ km^3
Mass	$(938.416 \pm 0.013) \times 10^{18}$ kg
Bulk density	2162 ± 8 kg/m^3 (±0.4%)
Gravitational flattening, J_2	0.026499 ± 0.000001
Spin pole (R.A., Decl.)	(291.412° ± 0.007°, 66.758° ± 0.002°)
Rotation rate	952.15326 ± 0.00004 deg/day
Global topography height range	−7.3 to +9.5 km

The Dawn VIR spectrometer obtained >24,000 VIS+IR spectral frames from the Survey and HAMO orbits, which resulted in detailed mapping of the surface mineralogy. These data revealed a surface that is ubiquitously covered by ammoniated phyllosilicates, indicating advanced aqueous alteration, and a likely outer solar system origin (De Sanctis *et al.*, 2015; Ammannito *et al.*, 2016). Detailed studies of the surface mineralogy suggest an association of carbonates, especially Na-carbonates with geologically young units and potentially active sites in the past (e.g., Carrozzo *et al.*, 2018). The identification of hydrated sodium chloride points to a deep-seated brine source and recent or even ongoing activity (De Sanctis *et al.*, 2020). The GRaND observations resulted in global maps of major elements such as iron and hydrogen, and constrains the abundance of other elements such as carbon within about one meter depth (Prettyman *et al.*, 2017). We describe the surface composition of Ceres based on the VIR and GRaND data and its implications in Chapter 4.

The Dawn FC mapped 99.9% of Ceres's surface at about 35 m/pixel in the clear filter and at 140 m/pixel in seven color filters. These images were used to study the topography, geology, and surface color, and they revealed a heavily cratered, mostly homogeneous surface punctuated by bright features (Fig. 3.7). The subtle color variations on Ceres reflect compositional variations and age-related changes in crater ejecta (Fig. 3.7; Nathues *et al.*, 2016; Stephan *et al.*, 2017). The topographic map covers 95% of Ceres's surface at a horizontal resolution of 100 m and an average vertical accuracy of 10.2 m and <20 m over 89% of the object (Park *et al.*, 2019). Geological features and units allow the study of geological processes (Williams *et al.*, 2018), as will be discussed in Chapter 5.

Extensive studies of subsurface water ice on Ceres were performed primarily based on the morphology derived from the FC imaging data and the hydrogen abundance map from the GRaND data. This will be discussed in Chapter 6. The crust of Ceres is found to be weak over large scales (> a few 100 km) in response to high strain rate upon impact, but strong over shorter scales and under low strain rate (e.g., Sizemore *et al.*, 2019). This constrains the crust of Ceres as composed of a mixture of about 30–40 vol.% ice, <20 vol.% salts and hydrated silicates, and >40 vol.% clathrates (Bland *et al.*, 2016; Ermakov *et al.*, 2017; Fu *et al.*, 2017). Subsurface water ice is found to be both widespread in Ceres's crust and displaying both vertical and lateral heterogeneity attributed to impacts (Sizemore *et al.*, 2019).

The gravity field of Ceres was measured globally with an 87-km-half-wavelength resolution (Konopliv *et al.*, 2018), and the result indicates that Ceres is nearly relaxed to hydrostatic equilibrium (Park *et al.*, 2016), leading to constraints on its internal structure (Ermakov *et al.*, 2017), lateral variations in crustal thickness, and the discovery of mascons associated with large craters such as Kerwan (Bland *et al.*, 2018). These results provide clues about the structure of the partially differentiated interior of Ceres, and constrain its thermal evolution and the drivers of the observed geological processes, as described in Chapter 7.

Altogether, the Dawn data led to the identification of a few sites that show possible recent activity, such as Occator crater, the Cerealia Facula (Scully *et al.*, 2019, 2020), Ahuna Mons, and other large montes (Ruesch *et al.*, 2016; Sori *et al.*, 2018). We will discuss evidence for the recent geological activity on Ceres in Chapter 8.

The existence of discrete brine reservoirs or extended liquid layers inside Ceres suggests Ceres is an ocean world (Hendrix *et al.*, 2019; Castillo-Rogez, 2020). The advanced aqueous processes and chemical evolution, the high abundance of carbon in organics and carbonates, and the cryovolcanic activity found on Ceres make it an interesting target for testing potential habitability in the past and at present (Castillo-Rogez *et al.*, 2020). Dawn's results at Ceres have brought up significant astrobiological implications, as will be discussed in Chapter 9.

The paradigm-shifting findings about Ceres allow us to recognize its profound scientific value in understanding a wide range of questions related to the formation and evolution of water rich planetesimals during planet formation, volatile transfer to the inner solar system, and the habitability of icy objects. Chapter 10 provides some considerations for the future exploration of Ceres.

In summary, the Dawn spacecraft performed successful rendezvous observations of Ceres for three and a half years at altitudes from 13,000 km down to 35 km. All three instruments and radio tracking collected observvrations that cover the entire surface of Ceres, providing high-resolution data to allow accurate determination of the bulk properties and detailed mapping for the geology, mineralogy, elemental abundances, topography, and gravity. The results fundamentally advanced our understanding about Ceres, the only dwarf planet in the inner solar system.

References

Ammannito, E., *et al.* (2016). Distribution of phyllosilicates on the surface of Ceres. *Science*, **353**, id.aaf4279.

Bland, M. T., *et al.* (2016). Composition and structure of the shallow subsurface of Ceres revealed by crater morphology. *Nature Geosci.*, **9**, 538–542.

Bland, M. T., *et al.* (2018). Morphological indicators of a mascon beneath Ceres's largest crater, Kerwan. *Geophys. Res. Lett.*, **45**, 1297–1304.

Brophy, J. (2011). The Dawn ion propulsion system. *Space Sci. Rev.*, **163**, 251–261.

Carrozzo, F. G., *et al.* (2018). Nature, formation, and distribution of carbonates on Ceres. *Sci. Adv.*, **4**, e1701645.

Castillo-Rogez, J. (2020). Future exploration of Ceres as an ocean world.

Castillo-Rogez, J. C. and Rayman, M. D. (2020). A bountiful harvest on Ceres. *Nature Astron.*, **4**, 807.

Castillo-Rogez, J. C., *et al.* (2020). Ceres: Astrobiological target and possible ocean world. *Astrobiology*, **20**, 269–291.

De Sanctis, M. C., *et al.* (2011). The VIR spectrometer. *Space Sci. Rev.*, **163**, 329–369.

De Sanctis, M. C., *et al.* (2015). Ammoniated phyllosilicates with a likely outer solar system origin on (1) Ceres. *Nature*, **528**, 241–244.

De Sanctis, M. C., *et al.* (2020). Fresh emplacement of hydrated sodium chloride on Ceres from ascending salty fluids. *Nat. Astron.*, **4**, 786–793.

Ermakov, A. I., *et al.* (2017). Constraints on Ceres' internal structure and evolution from its shape and gravity measured by the Dawn spacecraft. *J. Geophys. Res. Planet.*, **122**, 2267–2293.

Fu, R. R., *et al.* (2017). The interior structure of Ceres as revealed by surface topography. *Earth. Planet. Sci. Lett.*, **476**, 153–164.

Hendrix, A. R., *et al.* (2019). The NASA roadmap to ocean worlds. *Astrobiology*, **19**, 1–27.

Konopliv, A. S., *et al.* (2011). The Dawn gravity investigation at Vesta and Ceres. *Space Sci. Rev.*, **163**, 461–486.

Konopliv, A. S., *et al.* (2018). The Ceres gravity field, spin pole, rotation period and orbit from the Dawn radiometric tracking and optical data. *Icarus*, **299**, 411–429.

McCord, T. B., Adams, J. B. and Johnson, T. V. (1970). Asteroid Vesta: Spectral reflectivity and compositional implications. *Science*, **168**, 1445–1447.

McCord, T. B., Castillo-Rogez, J. and Rivkin, A. (2011). Ceres: Its origin, evolution and structure and Dawn's potential contribution. *Space Sci. Rev.*, **163**, 63–76.

McSween, H. Y. and Huss, G. R. (2010). Cosmochemistry. Cambridge University Press.

Nathues, A., *et al.* (2016). FC colour images of dwarf planet Ceres reveal a complicated geological history. Planet. *Space. Sci.*, **134**, 122–127.

Park, R. S., *et al.* (2016). A partially differentiated interior for (1) Ceres deduced from its gravity field and shape. *Nature*, **537**, 515–517.

Park, R.S., *et al.* (2019). High-resolution shape model of Ceres from stereophotoclinometry using Dawn imaging data. *Icarus*, **319**, 812–827.

Prettyman, T. H., *et al.* (2011). Dawn's gamma ray and neutron detector. *Space Sci. Rev.*, **163**, 371–459.

Prettyman, T. H., *et al.* (2017). Extensive water ice within Ceres' aqueously altered regolith: Evidence from nuclear spectroscopy. *Science*, **355**, 55–59.

Raymond, C. A. *et al.* (2011). The Dawn topography investigation. *Space Sci. Rev.*, **163**, 487–510.

Ruesch, O., *et al.* (2016). Cryovolcanism on Ceres. *Science*, **353**, id.aaf4286.

Russell, C. T. and Raymond, C. A. (2011). The Dawn mission to Vesta and Ceres. *Space Sci. Rev.*, **163**, 3–23.

Schröder, S. E., *et al.* (2013). In-flight calibration of the Dawn Framing Camera. *Icarus*, **226**, 1304–1317.

Schröder, S. E., Mottola, S., Matz, K.-D. and Roatsch, T. (2014). In-flight calibration of the Dawn Framing Camera II: Flat fields and stray light correction. *Icarus*, **234**, 99–108.

Scully, J. E. C., *et al.* (2019). Synthesis of the special issue: The formation and evolution of Ceres' Occator crater. *Icarus*, **320**, 213–225.

Scully, J. E. C., *et al.* (2020). The varied sources of faculae-forming brines in Ceres' Occator crater emplaced via hydrothermal brine effusion. *Nat. Comm.*, **11**, 3680.

Sierks, H., *et al.* (2011). The dawn framing camera. *Space Sci. Rev.*, **163**, 263–327.

Sizemore, H. G. *et al.* (2019). A global inventory of ice-related morphological features on dwarf planet Ceres: Implications for the evolution and current state of the cryosphere. *J. Geophys. Res. Planet.*, **124**, 1650–1689.

Sori, M. M., *et al*. (2018). Cryovolcanic rates on Ceres revealed by topography. *Nat. Astron*., **2**, 946–950.

Stephan, K., *et al*. (2017). An investigation of the blush material on Ceres. *Geophys. Res. Lett*., **44**, 1660–1668.

Thomas, V. C., *et al*. (2011). The Dawn spacecraft. *Space Sci. Rev*., **163**, 175–249.

Williams, D. A., *et al*. (2018). Introduction: The geologic mapping of Ceres. *Icarus*, **316**, 1–13.

Chapter 4

Surface Composition

The VIR and GRaND instruments permitted a more definitive determination of the surface composition of Ceres than ground-based observations. They also allowed the study of compositional variations and their association with surface topography and geology. Many minerals and elemental species that are key to understanding the evolution and current status of Ceres have been identified and their abundances quantified, including phyllosilicates, carbonates, organics, water ice, hydrogen, iron, and carbon.

Before Dawn arrived at Ceres, no definitive constraints about its surface composition had been possible due to the lack of spectral coverage in the 2.5–2.9 μm region in the ground-based data caused by telluric absorption (Chapman and Salisbury, 1973; McCord and Gaffey, 1974; Lebofsky *et al.*, 1981; King *et al.*, 1992; Rivkin *et al.*, 2006; Milliken and Rivkin, 2009). The Dawn VIR spectrometer collected high-quality data covering the 0.25–5.0 μm region and made a more reliable identification of the minerals on the surface of Ceres possible. GRaND measured the elemental abundance of the top one-meter depth of Ceres's surface. It constrained the relative abundances of major rock-forming elements relevant to carbonaceous chondrite materials, such as hydrogen, iron, potassium, and carbon. GRaND also probed subsurface water ice that cannot widely exist on the surface of Ceres. However, due to the poor directionality of the detector, the spatial resolution of the elemental abundance distribution measured by GRaND is much coarser than that of the VIR measurements at the same altitude.

Table 4.1 summarizes the global composition of Ceres, as well as the compositions of a few regions of special interest, as constrained by VIR and GRaND measurements. Widespread distribution of Mg- and ammoniated (NH_4-) phyllosilicates, together with Mg–Ca-carbonates and a large abundance of dark agents that do not show any diagnostic spectral features in the visible to near-infrared wavelengths, dominate the surface of Ceres (De Sanctis *et al.*, 2015; Ammannito *et al.*, 2016). Na-carbonates and ammonium salt were detected in Occator crater (for geological features and nomenclatures, please refer to Chapter 5 and Fig. 5.1), as well as some other bright regions at lower abundances (De Sanctis *et al.*, 2016; Raponi *et al.*, 2019). Abundant aliphatic organic materials were identified in the Ernutet crater region (De Sanctis *et al.*, 2017). Global

Table 4.1: Observational constraints on Ceres's surface mineralogy. Reprinted from De Sanctis *et al.* (2015, 2016), Raponi *et al.* (2019), and Kaplan *et al.* (2018) for the organics, and elemental composition from Prettyman *et al.* (2017, 2018). Concentrations of Fe and K are for Ceres's ice-free regolith composition.

Average surface mineralogy	**Abundances (vol.%)**
NH_4-clays	~6–7
Serpentine (antigorite used in spectral fits)	~9–10
Darkening agent	~60–80
Carbonate (magnesite, dolomite, calcite)	5–15
Occator	**Abundances (vol.%)**
Na_2CO_3	At least 30
Evidence for ammonium salt (NH_4Cl)	Up to ~5 wt%
Ernutet region	**Abundance (vol.%)**
Organics, with a predominant aliphatic signature and matched by chondritic insoluble organic material	Several % to 10 s%
Element	**Abundances**
Water equivalent hydrogen	~27 wt% (17% in hydrated minerals; 10% water ice within a meter of surface)
Iron	16 ± 1 wt%
Potassium	410 ± 40 $\mu g/g^{-1}$
Carbon	Data permit concentration in excess of CI chondrites (>3.5 wt%)

distribution of water ice was also detected within a meter of the surface (Prettyman *et al.*, 2017, 2018). Iron, potassium, and carbon are also present.

4.1 Phyllosilicates

The global average reflectance spectrum of Ceres in 2–4 μm region is shown in Fig. 4.1. The distinctive absorption features include the 2.72 μm OH stretch band associated with water of hydration, the 3.1 μm band that dominates the ground-based spectra in the 3 μm region, the 3.3–3.5 μm bands consistent with the C–H stretching band of organics, and the 3.95 μm feature associated with carbonates. Spectral mixing modeling with a variety of minerals suggested that a mixture of ammoniated phyllosilicates (montmorillonite and annite used in the analysis), Mg-serpentine (antigorite), magnesite, and a dark component best matched all the absorption bands in 2–4 μm. The 3.1 μm band is the diagnostic absorption feature of NH_4 on Ceres and can be used to characterize the composition and abundance of NH_4-phyllosilicates.

Global mapping of the 2.72 μm absorption feature shows little variation in the band center position across Ceres's surface, except for the small bright regions on the floor of Occator crater where the band center shifts

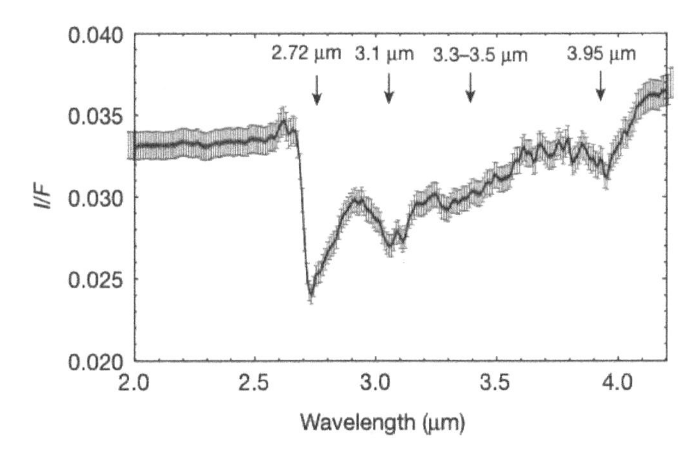

Figure 4.1: Global average reflectance spectrum of Ceres acquired by Dawn/VIR in the 2.0–4.4 μm region. The arrows indicate the major bands contained in this spectral range. Reprinted from De Sanctis *et al.* (2015). Copyright with permission from Springer Nature.

toward longer wavelengths (Ammannito *et al.*, 2016). The pervasive presence of Mg- rather than Fe-serpentine on Ceres indicates that aqueous alteration has been extensive. Similarly, the center of the 3.1 μm band also lacks spatial variations, suggesting a uniform NH_4-mineralogy across the surface of Ceres. The lack of variations based on the ammoniated phyllosilicate mineralogy suggests that the exposed upper layer of Ceres has no substantial compositional gradient. A global homogenization process is not likely because variations do exist in the absorption strength of both bands.

The strengths for these two absorption bands, which are dominated by the abundance of the corresponding minerals, vary across the surface. Such variations in band strengths are compatible with abundance variations of 6–12 vol. % for Mg-rich phyllosilicates, and 3–9 vol. % for NH_4-bearing minerals (Ammannito *et al.*, 2016). Figure 4.2 shows the qualitative distribution maps of phyllosilicates and NH_4 signature. On a global scale, the distribution of phyllosilicate minerals is correlated with that of NH_4 signature. Exceptions exist on the local scale. For example, in Urvara crater, relatively abundant NH_4 is correlated with less phyllosilicate than the global average. In addition, no correlation on the global scale is evident between the distribution of NH_4-phyllosilicates and surface albedo. But some bright areas, such as the bright crater and ejecta of Haulani, are correlated with less abundant NH_4-phyllosilicates. Furthermore, no broad correlation between the abundance of NH_4-phyllosilicates and global geomorphology was observed, such as global distribution of craters, crater size, and geological age. Analyses of the global distributions of ammoniated-phyllosilicates suggested possible global stratification and mixing in the upper layers of Ceres.

4.2 Carbonates

The global spectrum of Ceres suggests that carbonates are ubiquitous on the surface of Ceres (De Sanctis *et al.*, 2015). Carbonates exhibit diagnostic absorption features due to vibrational transitions of the CO_3^{2-} group that display overtone with combinations of bands at 3.3 to 3.5 μm and 3.9 to 4.0 μm. The band center positions are used to determine the specific carbonate species.

Figure 4.3 shows the global distributions of the 3.95 μm carbonate band center and band strength (Carrozzo *et al.*, 2018). For most of the surface, the band center is near 3.95 μm, characteristic of Mg- or Mg–Ca carbonates. A few localized areas show band centers shifted toward longer

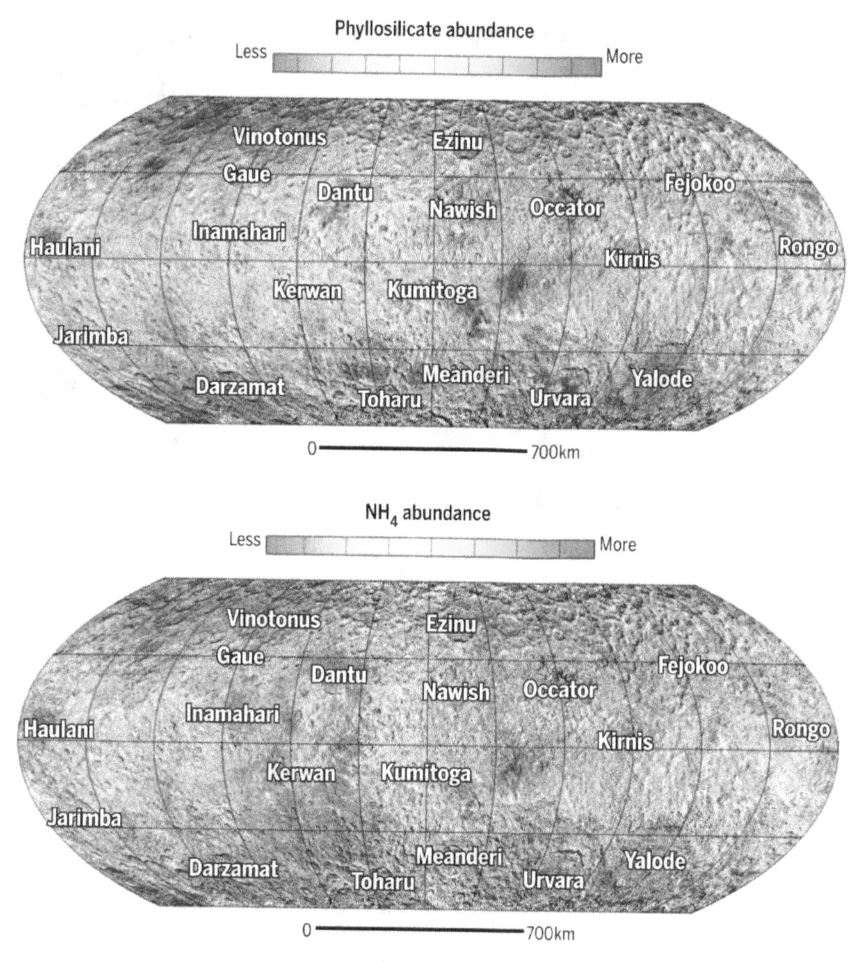

Figure 4.2: The distribution of phyllosilicates (top) and NH_4 (bottom) based on the depth of the 2.72 μm and 3.1 μm absorption strengths, respectively. Reprinted from Ammannito *et al.* (2016). Copyright with permission from AAAS.

wavelengths up to 4.02 μm, consistent with natrite (Na_2CO_3). These Na-carbonate-rich areas are all associated with relatively bright crater floors or ejecta materials of young craters, most notably the Cerealia Facula on the floor of Occator crater (De Sanctis *et al.*, 2016), Ahuna Mons (Zambon *et al.*, 2017), Oxo crater, Azacca crater, Kupalo crater, and Ikapati crater (Carrozzo *et al.*, 2018). Spectral mixing modeling suggested that the areas showing intermediate band center positions represent a mixture of Mg–Ca and Na-carbonates. This is consistent with the fact that those areas are always adjacent to the Na-carbonate-rich regions. High-resolution data

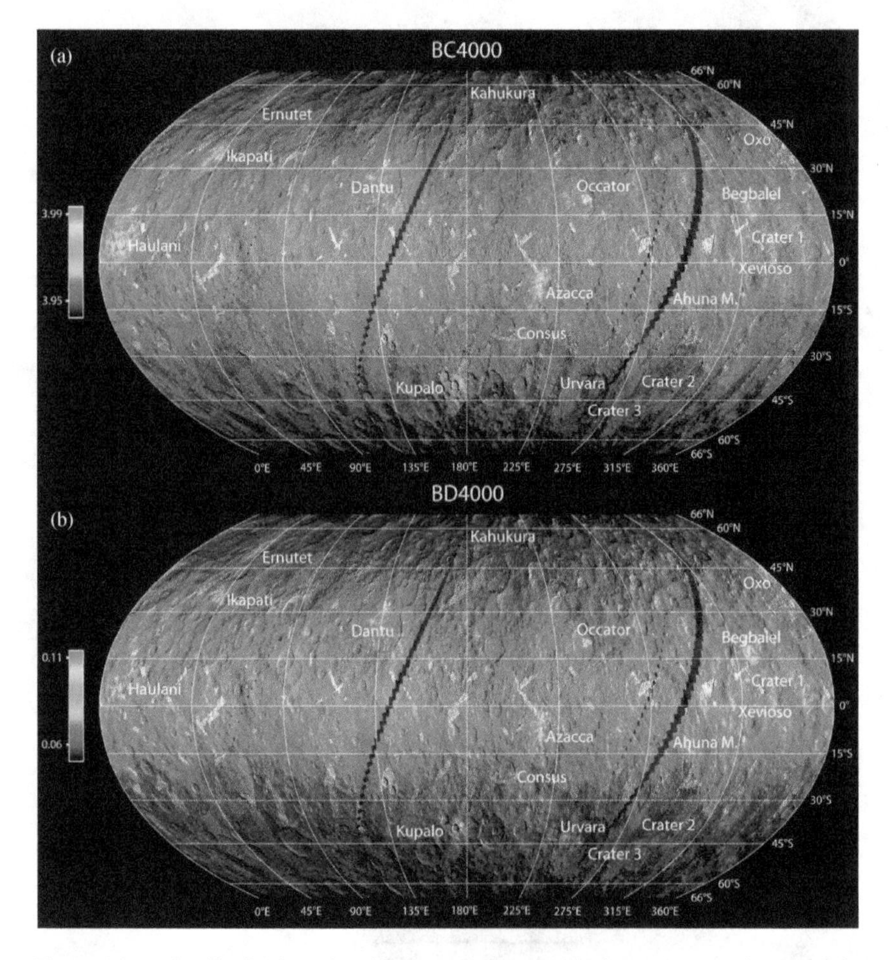

Figure 4.3: The distribution of carbonates on Ceres. (a) is for center wavelength of the 3.95 μm band as determined by the carbonate composition, where longer wavelength indicates Na-cabonates. (b) is the depth of the same band, indicative of the carbonate abundance. Reprinted from Carrozzo *et al.* (2018). Copyright with permission from AAAS.

of some of those regions, collected at lower orbital altitudes, often spatially resolve those bright materials into smaller Mg–Ca-carbonate areas and Na-carbonate areas.

Similar to the band center distribution, the 3.95 μm band strength map also shows a nearly uniform distribution on Ceres. Several localized kilometer-sized areas exhibit much stronger band strength relative to

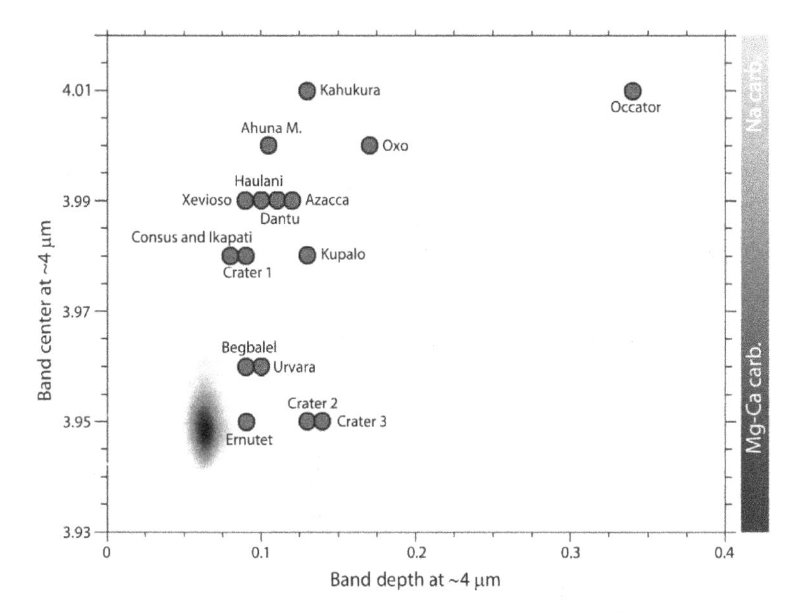

Figure 4.4: The carbonates properties in a few regions on Ceres as suggested by the center and depth of the 4 μm band. The carbonate composition corresponding to band center wavelengths is indicated by the gray bar on the right. Reprinted from Carrozzo *et al.* (2018). Copyright with permission from AAAS.

the background, mostly corresponding to the Na-carbonate-rich areas (Fig. 4.4). Exceptions exist in the Ernutet crater, the western side of Urvara crater, and some small areas in Baltay Catena, where relatively stronger carbonate bands do not correlate with Na-carbonates, but are associated with Mg–Ca-carbonates.

The Cerealia Facula near the center of Occator crater floor hosts the most abundant carbonate deposits on Ceres, and also represents the most concentrated known extraterrestrial occurrence of carbonate on kilometer-scales in the Solar System (De Sanctis *et al.*, 2016). This area is the brightest region on Ceres, having an albedo of 6–8 times the global average (Li *et al.*, 2016; Schröder *et al.*, 2017). The carbonates are mixed with a dark component, a small amount of phyllosilicates, as well as ammonium carbonate or chloride salts (Fig. 4.5). Toward the center of Cerealia Facula, the 3.4 μm and 3.95 μm absorptions increase significantly, indicating a substantial enrichment in carbonates, and the band center is consistent with natrite (Na_2CO_3). The center of the 2.72 μm absorption of Mg-phyllosilicates shifts to a slightly longer wavelength of 2.76 μm,

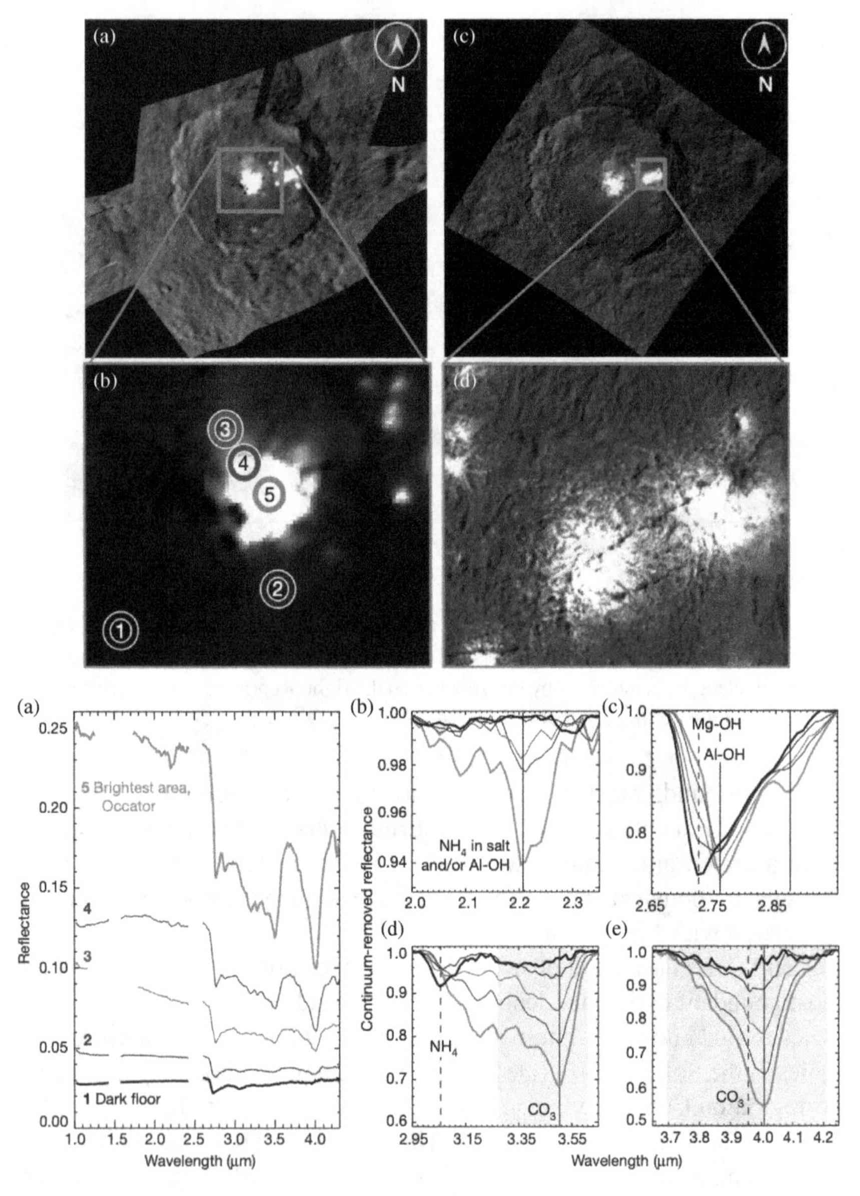

Figure 4.5: The spectra of carbonate-rich regions in Cerealia Facula and Vinalia Faculae. Upper panel shows the mosaic of Occator crater and the details of Cerealia Facula (left) and Vinalia Facula (right) at 2 μm based on VIR data. Lower panel shows the reflectance spectra of five locations marked in the upper panel (left), and the respective continuum removed spectral features at various spectral locations (right). Reprinted from De Sanctis *et al.* (2016). Copyright with permission from Springer Nature.

suggesting that the Mg-phyllosilicate is replaced by a different kind of phyllosilicate, possibly Al-phyllosilicate such as smectite, kaolinite or illite. The strength of the 3.1 μm absorption attributed to NH_4-bearing minerals decreases toward the center of the Facula and is completely absent in the brightest pixels, which suggests a compositional gradient across the facula. In the meantime, the absorptions at 2.20–2.22 μm, which are likely attributed to ammoniated salts in this case, appear only in the center of the Facula.

Figure 4.6 shows the distributions of carbonate, NH_4-bearing species, and NH_4-salts, as well as their correlations inside Occator crater.

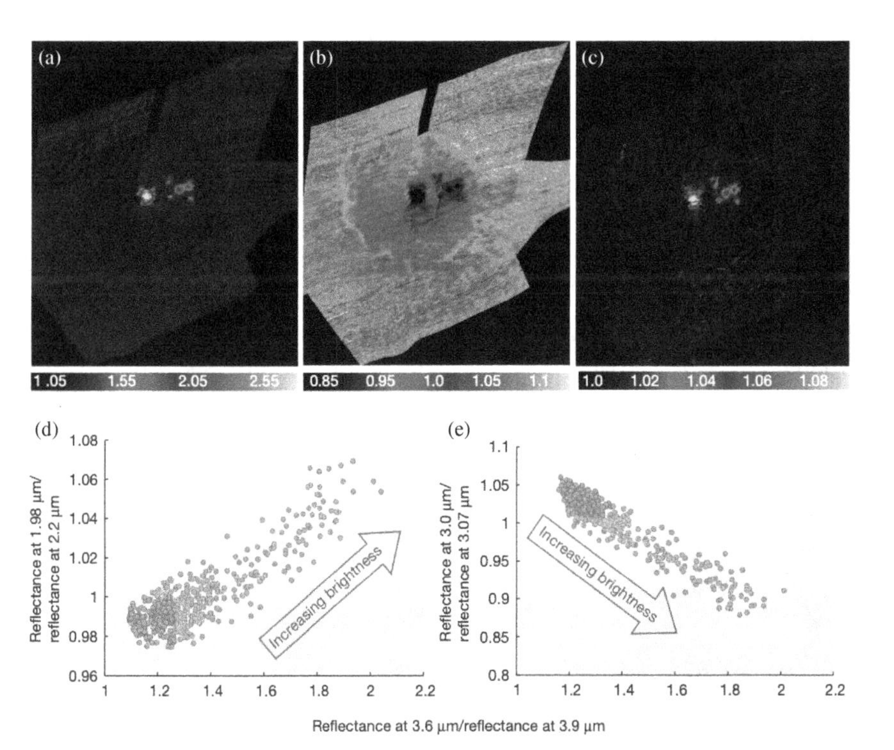

Figure 4.6: Spectral ratio maps representing the distribution of corresponding minerals: (a) Ratio of the reflectance at 3.6 μm and that at 3.9 μm as a proxy for carbonate abundance. (b) Ratio of the reflectance at 3.0 μm and that of 3.07 μm as a proxy for the abundance of NH_4-bearing phyllosilicates. (c) Ratio of the reflectance at 1.98 μm and that at 2.2 μm as a proxy for the abundance of NH_4 salts. (d) Shows a positive correlation between NH_4 salts proxy and carbonates proxy. (e) Shows a negative correlation between NH_4-phyllosilicates proxy and carbonates proxy. Reprinted from De Sanctis *et al.* (2016). Copyright with permission from Springer Nature.

In the center of Cerealia Facula, where carbonate is the most concentrated, NH_4-phyllosilicates are the most depleted and mostly replaced by NH_4-salts. The secondary bright spots, the Vinalia Faculae to the east of Cerealia Facula, show similar distributions of carbonates, NH_4-phyllosilicates, and NH_4-salts.

As the largest concentration beyond the Earth in the Solar System, the carbonates in Cerealia Facula should be of endogenous origin. Although carbonates also occur in carbonaceous chondrites, their amount is only a few volume percent, and no natrite has been reported. Therefore, the formation mechanism of carbonates on Ceres is distinctively different from that in carbonaceous chondrites. The correlation of carbonates with NH_4-bearing phyllosilicates and salts on Ceres suggests a complex geochemical process that is still subject to investigation (e.g., De Sanctis *et al.*, 2016).

4.3 Organics

An area of about 50 km across in the southwest floor and ejecta field of the Ernutet crater was first noticed to be distinctively redder than any regions on Ceres in visible images (Fig. 4.7) (Schröder *et al.*, 2017; Thangjam *et al.*, 2018). Detailed analysis of the VIR spectrum in this

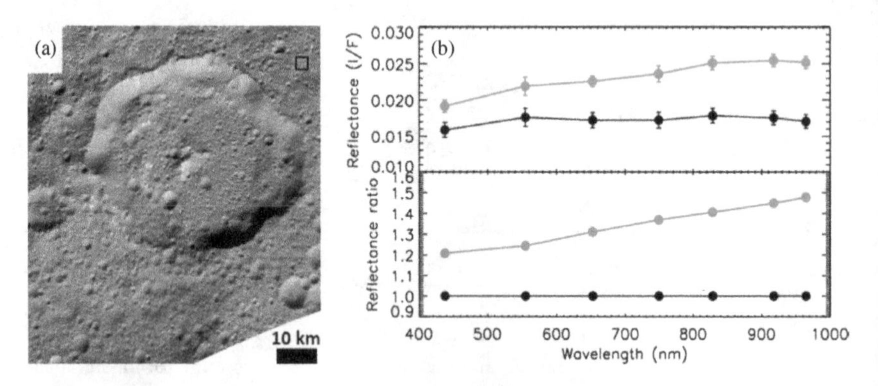

Figure 4.7: (a) Color composite of the red region near Ernutet crater based on HAMO images with (R, G, B) = (965, 555, 438) nm. (b) Seven-color spectra of red region (red line) and background material (black). Reprinted from Schröder *et al.* (2017). Copyright with permission from Elsevier.

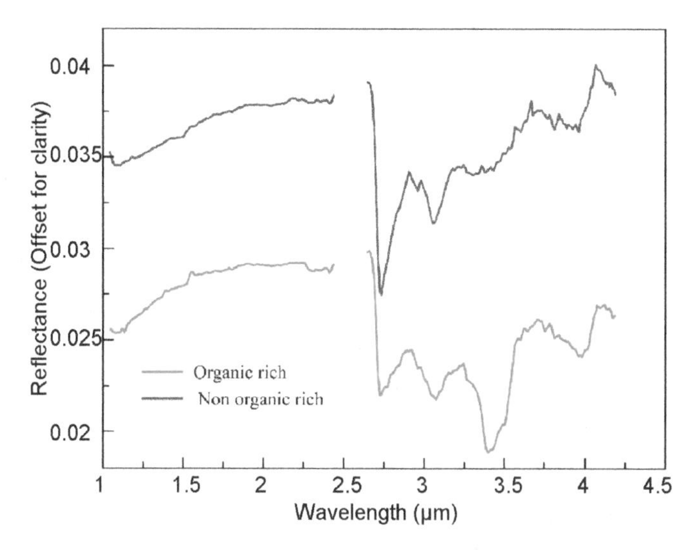

Figure 4.8: Spectrum of Ceres's organic material (red) in comparison with the spectrum of non-organic background material (black). Reprinted from De Sanctis *et al.* (2018). Copyright with permission from Wiley-VCH Verlag GmbH & Co. KGaA.

region revealed strong absorption features of aliphatic organics (organic matters with open chain structure) at 3.4 μm (Fig. 4.8) (De Sanctis *et al.*, 2017). Further search found a number of discrete organic-rich areas associated with small fresh craters less than a few hundred meters in diameter (Fig. 4.10) (Pieters *et al.*, 2018).

4.3.1 *Ernutet Crater*

The organic-rich area associated with the Ernutet crater represents the largest concentration of organic matter on Ceres. Compared to the spectra of the background material on Ceres, the spectrum of the organic-rich region shows prominent absorption features between 3.3 and 3.6 μm, while all other absorption features, such as the 2.72 μm hydroxyl feature, 3.1 μm NH_4 feature, and 3.95 μm carbonate feature, are similar. Materials containing C–H bonds, including a variety of organic compounds, are identified to be responsible for the 3.3–3.6 μm features. Comparing candidate organic species suggested that the best match for these features is aliphatic organic material, although it is difficult to narrow down their specific nature. If the aliphatic organic materials on Ceres are similar to terrestrial kerite-like materials, then their abundance could be up to ~9 vol% (De Sanctis *et al*., 2017). If, however, they are similar to the insoluble organic materials found in carbonaceous chondrite meteorites, then their abundance could be much higher, up to a few tens of vol% locally (Kaplan *et al*., 2018).

Other spectral features in the Ernutet organic-rich area also show some spatial distributions. The strength of the 3.95 μm band, commonly associated with carbonates, is enhanced in the organic-rich area (Fig. 4.8), suggesting an enrichment in carbonates. The 3.1 μm band that represents NH_4-bearing minerals is relatively enhanced around the rim of the crater, but not inside the organic-rich region.

Figure 4.9 shows the distribution of all areas on Ceres that contain organic materials as identified from the 3.3–3.6 μm features in the VIR data. All these organic-rich regions are within an area about 200 km across near the Ernutet crater. Other than the two relatively large organic-rich regions across the Ernutet crater rim, all other regions are about hundred meters in size or smaller, associated with fresh craters, and scattered in the region.

No obvious correlation between the organic-rich regions and geologic features such as craters and the associated ejecta fields could be identified, including the Ernutet crater (Fig. 4.9). The largest organic material deposit near the Ernutet crater is distributed on one side of the crater with no distinct geological boundaries visible. The small, discrete red organic-rich areas associated with fresh craters appear to be excavated by recent impacts, suggesting a continuous distribution of organic materials at a shallow depth beneath the top surface extending across the whole Ernutet area.

The lack of distinct correlations between the distribution of organic material and geology makes it challenging to understand the origin of the enriched organic matter in this area. Both endogenic and exogenic origins are possible (Fig. 4.10). Other processes, such as the production of organics in situ by impact (McKay and Borucki, 1997) could also be possible.

For the endogenic origin hypothesis, while the production of organic materials in Ceres's interior during its history of extended aqueous alteration is a possibility, identifying the processes to bring the organic materials to the surface consistent with observations seems to be

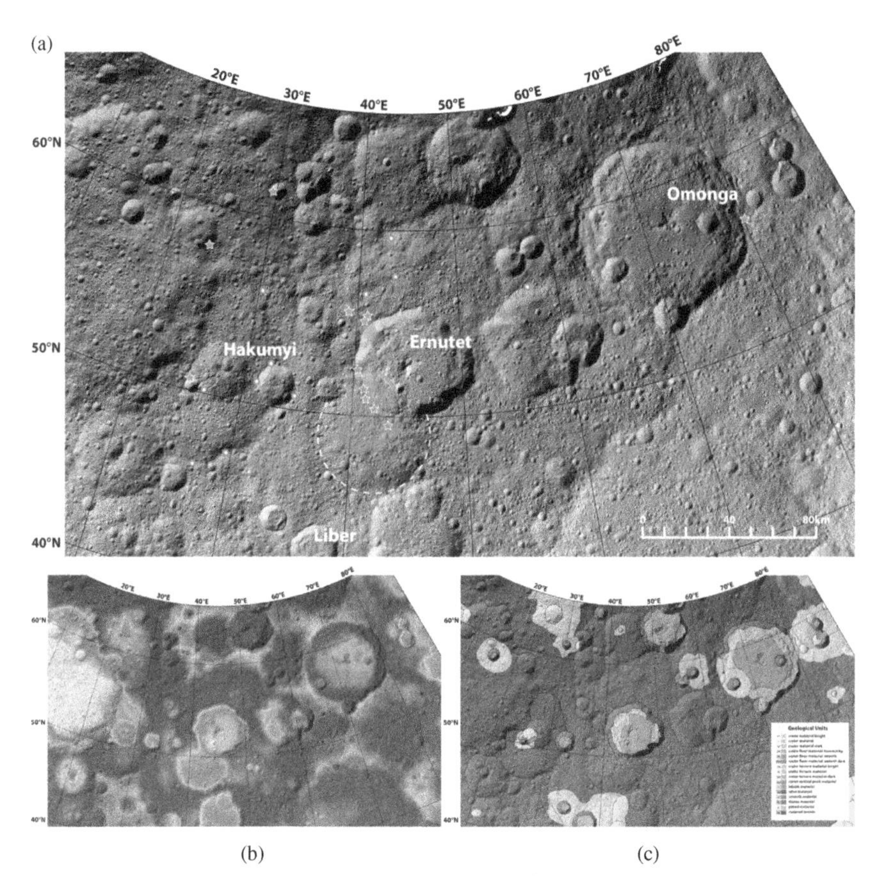

Figure 4.9: Overview of Ceres's organic-rich areas detected by VIR. (a) shows the mosaic of the region based on FC images with organic materials marked by the red overlay. (b) is the topography map, showing >10 km vertical relief. (c) is the geological map by Pasckert *et al.* (2017). Reprinted from Pieters *et al.* (2018). Copyright with permission from Wiley-VCH Verlag GmbH & Co. KGaA.

challenging. The cold surface temperature at Ernutet's latitude (~52° N) prohibits the exposure of material upwelled from the interior, leaving impact excavation and redeposition the only possible mechanism. If the organic materials were originally excavated by the Ernutet crater forming impact to shallow subsurface, then we would expect continuous distribution of excavated organic material distributed in the crater floor and the proximal ejecta field. However, the discrete pattern of red regions as

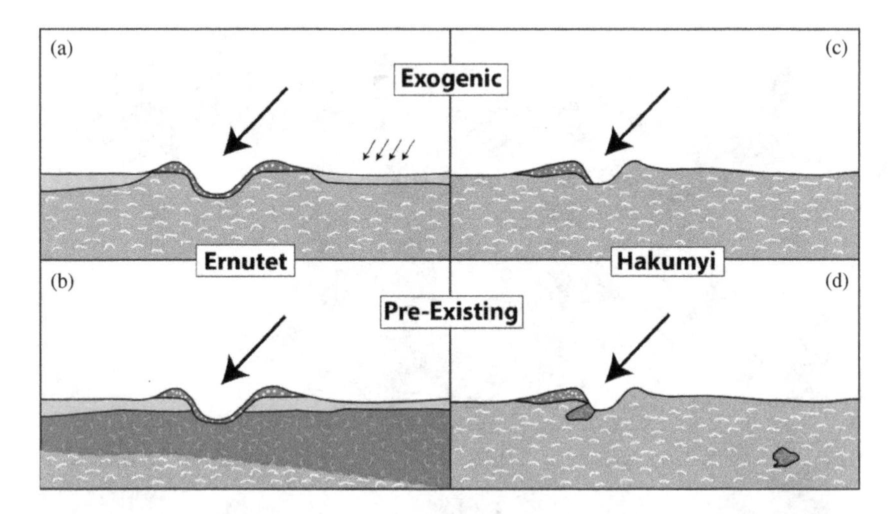

Figure 4.10: Schematic cross section of Ernutet and near Hakumyi showing the scenarios for the origin and exposure of organic materials on the surface of Ceres. Organic material is shown in red, regolith rich in organic materials is pink, and typcial Ceres surface materials are gray. The upper panels represent the delivery of organic materials from small impactors. The lower panels represent the exposure of pre-existing organic materials. Reprinted from Pieters *et al.* (2018). Copyright with permission from Wiley-VCH Verlag GmbH & Co. KGaA.

revealed by LAMO images contradicts this hypothesis. In addition, the distal, discrete small organic-rich areas cannot be directly derived from the Ernutet ejecta.

The assessment of possible exogenous origins of Ceres's organic materials is limited by our poor knowledge of organic-rich materials in the solar system, although we do have evidence for a widespread distribution of organic material from Mercury (Paige *et al.*, 2013) to the outer solar system. Our understanding about the impact process of low-density, organic-rich materials is also extremely limited from both natural impact and laboratory studies. The preservation of impactor materials does seem to be possible, as evidenced by the rich impact-delivered carbonaceous chondritic materials on the surface of Vesta (De Sanctis *et al.*, 2012; Prettyman *et al.*, 2012; Reddy *et al.*, 2012). The biggest problem for the exogenous origin hypothesis of Ceres's organics, however, is that the odds of producing just a single, localized 200 km field of organic-rich materials on Ceres in the past about 10 million years, which is the degradation timescale of organic signature, are low.

4.3.2 *Regolith*

GRaND data suggested a carbon abundance in Ceres's upper 1-meter regolith to be higher than that in carbonaceous chondrites (Prettyman *et al.*, 2017). The measured abundances of hydrogen and carbon in the upper one-meter depth of Ceres's regolith (Prettyman *et al.*, 2017), combined with the VIR spectral measurements, imply the widespread presence of organics in the regolith of Ceres with vertically varying H/C (Marchi *et al.*, 2019).

Dynamic simulations suggest that over the history of Ceres, it could have accumulated over 20 wt% exogenous materials in the shallow subsurface delivered by impacts, mixed with endogenic, aqueously altered materials. Spectral models suggested that up to 20% of carbonaceous chondritic materials could be mixed into the regolith without being spectroscopically detectable (Marchi *et al.*, 2019). In addition, about 80 vol% of dark material that does not show spectral features in the VIR spectral range was required to match the low albedo of Ceres in spectral modeling (De Sanctis *et al.*, 2015). Of the two most likely dark materials on Ceres, magnetite and amorphous carbon, the former cannot be more than ~2.5 vol% in order to match the measured elementary abundance of Fe, which is much lower than the abundance measured from carbonaceous chondritic materials (Prettyman *et al.*, 2017). Amorphous carbon is required on the surface to act as a darkening agent as also suggested by the UV spectral feature of Ceres at 100–200 nm wavelengths (Hendrix *et al.*, 2016; see Chapter 2). Amorphous carbon can be generated on the surface of Ceres in a relatively short timescale by UV and energetic proton irradiation that break the C–H bonds in organics and lower the H/C ratio. Combining the spectral and elemental data, the hydrogen concentration can be explained by assuming a H/C atomic ratio of ~0.6 for the amorphous carbon component within the ~1 m depth as measured by GRaND (Marchi *et al.*, 2019). Based on the existence of amorphous carbon and relatively high carbon concentration in Ceres's regolith (Section 4.5), geochemical calculation showed that a wide range of organic compounds are expected in the regolith of Ceres (Vinogradoff *et al.*, 2018), while the top layer exposed on the surface is subject to UV and energetic proton damage, resulting in a vertical gradient in the H/C.

4.4 Surface Water Ice

Both pre-Dawn observations (e.g., Lebofsky *et al.*, 1981) and theoretical calculation (e.g., Schörghofer, 2008; Titus, 2015) have demonstrated the possibility of water ice in high-latitude regions on the surface of Ceres. Therefore, searching for water ice was one of the primary science objectives of the Dawn mission. Water ice was first detected on Ceres on the pole-facing wall and adjacent floor of Oxo crater (Combe *et al.*, 2016), as well as the permanently shadowed crater floors in the polar regions (Platz *et al.*, 2016). Following the initial discovery, smaller water ice deposits were identified in about ten locations on Ceres.

Oxo crater is 9 km in diameter and located at about 42° N. It is the second brightest feature on Ceres with a normal albedo of 0.14–0.15, and one of the bluest regions together with the Haulani crater and Ahuna Mons (Schröder *et al.*, 2017). The sharp rim and few superposed craters imply a geologically young age of a few million years (Hughson *et al.*, 2018). A scarp in the southeastern part of the crater likely resulted from block collapse and slumping of the rim toward the center of the crater, forming a depression outside of the crater (Fig. 4.11). Active collapsing in the recent geological past is evident from the long, arcuate fractures subparallel to the terrace scarp, well-defined talus material, and an extensive boulder field within Oxo. Some kilometer- and subkilometer-scale lobate flow features on the northeastern and southeastern rims of the terrace block are

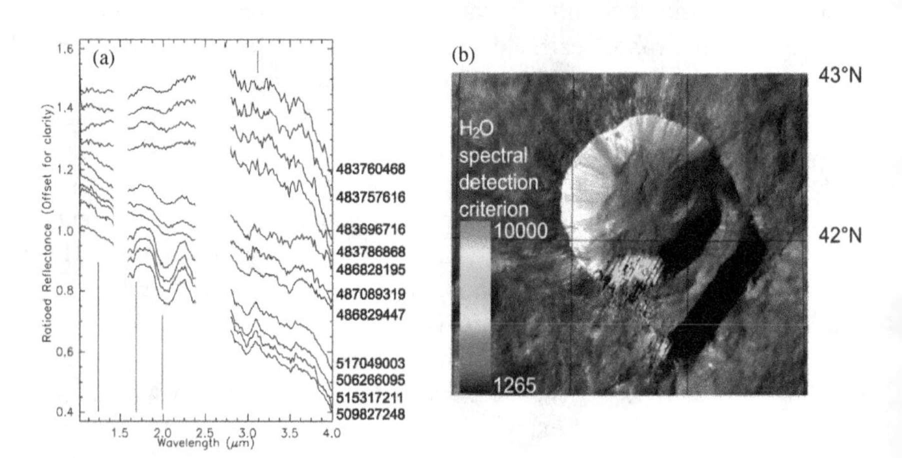

Figure 4.11: (a) IR spectra of H_2O-rich areas in Oxo crater ratio to Ceres average spectrum obtained by VIR. The vertical lines mark the expected wavelengths of H_2O absorption bands at 1.28, 1.65, and 2.0 μm, as well as the Fresnel peak of crystalline H_2O ice at 3.1 μm. (b) FC image of Oxo crater from LAMO with the color pixels overlaid representing the relative abundance of ice detected. Reprinted from Combe *et al.* (2019). Copyright with permission from Elsevier.

morphologically similar to many other features on Ceres that were interpreted as ice-cemented flows (e.g., Schmidt *et al.*, 2017, also see Chapter 6).

Water ice shows strong characteristic absorption bands at 2.0, 1.65, and 1.28 μm, which are clearly visible in the Oxo region spectra (Fig. 4.11). The strongest absorption feature of water ice appears on the north-facing wall and floor of the crater, where hummocky sloped materials are present. The morphology is consistent with water ice being exposed by slumping and mass wasting of the crater rim material, and preserved by the low temperature of the pole-facing slope. Other smaller water ice deposits identified on Ceres will be discussed in Chapter 6.

Although Ceres is too close to the Sun for water ice to be stable on the surface on large scales, permanently shadowed crater floors in the polar regions created by Ceres's low obliquity were expected to host stable surface ice deposits, as exemplified by the Moon (Paige *et al.*, 2010; Siegler *et al.*, 2011) and Mercury (Paige *et al.*, 2013).

The best examples of water ice deposit in permanently shadowed crater floors on Ceres are located in a 6.6-km-diameter crater at 86.19° N, 80.00° E, and a 3.8-km-diameter crater at 69.92° N, 114.04° E (Platz *et al.*, 2016). Illuminated by the dim reflected light from the crater wall, the bottoms of both craters show relatively bright deposits against the surroundings in the FC images (Fig. 4.12). When the bright deposit in the 3.8-km-diameter crater was partially illuminated by direct sunlight, VIR was able to collect spectra of this region (Fig. 4.13).

In the subsurface at mid- to high-latitude regions on Ceres, water ice can be stable within a meter depth over the age of the solar system (Fanale and Salvail, 1989; Titus, 2015). The GRaND measured the subsurface water ice content based on the hydrogen elemental abundance inferred from the thermal and epithermal neutron counts and 7.6-MeV gamma ray intensity. It was found that Ceres's surface regolith within about one meter is consistent with a layered structure, where a water ice-rich subsurface layer is covered by a dry top surface layer (Prettyman *et al.*, 2017). The derived water-equivalent hydrogen abundance shows a strong latitudinal trend, where high-latitude regions contain more water ice than low-latitude regions (Fig. 4.14). This trend is consistent with the theoretical predictions that water ice is preserved beneath the surface at a depth depending on the latitude. In addition, the northern hemisphere contains slightly more hydrogen than the southern hemisphere (Fig. 4.14). The difference between the poles is about 2.5 ± 1.1 wt% water-equivalent

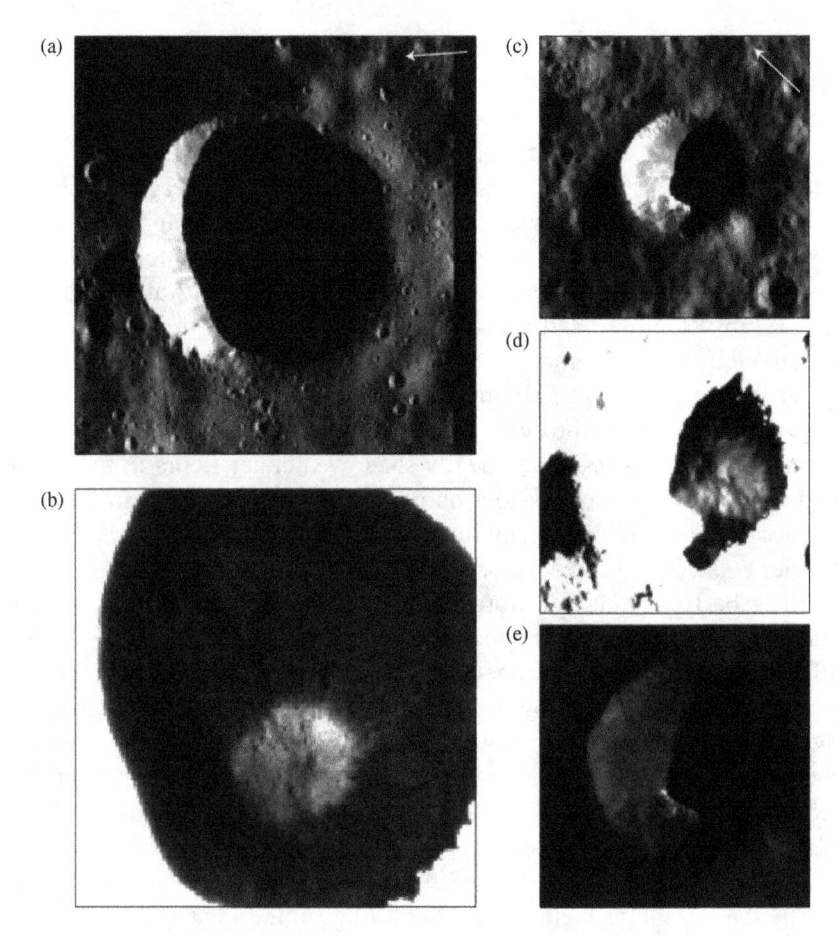

Figure 4.12: Water ice in permanent shadow. (a) is a crater of 6.6 km diameter centered at 86.19° N, 80.00° E. (b) is the close up of the floor of the crater shown in (a) and highly stretched in brightness to reveal the dark interior as illuminated by the bright crater wall. (c) shows another crater of 3.8 km diameter at 69.92° N, 114.04° E, and (d) is the close up view of its floor showing the bright interior. (e) displays the edge of the bright deposit in the crater shown in (c) that is partially illuminated by the Sun. Reprinted from Platz *et al.* (2016). Copyright with permission from Springer Nature.

hydrogen, which is larger than predicted by ice stability models considering Ceres's precessing orbital elements (Ermakov *et al.* 2017). Combining with the distribution of phyllosilicate on the surface of Ceres, it was inferred that the ice table on Ceres contains up to 10 wt% water ice.

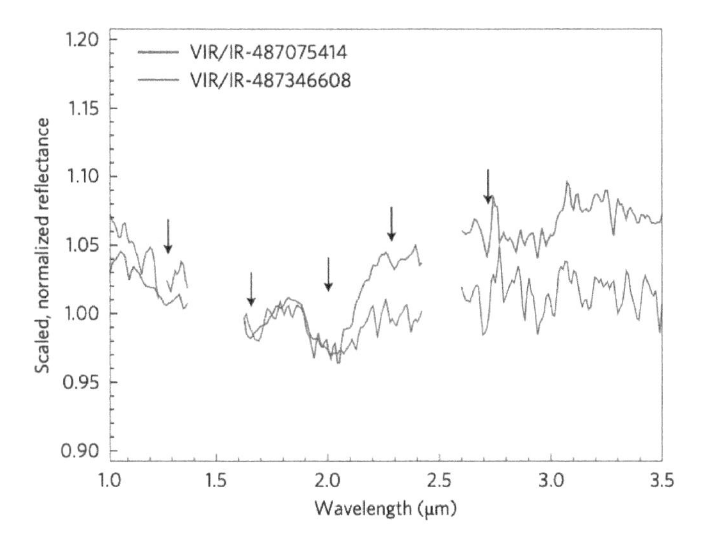

Figure 4.13: Spectrum of the partially illuminated crater floor in Figure 4.12e showing the absorption features diagnostic of water ice (marked by arrows). Reprinted from Platz *et al.* (2016). Copyright with permission from Springer Nature.

4.5 Iron and Potassium

Neutron capture by Fe produces diagnostic gamma ray emissions at 7.6-MeV. The hydrogen content in the regolith decelerates thermal and epithermal neutrons from cosmic rays, enhancing the neutron capture process in Fe. Therefore, at low abundance, increase of hydrogen increases the 7.6-MeV gamma ray counts. But because the presence of hydrogen dilutes Fe, at a higher hydrogen abundance, increasing hydrogen decreases the 7.6-MeV counts. Therefore, the 7.6-MeV gamma ray measurements need to be detrended by removing the effects of varying hydrogen abundance using the thermal and epithermal neutron counts in order to derive the abundance of Fe. With this approach, the mean Fe abundance on Ceres was measured to be 16 ± 1 wt% in its non-hydrous composition, which is depleted relative to the CM and CI chondrites (Fig. 4.15) (Prettyman *et al.*, 2017).

Additionally, the equatorial concentration of potassium was measured from the 1.461-MeV gamma ray emission to be 410 ± 40 μg/g, which is between the average abundances in the CI and CM chondrites. Without a priori knowledge of Ceres's bulk potassium composition, it is not clear

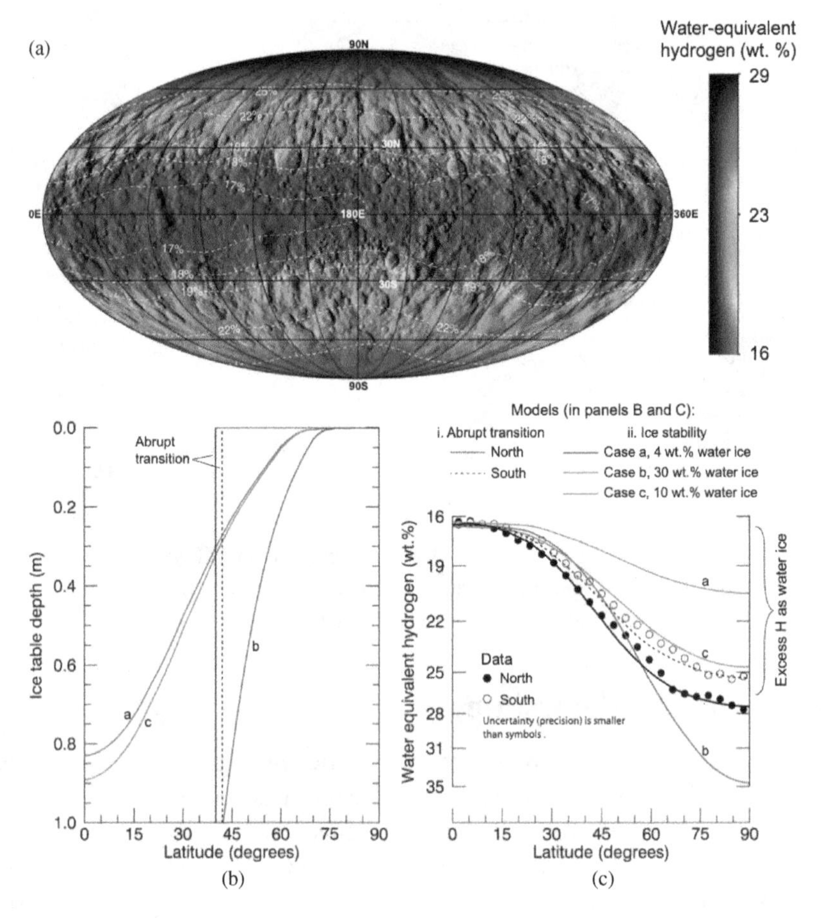

Figure 4.14: The distribution of water-equivalent hydrogen (lower limit) within Ceres's regolith determined from thermal and epithermal neutron counting data. Reprinted from Prettyman *et al.* (2017). Copyright with permission from AAAS.

whether potassium is fractionated in Ceres or if the observed value reflects the difference between the Ceres-forming material and the CI/CM parent bodies.

The nearly uniform elemental distributions of the ice-free, equatorial regolith from the GRaND measurements indicate a global-scale rock-ice fractionation. The low Fe abundance compared to the CM and CI chondrites is probably a result of global concentration of the heavy Fe at depth inside Ceres. Hydrogen is expected to be partitioned primarily between phyllosilicates and water ice.

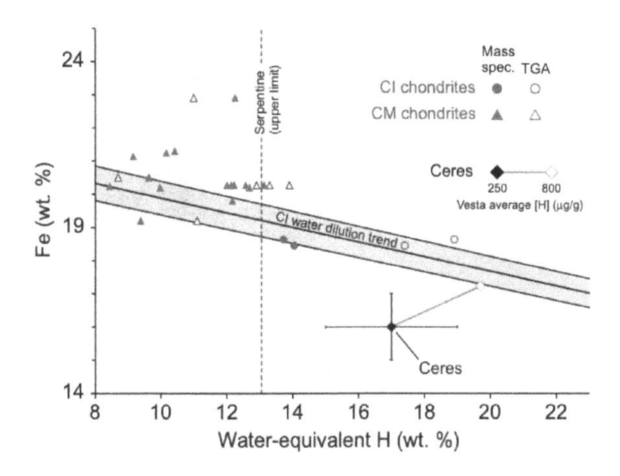

Figure 4.15: Fe versus water-equivalent H for the CI and CM chondrites and Ceres. The black diamond with error bars indicate Ceres's equatorial average values. Ceres is clearly below the overall trend line of CI and CM chondrites. Reprinted from Prettyman *et al.* (2017). Copyright with permission from AAAS.

The spatial distribution of Fe on Ceres was inferred by mapping the high-energy gamma ray (HEGR), defined as a broad-band emission in the energy range of 8 to ~9-MeV. After removing the dilution effect of hydrogen, HEGR is directly scalable to the average atomic mass <A> of the regolith (Peplowski and Lawrence, 2013). Modeling with the CM and CI chondrite elemental abundances suggested that <A> for Ceres's regolith is dominated by Fe, although other elements such as Mg and S could also contribute. Using this technique, Lawrence *et al.* (2018) derived a map of <A> for Ceres's anhydrous regolith (Fig. 4.16).

Overall, the hydrogen-free HEGR counts on Ceres vary by about ±3.7%, corresponding to a variation in <A> of about ±0.5 atomic mass unit (amu), dominated by the spatial variations in Fe. Comparison with various geological maps and mineral abundance maps showed that high <A>, which possibly corresponds to high Fe, tends to be correlated with younger, less cratered surfaces covered by impact ejecta of the largest craters. Older, more heavily cratered terrains have relatively lower Fe concentration. Because the ejecta of young, large craters represents materials excavated from deep inside the crust of Ceres and not yet well mixed with preexisting regolith, the high Fe abundance in this region is consistent with rock-ice fractionation that resulted in compositional stratigraphy, where the Fe concentration increases with depth.

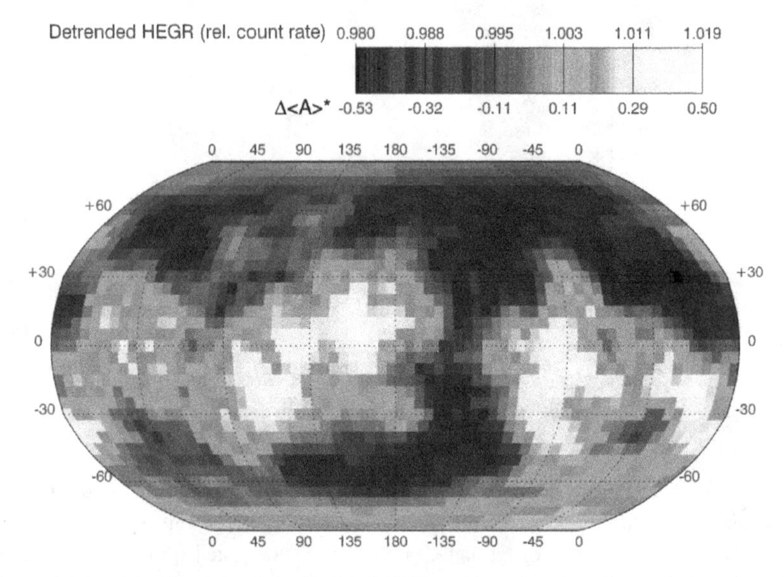

Figure 4.16: Distribution of detrended HEGR counts showing the variations in <A>, which is dominated by variations of Fe. Reprinted from Lawrence *et al.* (2018). Copyright with permission from Wiley-VCH Verlag GmbH & Co. KGaA.

4.6 Interpretation of Ceres's Surface Composition

Ceres's surface mineralogy provides evidence for pervasive aqueous alteration, suggesting water–rock alteration on a global scale in its interior. Key inferences can be made from the combined VIR and GRaND observations (Castillo-Rogez *et al.*, 2018). First, the mineralogy is characteristic of a rather reducing and alkaline environment. The simultaneous presence of ammonium-bearing clays and of carbonates constrains pH to lie in the range 7–11. The log pH_2, which is similar to the fugacity of hydrogen, has to be greater than −5 bar. Hydrogen was produced from serpentinization and accumulated under high pressure in a mostly closed aqueous system. The presence of ammoniated clays, in similar fractions to serpentine, constrain the temperature of the early ocean to <50°C. Sulfur is expected to be in reduced form, combined with metals, while chlorides and carbonates are the main forms of salts (Fig. 4.17).

A very large fraction of the water could be in the form of clathrate hydrates, which supports geophysical interpretations for the abundance of that material in Ceres's crust (see Chapter 7).

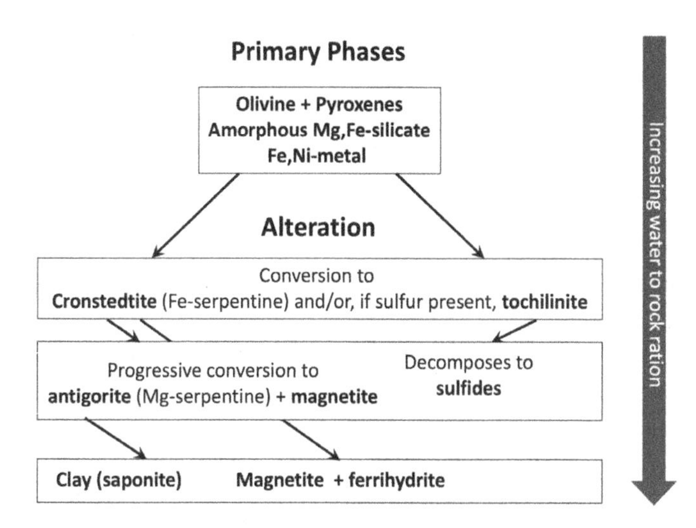

Figure 4.17: Mineralogy evolution under reducing conditions and increasing water-to-rock ratio. The mineralogy found on Ceres's surface is consistent with advanced aqueous alteration. Reprinted from McSween *et al.* (2018).

The relatively reducing conditions, while conducive to the production of carbonates, are similar to those expected in large icy satellites (McKinnon and Zolensky, 2003). Indeed, Ceres's salt chemistry resembles that of Enceladus (Postberg *et al.*, 2011) and possibly Europa (Brown and Hand, 2013). More generally, these results add to our knowledge of large volatile-rich bodies. The presence at multiple sites of evaporites rich in sodium carbonate and ammonium chloride suggests that oceanic material is frozen in the near surface (first tens of kilometers, and perhaps shallower), consistent with geophysical data (Ermakov *et al.*, 2017; Fu *et al.*, 2017).

A key open question is about the conditions under which Ceres acquired its surface regolith, tens to hundreds of meters of carbonaceous material. A simple lag deposit built from particles trapped in the crust is not a sufficient explanation because ice is stable below ten meters of regolith at the equator (Landis, personnel communication) and a few centimeters at high latitude. Neveu and Desch (2015) suggested that in its early history, impacts breaching through the thin crust could have exposed ocean material loaded in fines. These authors inferred that the regolith could be very old, of the order of 50 million years. An alternative origin is via the accretion of impacting material. This hypothesis is supported by observations and is consistent with the state of understanding of impactor material retention in icy crusts (Daly and Schultz, 2015). Marchi *et al.* (2019) suggested that impactor material could accumulate in the first five kilometers of Ceres's crust. Using numerical modeling, Bowling *et al.* (2019) showed that up to 80% of an impactor mass could be accreted in the impact melt chamber resulting from the formation of Occator crater. This result implies that the chemistry of impact-generated melt could be significantly influenced by the composition of the impactor. Moreover, Mao and McKinnon (2020) demonstrated that impactor material could lead to the accumulation of hundreds of meters of regolith on Ceres's surface. This scenario cannot explain the abundance of ammoniated clays on Ceres's surface, a kind of material that has not been found in carbonaceous chondrites. It also cannot account for the large abundance of carbon, 10 to 20 wt%, found in the regolith by Dawn's GRaND instrument (carbonaceous chondrites have <~4 wt% C in bulk). Hence, additional mechanisms need to be invoked in order to fully explain the origin of Ceres's regolith. A combination of these various origins is possible. Lastly, exogenous, infallen material has been identified on the protoplanet Vesta in the form of carbonaceous material with distinct signatures as measured with Dawn's GRaND and VIR instruments. Recent results from Raponi *et al.* (2021) suggested the presence of serpentine on Ceres that has been heated to several 100°C, conditions that are not expected on Ceres's surface. The presence of anhydrous silicates was also suggested based on observations in the mid-infrared (Vernazza *et al.*, 2017) and explained as an exogenic contribution.

The Dawn mission determined that the surface of Ceres is almost entirely covered by serpentine, ammoniated phyllosilicates, carbonates, and salts, with variations associated with geologically young impact craters and large mounds. Exposed water ice patches exist only in a few isolated areas associated with impact craters in mid- to high-latitude regions, and in some permanently shadowed craters in the polar regions, but subsurface ice is present in the top meter of the subsurface at latitude higher than about 40°. Organic material was identified on the surface in a single area in the Ernutet crater region. Iron appears to be depleted in the upper meter of Ceres's regolith, but carbon is enriched relative to carbonaceous meteorite samples. The surface composition of Ceres indicates pervasive water–rock alteration on the global scale, and provides constraints on its thermal history and chemical evolution.

References

Ammannito, E., *et al.* (2016). Distribution of phyllosilicates on the surface of Ceres. *Science*, **353**, aaf4279.

Bowling, T. J., Ciesla, F. J., Davison, T. M., Scully, J. E. C., Castillo-Rogez, J. C. and Marchi, S. (2019). Post-impact thermal structure and cooling timescales of Occator Crater on Asteroid 1 Ceres. *Icarus*, **320**, 110–118.

Brown, M. E. and Hand, K. P. (2013). Salts and radiation products on the surface of Europa. *Astron. J.*, **145**, 110 (7pp).

Carrozzo, F. G., *et al.* (2018). Nature, formation, and distribution of carbonates on Ceres. *Sci. Adv.*, **4**, e1701645.

Castillo-Rogez, J. C., Neveu, M., McSween, H. Y., Fu R. R., Toplis, M. J. and Prettyman, T. (2018). Insights into Ceres' evolution from surface composition. *Meteorit. Planet. Sci.,* **53**, 1820–1843.

Chapman, C. R. and Salisbury, J. W. (1973). Comparisons of meteorite and asteroid spectral reflectivities. *Icarus,* **19**, 507–522.

Combe, J.-P., *et al.* (2016). Detection of local H_2O exposed at the surface of Ceres. *Science,* **353**, aaf3010.

Combe, J.-P., *et al.* (2019). Exposed H_2O-rich areas detected on Ceres with the Dawn visible and infrared spectrometer. *Icarus*, **318**, 22–41.

Daly, R. T. and Schultz, P. H. (2015). Predictions for impactor contamination on Ceres based on hypervelocity impact experiments. *Geophys. Res. Lett*, **42**, 7890–7898.

De Sanctis, M. C., *et al.* (2012). Detection of widespread hydrated materials on Vesta by the VIR imaging spectrometer on board the Dawn mission. *Astrophys. J. Lett.*, **758**, 36.

De Sanctis, M. C., *et al.* (2015). Ammoniated phyllosilicates with a likely outer solar system origin on (1) Ceres. *Nature,* **528**, 241–244.

De Sanctis, M. C., *et al.* (2016). Bright carbonate deposits as evidence of aqueous alteration on (1) Ceres. *Nature,* **536**, 54–57.

De Sanctis, M. C., *et al.* (2017). Localized aliphatic organic material on the surface of Ceres. *Science,* **355**, 719–722.

De Sanctis, M. C., *et al.* (2018). Ceres's global and localized mineralogical composition determined by Dawn's Visible and Infrared Spectrometer (VIR). *Meteorit. Planet. Sci.*, **53**, 1844–1865.

Ermakov, A. I., *et al.* (2017). Ceres's obliquity history and its implications for the permanently shadowed regions. *Geophys. Res. Lett.*, **44**, 2652–2661.

Fanale, F. P. and Salvail, J. R. (1989). The water regime of asteroid (1) Ceres. *Icarus*, **82**, 97–110.

Fu, R., *et al.* (2017). The interior structure of Ceres as revealed by surface topography. *Earth and Planet. Sci. Lett.,* **476**, 153–164.

Hughson, K. H. G., *et al.* (2018). The Ac-5 (Fejokoo) quadrangle of Ceres: Geologic map and geomorphological evidence for ground ice mediated surface processes. *Icarus*, **316**, 63–83.

Kaplan, H. H., Milliken, R. E. and Alexander, C. M. O'D. (2018). New constraints on the abundance and composition of organic matter on Ceres. *Geophys. Res. Lett.*, **45**, 5274–5282.

King, T. V. V., Clark, R. N., Calvin, W. M., Sherman, D. M. and Brown, R. H. (1992). Evidence for ammonium-bearing minerals on Ceres. *Science*, **255**, 1551–1553.

Lawrence, D. J., *et al.* (2018). Compositional variability on the surface of 1 Ceres revealed through GRaND measurements of high-energy gamma rays. *Meteorit. Planet. Sci.*, **53**, 1805–1819.

Lebofsky, L. A., Feierberg, M. A., Tokunaga, A. T., Larson, H. P. and Johnson, J. R. (1981). The 1.7- to 4.2 μm spectrum of asteroid 1 Ceres: Evidence for structural water in clay minerals. *Icarus*, **48**, 453–459.

Li, J.-Y., *et al.* (2016). Surface albedo and spectral variability of Ceres. *Astrophys. J. Lett.*, **817**, 22.

Mao, X. and McKinnon, W. B. (2020). Spin evolution of Ceres and Vesta due to impacts. *Meteorit. Planet. Sci.*, **55**, 2493–2518.

Marchi, S., *et al.* (2019). An aqueously altered carbon-rich Ceres. *Nat. Astron.*, **3**, 140–145.

McCord, T. B. and Gaffey, M. J. (1974). Asteroids: Surface composition from reflection spectroscopy. *Science,* **186**, 352–355.

McKay, C. P. and Borucki, W. J. (1997). Organic synthesis in experimental impact shocks. *Science,* **276**, 390–392.

McKinnon, W. B. and Zolensky, M. E. (2003). Sulfate content of Europa's ocean and shell: Evolutionary considerations and some geological and astrobiological implications. *Astrobiology*, **3**, 879–897.

McSween, H. Y., *et al.* (2018). Carbonaceous chondrites as analogs for the composition and alteration of Ceres. *Meteorit. Planet. Sci.,* **53**, 1793–1804.

Milliken, R. E. and Rivkin, A. S. (2009). Brucite and carbonate assemblages from altered olivine-rich materials on Ceres. *Nat. Geosci.*, **2**, 258–261.

Neveu, M. and Desch, S. J. (2015). Geochemistry, thermal evolution, and cryovolcanism on Ceres with a muddy mantle. *Geophys. Res. Lett.*, **42**, 10,197–10,206.

Paige, D. A., *et al.* (2010). Diviner lunar radiometer observations of cold traps in the Moon's south polar region. *Science,* **330**, 479.

Paige, D. A., *et al.* (2013). Thermal stability of volatiles in the north polar region of Mercury. *Science,* **339**, 300.

Pasckert, J. H., *et al.* (2017). Geologic mapping of the Ac-2 Coniraya quadrangle of Ceres from NASA's Dawn mission: Implications for a heterogeneously composed crust. *Icarus*, **316**, 28–45.

Peplowski, P. N. and Lawrence, D. J. (2013). New insights into the global composition of the lunar surface from high-energy gamma rays measured by Lunar Prospector. *J. Geophys. Res. Planet.*, **118**, 671–688.

Pieters, C. M., *et al.* (2018). Geologic constraints on the origin of red organic-rich material on Ceres. *Meteorit. Planet. Sci.*, **53**, 1983–1998.

Platz, T., *et al.* (2016). Surface water-ice deposits in the northern shadowed regions of Ceres. *Nat. Astron.*, **1**, 0007.

Postberg, F., Schmidt, J., Hillier, J., Kempf, S. and Srama, R. (2011). A salt-water reservoir as a source of compositionally stratified plume on Enceladus *Nature*, **474**, 620–622.

Prettyman, T. H., *et al.* (2012). Elemental mapping by Dawn reveals exogenic H in Vesta's regolith. *Science*, **338**, 242.

Prettyman, T. H., *et al.* (2017). Extensive water ice within Ceres' aqueously altered regolith: Evidence from nuclear spectroscopy. *Science*, **355**, 55–59.

Prettyman, T. H., *et al.* (2018). High spatial resolution measurements of Ceres' elemental composition. AGU Fall Meeting, abstract #P24A-06.

Raponi, A., *et al.* (2019). Mineralogy of Occator crater on Ceres and insight into its evolution from the properties of carbonates, phyllosilicates, and chlorides. *Icarus*, **320**, 83–96.

Raponi, A., *et al.* (2021). Organic material on Ceres: Insights from visible and infrared space observations. *Life*, **11**, 9.

Reddy, V., *et al.* (2012). Delivery of dark material to Vesta via carbonaceous chondritic impacts. *Icarus*, **221**, 544–559.

Rivkin, A. S., Volquardsen, E. L. and Clark, B. E. (2006). The surface composition of Ceres: Discovery of carbonates and iron-rich clays. *Icarus*, **185**, 563–567.

Siegler, M. A., Bills, B. G. and Paige, D. A. (2011). Effects of orbital evolution on lunar ice stability. *J. Geophys. Res.*, **116**, E03010.

Schmidt, B. E., *et al.* (2017). Geomorphological evidence for ground ice on dwarf planet Ceres. *Nat. Geosci.*, **10**, 338–343.

Schörghofer, N. (2008). The lifetime of ice on main belt asteroids. *Astrophys. J.*, **682**, 697–705.

Schröder, S. E., *et al.* (2017). Resolved spectrophotometric properties of the Ceres surface from Dawn Framing Camera images. *Icarus,* **288**, 201–225.

Thangjam, G., *et al.* (2018). Spectral properties and geology of bright and dark material on dwarf planet Ceres. *Meteorit. Planet. Sci.*, **53**, 1961–1982.

Titus, T. N. (2015). Ceres: Predictions for near-surface water ice stability and implications for plume generating processes. *Geophys. Res. Lett.*, **42**, 2130–2136.

Vernazza, P., *et al.* (2017). Different origins or different evolutions? Decoding the spectral diversity among C-type asteroids. *Astron. J.*, **153**, 72 (10pp).

Vinogradoff, V., Bernard, S., Le Guillou, C., Remusat, L., 2018. Evolution of interstellar organic compounds under asteroidal hydrothermal conditions. *Icarus*, **305**, 358–370.

Zambon, F., *et al*. (2017). Spectral analysis of Ahuna Mons from Dawn mission's visible-infrared spectrometer. *Geophys. Res. Lett*., **44**, 97–104.

Chapter 5

Geology

Ceres's surface geology has been primarily shaped by impact craters, which are responsible for its morphology on regional and local scales, as well as for partial resurfacing via blanketing by ejecta from large impacts. Mass wasting (landslides and slumping), triggered in part by micrometeorite bombardment, further acts in long-term surface modification. Ceres also displays evidence for limited tectonic features on a global scale and crater-generated fractures on a local scale. Lastly, Ceres exhibits evidence for some form of volcanic activity driven by brines in a few places (see more detail in Chapter 8). Crater morphologies as well as expressions of melting and viscous flow indicate the existence of ice in the crust (see also Chapter 6).

5.1 Global Geology

Ceres's geological units are in large part based on large ejecta blankets generated by large (>200 km) impact craters, including Kerwan, Urvara, and Yalode (Buczkowski *et al.*, 2016; Hiesinger *et al.*, 2016). These ejecta blankets partially resurfaced Ceres. Other geological features include montes and tholi, catenae, faculae, fossae, and rupes. Figure 5.1 shows Ceres's major craters and geological features (Williams *et al.*, 2018).

Global geologic mapping defines three globally distributed units on Ceres and a series of widely distributed impact-related units, the former including cratered terrain, smooth material, and the units of Urvara/Yalode system (Fig. 5.2; Mest *et al.*, 2018). The cratered terrain exhibits rugged surfaces that are heavily cratered. This unit covers most of Ceres's surface

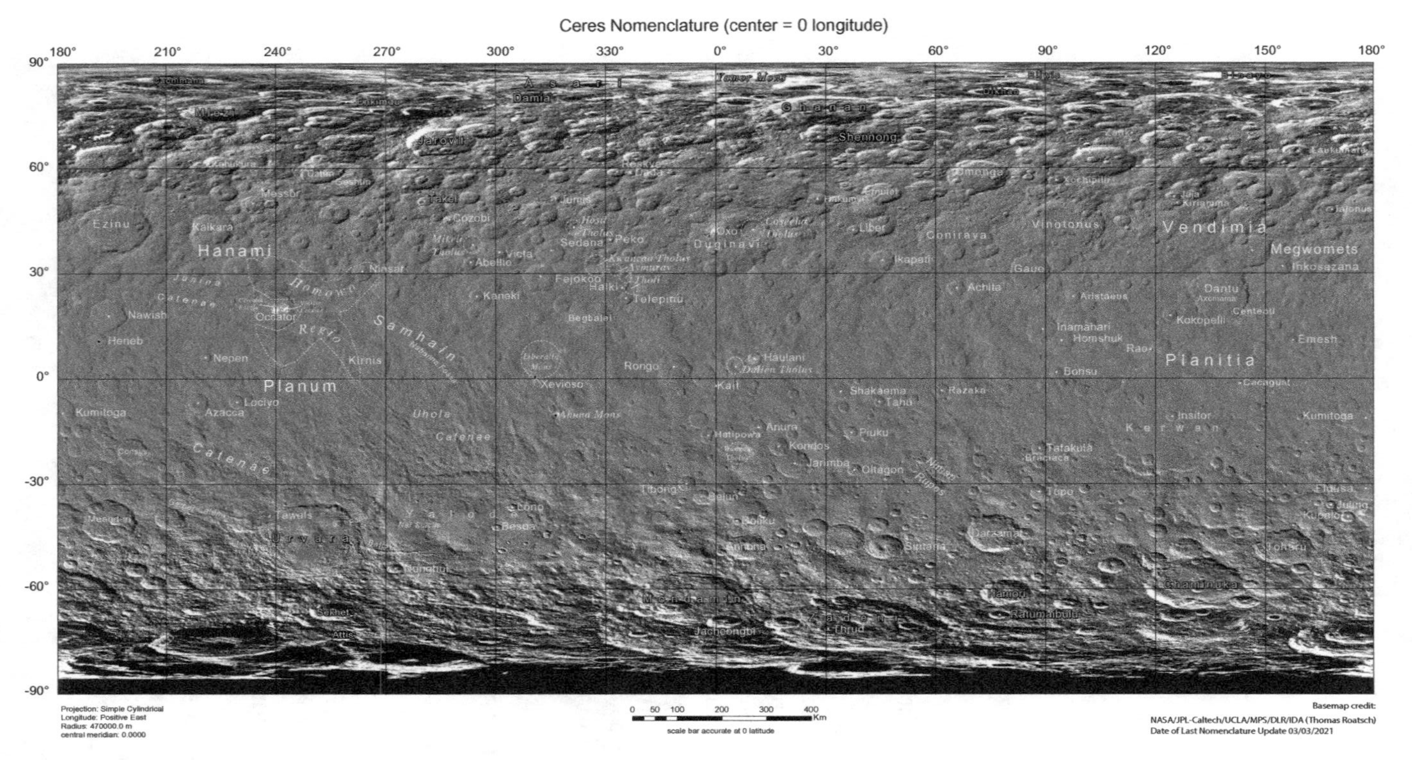

Figure 5.1: Global map of Ceres based on a mosaic derived from FC images obtained in Dawn's low altitude mapping orbit with named surface features (from https://planetarynames.wr.usgs.gov/images/ceres.pdf). For an up-to-date list of named features on Ceres, refer to the Gazetteer of Planetary Nomenclature (https://planetarynames.wr.usgs.gov/Page/CERES/target).

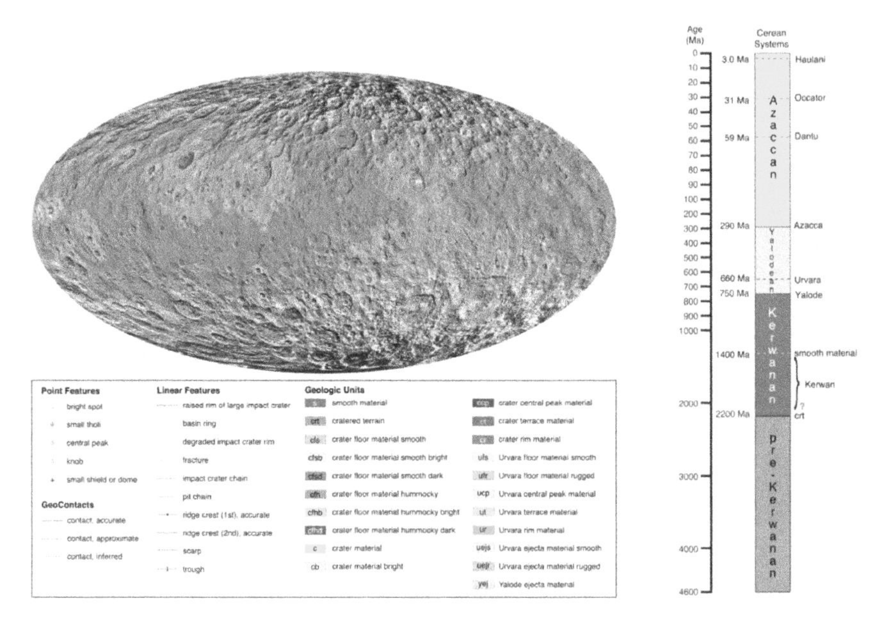

Figure 5.2: Global geologic map of Ceres based on a mosaic derived from FC images obtained in Dawn's high altitude mapping orbit (left) and Ceres's chronostratigraphic system (right). Center longitude is 180° in the map. The boundary ages are preliminary and based on lunar-derived model. Reprinted from Mest *et al.* (2018).

and represents the oldest geologic unit on Ceres. The surface material likely consists of crustal material mixed with various impact materials. Smooth material forms nearly flat to hummocky plains in the western equatorial hemisphere. It is mostly found on the floor of and surrounding Kerwan crater. The geologic unit related to Urvara and Yalode basins consists of impact materials that cover a large part of Ceres's eastern and southern hemispheres. The ejecta deposits and structures from Urvara superpose those of Yalode, indicating a slightly younger age of the former.

Crater floor materials can be smooth, hummocky, bright and dark. The floor may also display terraces and a central peak. The ejecta deposits of some morphologically fresh craters, such as Haulani, Occator, Dantu, and Azacca, are associated with a blue to light blue color in the FC color mosaics that correlates with rayed patterns.

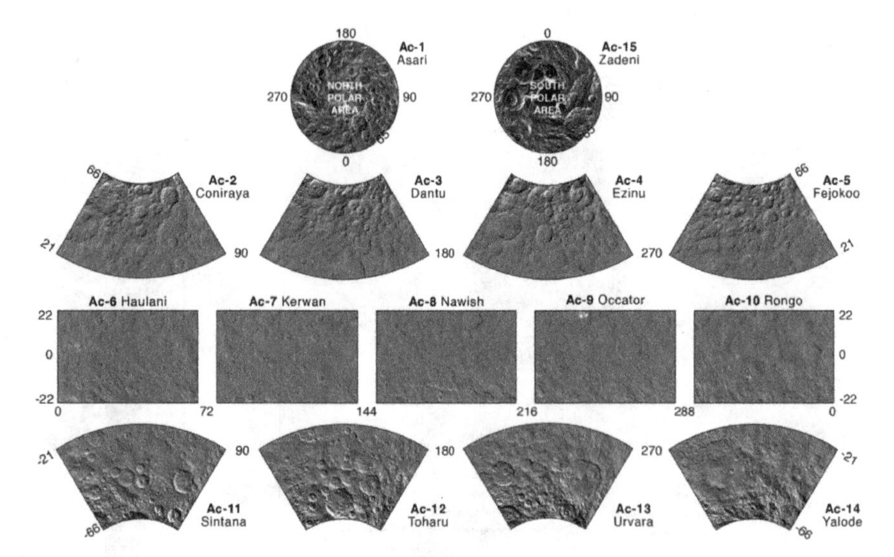

Figure 5.3: The fifteen-quadrangle scheme adopted for the regional geologic mapping of Ceres. Reprinted from Roatsch *et al.* (2016). Copyright with permission from Elsevier.

Based on the global geologic mapping and their relative ages and absolute model ages (AMA, see Section 3), a chronostratigraphic system was proposed to contain four major systems: pre-Kerwanan, Kerwanan, Yalodean, and Azaccan (Fig. 5.2). Kerwan crater is likely among the oldest recognizable impacts preserved on Ceres, and is used to define the two oldest systems in Ceres's chronostratigraphic system; pre-Kerwanan and Kerwanan systems. The formation of Yalode impact basin marks the end of the Kerwanan system. The Urvara basin formed during the Yalodean. The Yalodean system ended with the formation and preservation of the youngest, rayed craters on Ceres. The Azaccan system represents the youngest chronostratigraphic unit on Ceres.

Detailed geologic mapping of Ceres was performed with the FC images collected during all three orbital phases of the Dawn primary mission. The geologic maps are organized in a 15-quadrangle scheme at 1:500,000 scale (Fig. 5.3; Roatsch *et al.*, 2016). Six classes of features that cover 45 geologic units are defined: cratered terrain, smooth material, tholus material, pitted terrain, crater materials, and lobate materials. Readers are referred to Williams *et al.* (2018) and other articles in the collection of "The geologic mapping of Ceres" in Icarus Volume 316 for the detailed quadrangle maps.

5.2 General Crater Properties

Craters played a key role in the resurfacing on Ceres (Fig. 5.4; Buczkowski *et al.*, 2016; Hiesinger *et al.*, 2016). The few largest craters that dominate the global crater distribution on Ceres (Kerwan, Urvara, and Yalode) are all located in the southern hemisphere. As a result, significantly more craters >20 km in diameter are distributed in the northern hemisphere. On a regional scale, some regions of low crater densities found in the northern hemisphere are associated with the youngest craters on Ceres, such as Haulani, Occator, Dantu, Oxo, and Ezinu.

Analysis of the size frequency distribution of Ceres's craters revealed a depletion of large craters (Fig. 5.5) (Marchi *et al.*, 2016). While craters <60 km diameter are nearly saturated on Ceres, those in the 100–150-km-diameter range are significantly less abundant than the extrapolation of crater size-frequency distribution (CSFD) from smaller sizes. No craters larger than 300 km in diameter have been identified. This depletion of large craters is inconsistent with the prediction by the reference collisional

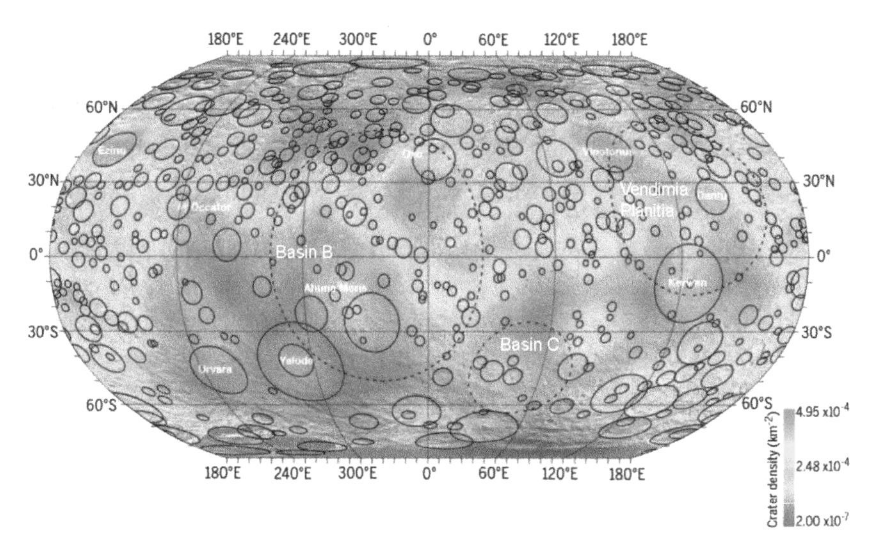

Figure 5.4: Spatial density of craters >20 km in diameter marked by black circles. The three dashed circles mark the outlines of putative basins recognizable from the global digital elevation model, but barely visible in images. Marchi *et al.* (2016) discussed these putative large basins on Ceres. Reprinted from Hiesinger *et al.* (2016). Copyright with permission from AAAS.

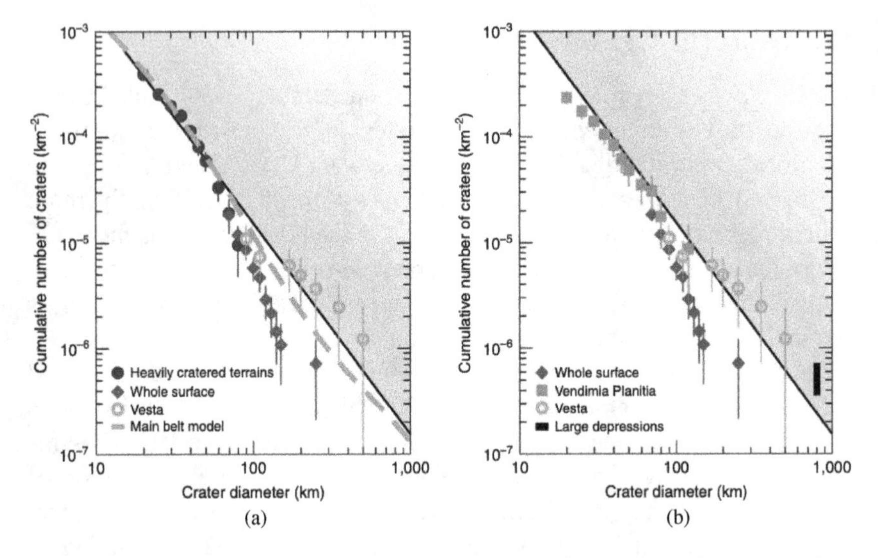

Figure 5.5: Size frequency distributions of craters in various regions of Ceres's surface, compared to Vesta and the reference main belt model used by O'Brien *et al.* (2014). This plot highlights a deficit of craters in the 60–300 km range across Ceres' surface. Reprinted from Marchi *et al.* (2016). Copyright with permission from Springer Nature.

model over a range of assumptions, including late implantation of Ceres into the main belt, and with the extrapolation of large craters on Vesta, which has a similar collisional environment as Ceres (Marchi *et al.*, 2016; Roig and Nesvorny, 2020).

To explain the apparent depletion of large craters, Marchi *et al.* (2016) searched for and identified three possible relict impact basins, as also indicated by the analysis of Hiesinger *et al.* (2016), including Vendimia Planitia (~800-km-diameter and 3–4 km deep), and two unnamed basins (~800 km wide and 2–3 km deep, and ~500 km wide). These basins are generally associated with increased abundance of ammoniated phyllosilicates (Ammannito *et al.*, 2016) and positive gravity anomalies (Ermakov *et al.*, 2017). Their presence is in line with extrapolation of Vesta's CSFD. Therefore, large craters could have formed on Ceres, but been degraded due to Ceres's water-rich composition, for example via viscous relaxation.

Ceres's craters exhibit a variety of morphologies from simple bowl-shaped craters for the smallest ones to complex craters. The latter may show multiple terraces, floor deposits, a central peak, and/or a pit (Fig. 5.6; Hiesinger *et al.*, 2016; Schenk *et al.*, 2021). Comparison

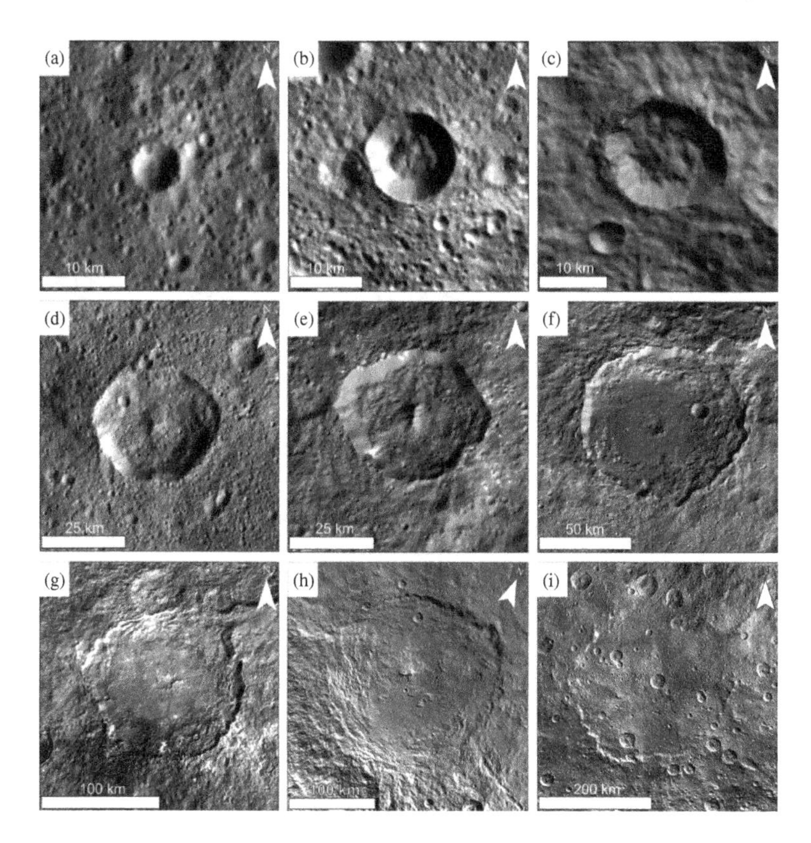

Figure 5.6: Morphologies of impact craters on Ceres with increasing size from left to right and top to bottom. Crater morphology evolves from a simple bowl shape (a) to increasing complex structures; (b) modified simple crater with mass wasting deposits; (c) complex crater with possible terraces and signatures of mass wasting on the floor and walls; (d) crater with central peak; (e) polygonal crater with mass wasting ridges on the floor; (f) terraces, a central pit, a smooth and flat floor, and a small peak close to the central pit; (g) concentric terraces, a possible peak ring structure or central pit; (h) concentric terraces, a small elongated central peak, and a relaxed morphology; (i) partially relaxed morphology and a central depression. Larger craters (f–i) display a smooth and flat floor and evidence for relaxation, the signature of impact produced heating decreasing the viscosity and even partially melting ice rich material. Arrowheads point north. Reprinted from Hiesinger *et al.* (2016). Copyright with permission from AAAS.

between the different crater morphologies on Ceres and those on other objects such as Vesta, as well as the icy satellites of Saturn, Uranus, and Pluto combined with their corresponding sizes, put constraints on the rheological properties of the upper crust of Ceres.

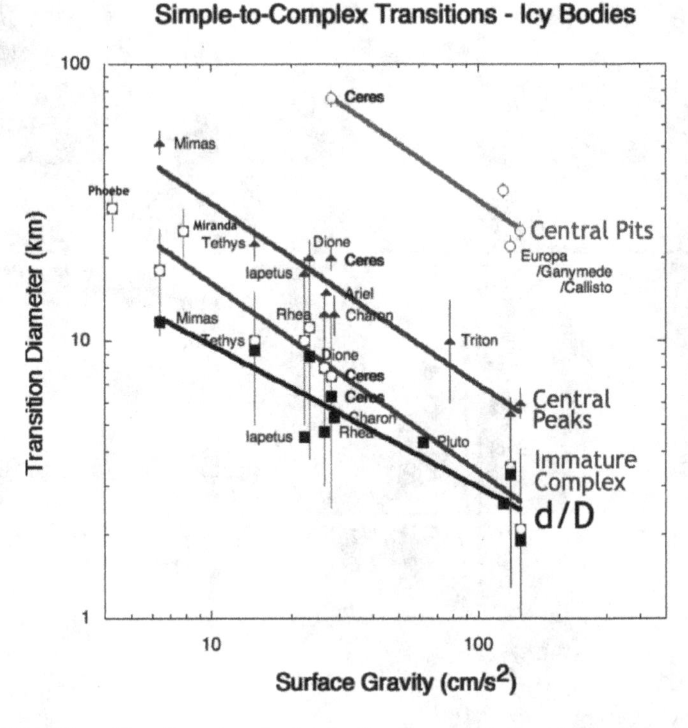

Figure 5.7: Transition diameters for icy bodies throughout the solar system. Reprinted from Schenk *et al.* (2021). Copyright with permission from Elsevier.

The simple craters on Ceres show a broadly similar morphology as those on Vesta and icy satellites, although more boulders and less floor fill are observed for Ceres's craters than on ice-free Vesta. For complex craters, to the first order, Ceres's crater morphologies are similar to those of icy satellites at all diameters, but very different from those on Vesta (Schenk *et al.*, 2021). The transition sizes from simple to complex craters, then to central peak craters, and to central pit craters on Ceres, as well as the size at which the depth-to-diameter (d/D) trend line breaks to a shallower slope for Ceres, are all consistent with the general dependence on surface gravity for icy satellites rather than for anhydrous bodies, following a $\sim g^{-0.65}$ relationship (Fig. 5.7), where g is the surface gravitational acceleration. This broad similarity indicates an outer shell rheology for Ceres dominated by weak material in response to impacts compared to that of Vesta or the Moon.

On the other hand, most craters on Ceres do not show signatures of viscous relaxation except for some of the largest ones, indicating the presence of high-strength crustal material. This requires non-ice material and limits water ice to represent less than ~40 vol.% (Bland *et al.*, 2016). Clathrates, which behave like ice upon impact, but are stronger than ice at low strain rate, together with ice could make up 80 vol.% of Ceres's crust (Schenk *et al.*, 2021).

Evidence of impact melt, in the form of very smooth material, is found in or around Ceres craters >30 km in diameter, but is lacking for polar craters and on mid-sized icy satellites. This difference could be attributed to the higher surface and internal temperature of Ceres compared to icy satellites, because thermal gradients may be a strong factor influencing melt production on ice-rich objects (Schenk *et al.*, 2021).

5.3 Surface Ages from Crater Counting

Crater size-frequency distribution (CSFD) is commonly used to derive the relative and absolute model ages (AMA) of planetary surfaces (e.g., Neukum *et al.*, 2001; O'Brien *et al.*, 2014). The AMA depends on two functions: the production function (PF) and the chronology function (CF) (Fig. 5.8). The PF describes the crater frequency distribution averaged over the past, and is used to fit the observed CSFD and extrapolate it to a particular reference crater diameter in order to compare with the CF. The PF characterizes the time-averaged size-frequency distribution of impactors and how a particular planetary surface responds to impacts in the sizes of craters formed. Therefore, it depends on the size, velocity, and density of impactors, and gravity and material properties of planetary surfaces. The CF is the cumulative crater frequency of particularly sized craters over time. It depends on the temporal evolution of potential impactors in the vicinity of a planetary body. Comparing the measured crater frequency with CF yields the AMA of a particular planetary surface.

The CF and PF for Ceres were derived with two approaches: lunar-derived model (LDM) and asteroid-derived model (ADM) (Fig. 5.8). The LDM adapts the lunar PF and CF to impact conditions on Ceres, taking into account the various factors that affect the two functions in a similar manner as has been done for Mars and Mercury (Neukum *et al.*, 2001). The LDM benefits from direct observations of craters down to the smallest crater diameter range and the absolute calibration of the lunar CF using radiometric ages from lunar samples. However, it has to assume the same flux characteristics of the impactors in the asteroid belt as in the near-Earth environment, which may not be true. Also, as shown in Fig. 5.8, the exponential decay of the impactor flux from ~4.1 to ~3 billion

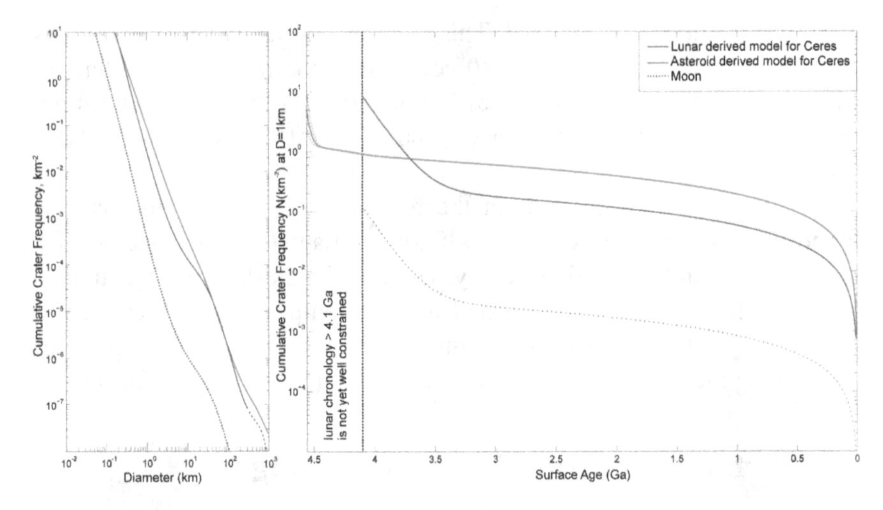

Figure 5.8: Production functions (PF; left) and chronology of function (CF; right) for Ceres, in comparison to those of the Moon. The blue and red lines are based on the lunar-derived model (LDM) and asteroid-derived model (ADM) for Ceres. The dotted lines are for the Moon. Reprinted from Hiesinger *et al.* (2016). Copyright with permission from AAAS.

years ago would lead to a primordial main belt too massive to be consistent with observations (Hiesinger *et al.*, 2016).

On the other hand, the ADM relies on the observed collision rates in the asteroid belt in combination with dynamical models for the early evolution of the asteroid belt (O'Brien *et al.*, 2014). However, the ADM-based PF has to be extrapolated to the size of craters too small for the impactors to be observed from the ground in order to model the majority of observed craters. The absolute calibration of ADM is also lacking. The main difference between LDM and ADM is in their absolute scales from ~3.2 billion years ago to the present, and the different trends before that (Fig. 5.8). This difference typically results in relatively younger AMA from the ADM than from LDM for surface ages <~3.2 billion years, and the opposite for surface ages >~3.7 billion years. A recent analysis based on the CSFDs of craters >90 km on Ceres and Vesta favored ADM for main-belt asteroids, because it provided self-consistent chronological models for both objects, and the models were consistent with the observed characteristics of the present-day asteroid belt (Roig and Nesvorny, 2020).

An example for the chronology modeling of Ceres is shown in Fig. 5.9 for the smooth deposits around Kerwan crater. This region

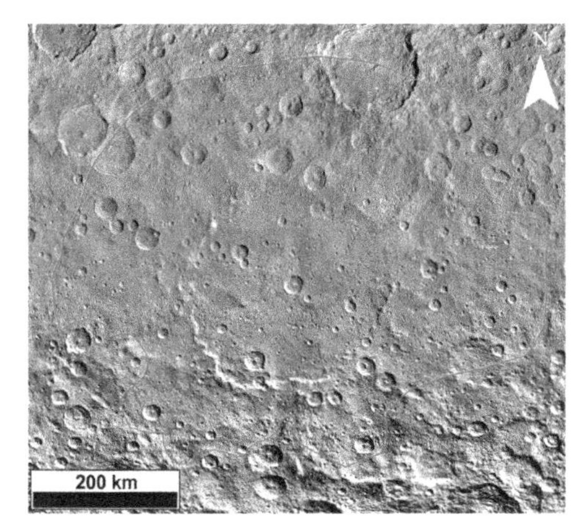

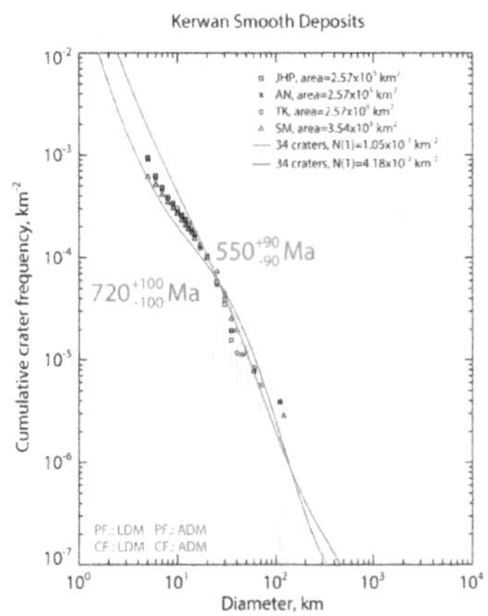

Figure 5.9: Age determination for Kerwan crater on Ceres. (Left) The blue outline marks the area used for crater counting analysis. The base mosaic is from HAMO images. (Right) The crater size frequency distribution plot for the counting area shown in the left, and the best fit age determination based on LDM (blue) and ADM (red). Reprinted from Hiesinger *et al.* (2016). Copyright with permission from AAAS.

represents a large, first-order homogeneous unit for CSFD study. The ADM led to an estimated AMA of 550 million years for this region, and the LDM yielded 720 million years (Hiesinger *et al.*, 2016). Similarly, the effort to determine the ages of the putative large basins on Ceres resulted in 3.5 billion years for the smallest one and 3.7 billion years for the two larger ones based on the LDM. The ADM-based ages for the two larger basins were 2.8 billion years and beyond 4 billion years, respectively. These ages are all consistent with the formation of the youngest basins on other planetary bodies such as Vesta (Schmedemann *et al.*, 2014).

5.4 Tectonics

Tectonic activity on Ceres is expressed in three types of features: sets of large parallel fractures (catenae) found in two regions on Ceres, fractures found on crater floors, and faults revealed by the presence of polygonal craters.

Catenae are large fractures of extensional nature. The surface expression of these fractures is in the form of pit chains, i.e., a succession of small depressions filled with regolith. Two sets have been identified by Scully *et al.* (2017): the Junina and Samhain Catenae (Fig. 5.10). They are

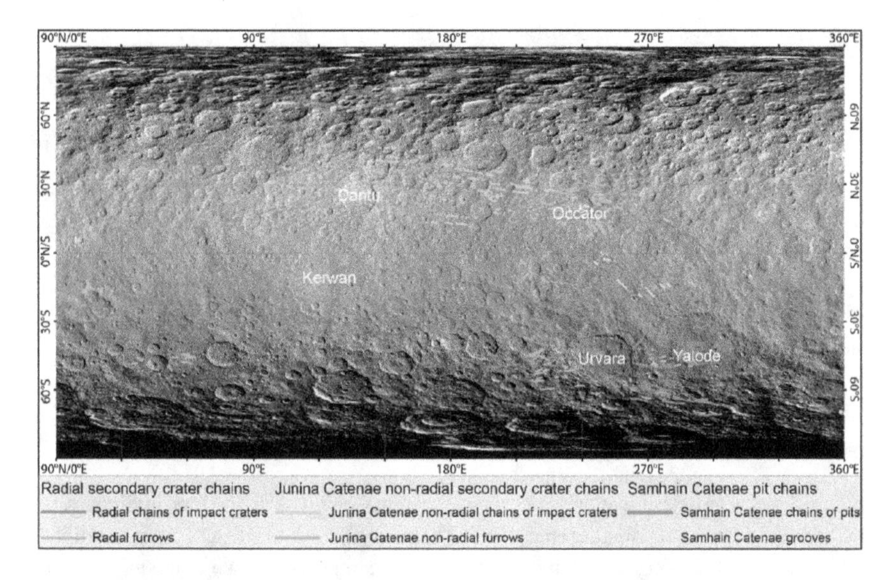

Figure 5.10: Distribution of the various types of large faults and fractures found at Ceres. Reprinted from Scully *et al.* (2017). Copyright with permission from Wiley-VCH Verlag GmbH & Co. KGaA.

both associated with Hanami Planum, but their origin is unknown. Scully *et al.* (2017) suggested these fractures were created by a large convective plume that would also be responsible for the high topography of Hanami Planum against its surroundings.

Floor-fractured craters (FFC) are abundant on Ceres. Buczkowski *et al.* (2018) reported 21 FFCs with diameters ranging from ~15 to ~120 km. Two classes of FFCs were identified: Class 1 FFCs show both radial and concentric fractures and complex central peaks; Class 4 FFCs are characterized by the presence of V-shaped moats with various types of fractures.

By analogy with lunar craters, these features have been interpreted as the product of cryomagma intrusions driving floor uplift (Buczkowski *et al.*, 2018). Hence, FFCs are another piece of evidence for abundant ice below the surface that is melted upon impact-produced heating. Class 1 FCCs are also frequently associated with melt. Dantu crater (Fig. 5.11) is an example of a crater whose floor displays evidence of salts in association with fractures. It is possible that, similarly to Occator crater, the Dantu crater-forming impact created a local melt chamber and introduced fractures that could reach a deeper brine

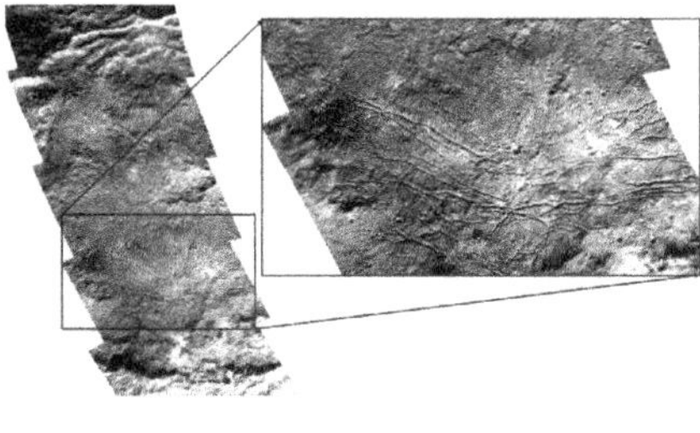

Figure 5.11: Dantu crater as an example of a crater that displays fractures on its floor. Left: Dantu crater is 126 kilometers across. It displays a central pit and a shallow floor suggesting the occurrence of melting (https://photojournal.jpl.nasa.gov/catalog/PIA22985). Right: This color mosaic reveals brightness variations that are explained by hydrothermal activity and deposits of evaporites following impact (https://photojournal.jpl.nasa.gov/catalog/PIA22471) Credit: NASA/JPL-Caltech/UCLA/MPS/DLR/IDA.

reservoir. See Chapter 6 for more discussion about the implications of FFCs in Ceres's subsurface ice.

Polygonal craters define craters whose rims are straight. Only one part of the crater may present straight rims or a crater may have 5 to 12 straight rims (Zeilnhofer and Barlow, 2021). The formation of polygonal craters is explained by the presence of a fracture network at depth that drives the redistribution of crustal material following impact. An example of polygonal crater is shown in Fig. 5.12.

Lastly, Ceres presents an outstanding tectonic feature, Nar Sulcus, located in Yalode crater (Fig. 5.13). The structure consists of a series of almost parallel grooves amidst the smooth material of Yalode's crater floor. It may point to an episode of tectonic deformation following the subsurface mixing of ice, rock, and salt, perhaps causing a large volume to melt. When this material subsequently refroze, it would expand and create stresses that fractured the ground, leading to the formation of the sulcus (Hughson *et al.*, 2018). The uniqueness of this feature may be related to its origin in Yalode, the second largest crater on Ceres, whose formation involved significant heat production.

Ceres's surface is mainly shaped by craters and their ejecta. Its overall geology indicates that this body has been less active than bodies that experienced more heating (e.g., due to tides). However, craters also played a

Figure 5.12: These long fractures are two of the Samhain Catenae. The catena in the center intersects a crater, giving it its polygonal shape. https://photojournal.jpl.nasa.gov/catalog/PIA22086. Credit: NASA/JPL-Caltech/UCLA/MPS/DLR/IDA.

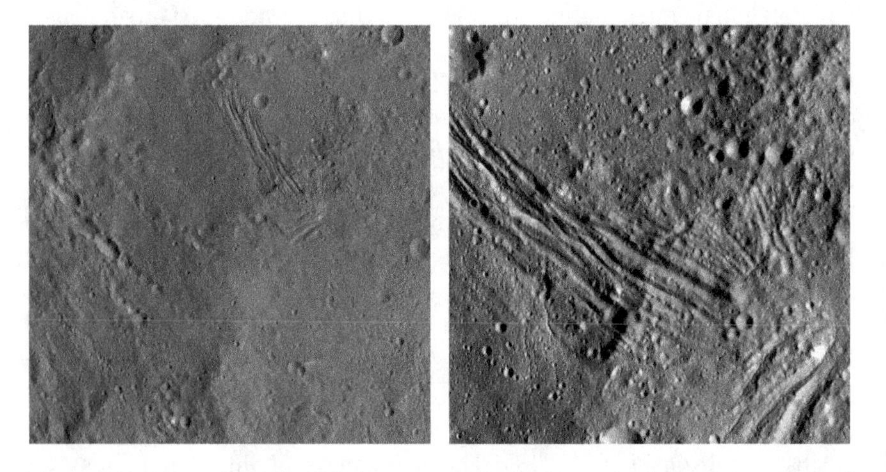

Figure 5.13: Nar Sulcus in Yalode crater (Left) is about 50 kilometer long (https://photojournal.jpl.nasa.gov/catalog/PIA22469). A close-up image shown on the right highlights the extensional deformation characterizing this feature (https://photojournal.jpl.nasa.gov/catalog/PIA21400). Credit: NASA/JPL-Caltech/UCLA/MPS/DLR/IDA.

major role in the mobilization and exposure of subsurface ice and salts as a consequence of impact-generated heating, leading to smooth floors and floor fractures. The implications of impact heat in an ice-rich crust are significant and further addressed in Chapters 8 and 9.

References

Ammannito, E., *et al.* (2016). Distribution of phyllosilicates on the surface of Ceres. *Science*, **353**, id.aaf4279.

Bland, M. T., *et al.* (2016). Composition and structure of the shallow subsurface of Ceres revealed by crater morphology. *Nat. Geosci.*, **9**, 538–542.

Buczkowski, D. L., *et al.* (2016). The geomorphology of Ceres, *Science*, **353**, 6303.

Buczkowski, D. L., *et al.* (2018). Floor-fractured craters on Ceres and implications for interior processes. *J. Geophys. Res.*, **123**, 3188–3204.

Ermakov, A. I., *et al.* (2017). Constraints on Ceres' internal structure and evolution from its shape and gravity measured by the Dawn spacecraft. *J. Geophys. Res. Planets*, **122**, 2267–2293.

Hiesinger, H., *et al.* (2016). Cratering on Ceres: Implications for its crust and evolution. *Science*, **353**, 6303.

Hughson, K. H. G., *et al.* (2018). Normal faults on Ceres: Insights into the mechanical properties and thermal history of Nar Sulcus. *Geophys. Res. Lett.*, **46**, 80–88.

Marchi, S., *et al.* (2016). The missing large impact craters on Ceres. *Nat. Comm.*, 7, 12257.

Mest, S. C., *et al.* (2018). The HAMO-based global geologic map and chronostratigraphy of ceres, 49th Lunar and Planetary Science Conference 2018 (LPI Contrib. No. 2083), 2730.

Neukum, G., Ivanov, B. A. and Hartmann, W. K. (2001). Cratering records in the inner solar system in relation to the lunar reference system. *Space Sci. Rev.*, **96**, 55–86.

O'Brien, D. P., *et al.* (2014). Constraining the cratering chronology of Vesta. *Planet. Space Sci.*, **103**, 131–142.

Roatsch, T., *et al.* (2016). High-resolution Ceres high altitude mapping orbit atlas derived from Dawn framing camera images. *Planet. Space Sci.*, **129**, 103–107.

Roig, F. and Nesvorny, D. (2020). Modeling the chronologies and size distribution of Ceres and Vesta craters. *Astrono. J.*, **160**, 110.

Schenk, P., *et al.* (2021). Compositional control on impact crater formation on mid-sized planetary bodies: Dawn at Ceres and Vesta, Cassini at Saturn. *Icarus*, **359**, 114343.

Schmedemann, N., *et al.* (2014). The cratering record, chronology and surface ages of (4) Vesta in comparison to smaller asteroids and the ages of HED meteorites. *Planet. Space Sci.*, **103**, 104–130.

Scully, J. E. C., *et al.* (2017). Evidence for the interior evolution of Ceres from geologic analysis of fractures. *Geophys. Res. Lett.*, **44**, 9564–9572.

Williams, D. A., Buczkowski, D. L., Mest, S. C., Scully, J. E. C., Platz, T. and Kneissl, T. (2018). Introduction: The geological mapping of Ceres. *Icarus*, **316**, 1–13.

Zeilnhofer, M. and Barlow, N. (2021). The characterization and distribution of polygonal impact craters on Ceres and their implications for the Cerean crust. *Icarus*, 114586.

Chapter 6

Water Ice

Many pieces of evidence from ground-based observations and theoretical modeling point to the existence of subsurface water ice on Ceres. Coordinated studies of the water ice on Ceres from its surface to the expected crust-mantle boundary have been performed with the compositional, morphological, geological, and gravitational mapping achieved by the Dawn mission, supplemented by theoretical modeling. This effort resulted in a rough picture of the current status of Ceres's cryosphere and its history. The surface and subsurface water ice could have contributed to the production of the putative Ceres's exosphere.

Before Dawn arrived at Ceres, it was generally accepted that Ceres contains about 25% mass in the form of free water (Thomas *et al.*, 2005). Thermal, physical, and chemical modeling (McCord and Sotin, 2005; Castillo-Rogez and McCord, 2010) concluded that Ceres has undergone at least partial differentiation and rock-ice fractionation on a global scale, and pockets of brine may still exist in the interior today. The possible discovery (A'Hearn and Feldman, 1992) and the definitive detection of water vapor around Ceres (Küppers *et al.*, 2014) confirmed the prediction that water ice could be preserved within 100 meters from the surface at low latitudes and close to the surface at high latitudes (Fanale and Savail, 1989; Schörghofer, 2008; Titus, 2015). The shadowing effect of local topography could protect local surface ice deposits even in mid-latitude (Hayne and Aharonson, 2015).

Many coordinated investigations were performed to study water on Ceres from the surface to the expected crust-mantle boundary (Castillo-Rogez and McCord, 2010) at a few tens of kilometers deep, and in scale lengths from tens to hundreds of meters to global. Different techniques were needed to cover the wide ranges of depths and scale lengths. Dawn's FC and VIR instruments directly observed surface water ice deposits. Dawn's GRaND detected ice within the top meter of the surface. The geomorphological features of various scales were related to the properties of materials at different depths. Geophysical modeling based on the shape and gravity models revealed the interior structures and state of water near the mantle–crust boundary. Combining these analyses, a full picture of water on Ceres emerged.

Dawn discovered extensive evidence for the presence of ice in Ceres's shallow subsurface. As discussed in Section 4.4, spectroscopic observations revealed unequivocal spectral features from localized water ice patches. GRaND detected enriched hydrogen associated with a water ice table just below the surface at latitudes greater than ~45°. In addition to those direct detections, geomorphological signatures of water ice, including flow features, cryovolcanic features, cryogenic signatures, and crater morphologies, were found almost everywhere on Ceres. Many geological features that also attest to the role of volatiles in driving the near- and long-term response of the crust to impacts were found at all latitudes. Independent analysis of multiple feature types suggested that stratigraphy may be common in the upper ~10 km of the crust. Regional deficits and clusters of features indicate that ice concentration is heterogeneous on nearly all length scales from 100s of km to <1 km. Impacts are likely the key driver of heterogeneity, not only causing progressive devolatilization of the low- and mid-latitude crust on billion-year timescales, but also producing localized enhancements in near-surface ice content via excavation of deep ice-rich material and triggering of cryovolcanic activity. Impacts and landslides may be the dominant mechanism for ice loss on modern Ceres (Sizemore *et al.*, 2019; Landis *et al.*, 2019).

6.1 Exposed Surface Water Ice

After the detection of the first and the largest water ice deposit in Oxo crater (Combe *et al.*, 2016), a total of nine locations were identified to contain spectral absorption features diagnostic of water ice (Fig. 6.1; Combe *et al.*, 2019). All of them occur in fresh craters near the shadows along rims at north and south latitudes between 30° and 70°. The largest water ice deposit in Oxo crater has a total area of 6.8 km^2, and the smallest deposits are only <0.1 km^2. They are all associated with one or more

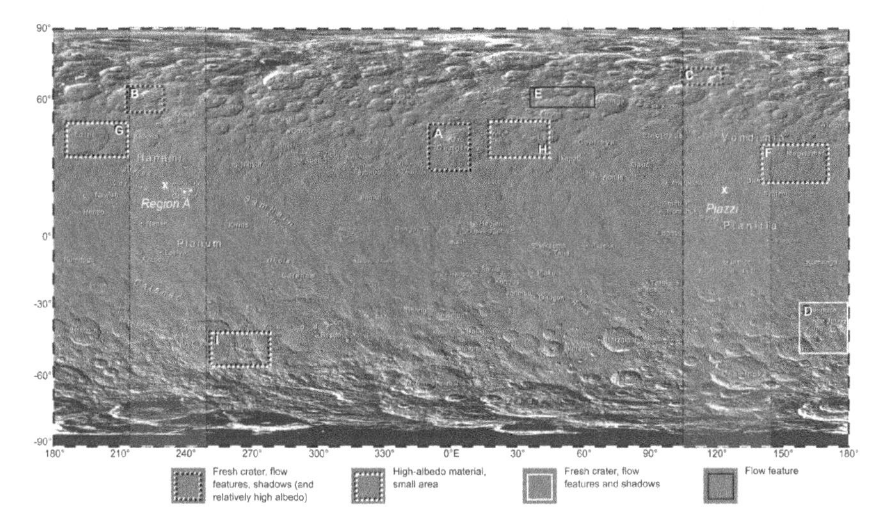

Figure 6.1: Distribution of ice exposures on Ceres. The various types of ice deposits are indicated by different line styles. The two vertical longitudinal bands correspond to the peak water vapor production as reported by Küppers *et al.* (2014). Reprinted from Combe *et al.* (2019). Copyright with permission from Elsevier.

surface features such as a flow or landslide, fractures, high albedo areas, or a pole-facing slope.

The water ice deposits on Ceres were classified into four types based on their associated geological characteristics and albedos (letters refer to the areas marked in Fig. 6.1):

1. Fresh crater, flow features, shadows, and high albedo in three locations (A, B, C), all in the northern hemisphere.
2. Fresh crater, flow features, and shadows (type 1 above but without high albedo) in Juling crater (D).
3. Flow feature with moderate albedo (not associated with fresh craters) in one location (E).
4. Small, high-albedo spots in four locations (F, G, H, I), three of which (F, G, I) are associated with pole-facing slopes of small craters.

In the mid- to high-latitude regions, the distribution of water ice is consistent with temperature-dependent surface ice stability. The distribution of surface ice patches does not correspond to the longitudes of the water vapor production peaks observed by the Herschel Space Observatory (HSO) (Küppers *et al.*, 2014; see Chapter 2), probably indicating that these surface water ice sites are not directly responsible for the majority of the observed water outgassing. Because water ice is not expected to be stable on the surface at low latitudes, the water ice sites below 40° latitude could be associated with recent exposure of subsurface ice by small impacts or mass wasting.

Surface water ice has also been unambiguously identified inside the permanently shadowed regions (PSR) in the northern polar region (Platz *et al.*, 2016; see Chapter 4). Based on the HAMO images, a total of 634 craters of the size range 0.5–74 km at latitudes >65° N were mapped out to host PSRs, and another 37 craters between 60° and 65° N possibly host PSRs (Fig. 6.2). The total area of the mapped PSRs is in the order of 2000 km^2, accounting for about 0.15% of the area of the northern hemisphere, comparable to the fraction of PSRs for Mercury's southern hemisphere

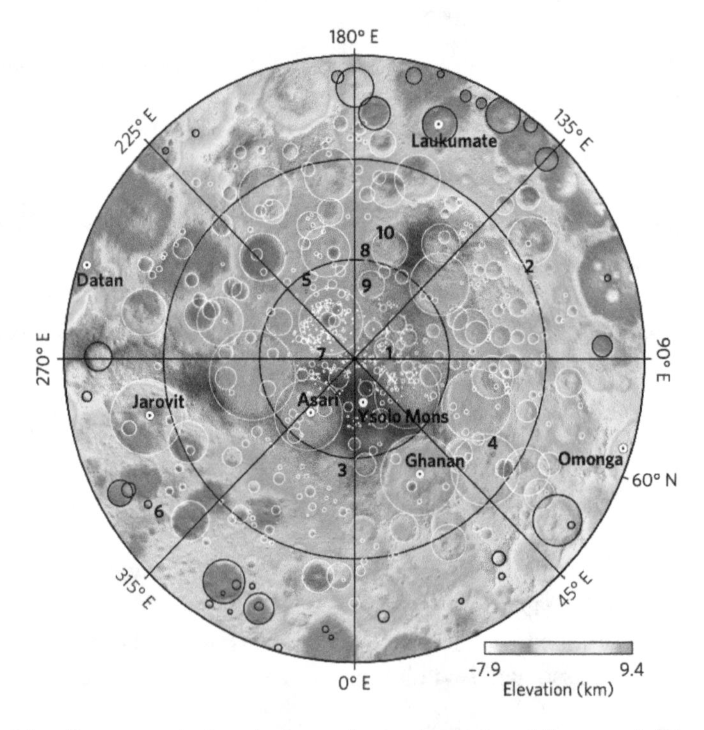

Figure 6.2: Permanent shadows in the northern polar region of Ceres overlaid on a topographic map. White circles indicate craters hosting permanent shadows. Red filled circles are craters with water ice. Black circles between 60° and 65° N are craters hosting potential permanent shadows. Reprinted from Platz *et al.* (2016). Copyright with permission from Springer Nature.

(Chabot *et al*., 2012) and for both poles of the Moon (Mazarico *et al*., 2011). The largest PSR has an area of about 140 km^2, occurring inside a crater 18 km in diameter located at 81.75° N, 78.22° E. Of these PSRs, 10 locations show high albedo or spectral signatures of water ice or both in the imaging and spectral data collected during HAMO and LAMO.

Thermophysical modeling showed that the upper bound of summertime temperatures within these PSRs is about 57 K. Ices of H_2O, CO_2, NH_3, and SO_2 are stable for billions of years under these temperature conditions. Obliquity variations due to the spin axis precession of Ceres on a timescale of 24.5 kyr (Ermakov *et al*., 2017a) are the limiting factor of the lifetime of ices in Ceres's PSRs.

The number of only ten bright sites identified in the PSRs is surprisingly small, even considering the limited detectability under the low-illumination conditions. This fraction is much smaller than that of the PSRs on Mercury and the Moon with water ice identified. Plausible explanations include the continuous mantling process from infall of ejecta from distant impacts, erosion from impact gardening, and space weathering. The oscillation of Ceres's pole may also be a contributing factor as suggested by the apparent correlation between ice deposits and the persistence of PSRs during the obliquity change (Ermakov *et al*., 2017a).

Modeling (Schörghofer *et al*., 2016) showed that most of the PSRs are cold enough to trap water ice over geological time periods. The calculation suggested that 0.14% water molecules in the exosphere could be trapped in the permanently shadowed craters, leading to fresh ice deposits in those cold traps. The estimated ages of the craters that host water ice in the PSRs are consistent with the timescale calculated by the cold-trapping model that is both long enough to accumulate water ice that is optically detectable, and short enough not to be destroyed by impact gardening. In other areas, cold-trapped ice could be too optically thin to be detected, but could produce transient water outgassing when obliterated by, e.g., solar energetic particle events (Schörghofer *et al*., 2017). Still, the dearth of water ice deposits in Ceres's PSRs compared to Mercury and the Moon is not fully explained.

One unexpected discovery about surface water ice on Ceres is the rapid increase of ice abundance on the wall of Juling crater over a period of six months observed by the Dawn spacecraft (Raponi *et al*., 2018). The Juling crater's water ice deposit is unusual compared to others on Ceres in that it is one of the only two located in the southern hemisphere (Fig. 6.3),

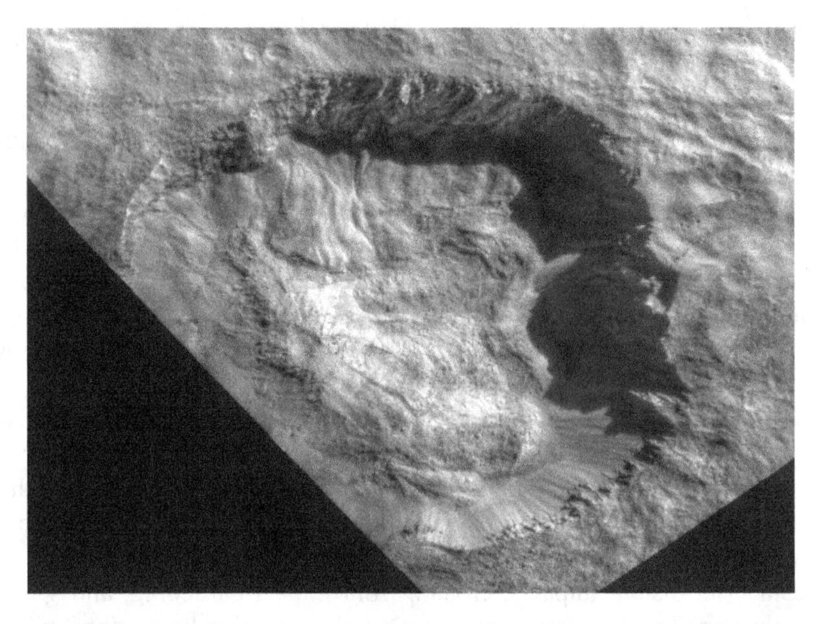

Figure 6.3: Juling crater imaged on April 30, 2016. North is up. The morphology shows evidence of the flow of ice and rock, similar to rock glaciers in Earth's Polar Regions. The northern cliff hosts a water ice deposit detected by the VIR instrument. Image credit: NASA/JPL-Caltech/UCLA/MPS/DLR/IDA/ASI/INAF.

and at a relatively low latitude (35° S). Water ice is distributed on the northern (pole facing) cliff of the crater. Unlike those associated with young craters in the northern hemisphere, the Juling crater ice deposit does not show elevated albedo, although flow features and shadows along the rim are present.

Dawn observed this water ice deposit twice during the LAMO phase and three times during the XMO2 phase, which was dedicated to confirm and study the suspected increase of ice in the Juling crater. The strength of the 2.0-μm absorption feature from water ice showed clear changes over time (Fig. 6.4). After rejecting other possible causes, such as illumination conditions, spatial resolution, and grain size, the change in absorption strength could only be attributed to an increase in water ice abundance. Spectral modeling with an areal mixing model suggested about 9% water ice in the first observation and 14% in the last.

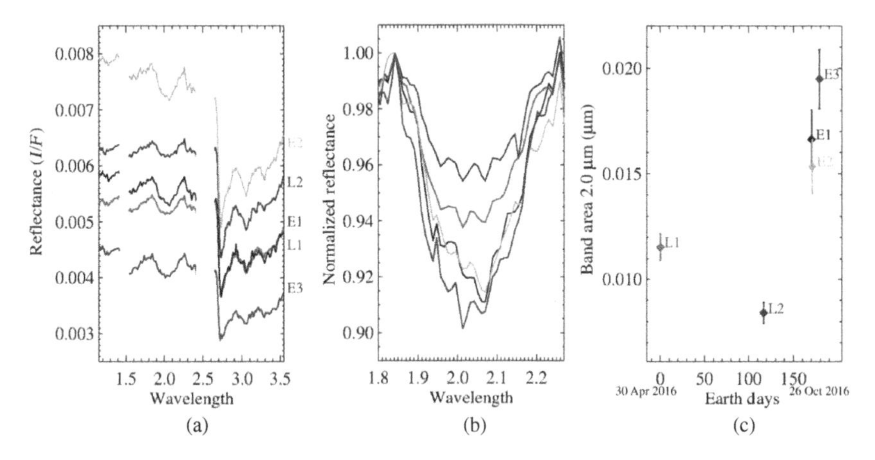

Figure 6.4: Change of water ice absorption strength in Juling crater. (a) The reflectance spectra of an area on the wall of Juling crater in five epochs. (b) The absorption band at 2.0 μm normalized at 1.83 μm. (c) The band areas of five epochs with respect to time. Reprinted from Raponi *et al.* (2018).

Possible explanations for this observation include liquid brine percolating from the subsurface freezing on the surface, exposure of subsurface water ice via mass wasting, and cold trapping of water vapor. Interior evolution models of Ceres (McCord *et al.*, 2011) suggested that subsurface brine percolation is difficult although not impossible. Exposure of subsurface water due to mass wasting would cause a sudden increase of exposed ice and is not consistent with the gradual increase as observed, although continuous erosion of the wall by regolith falls cannot be ruled out. On the other hand, the correlation between the increasing water ice on the wall and the increasing solar heating on the crater floor and the decreasing heliocentric distance of Ceres as it moved away from the aphelion (Fig. 6.5) during the course of observations support the cold-trapping scenario. Based on thermophysical modeling (Formisano *et al.*, 2018), the change of illumination conditions over the 6-month period increased the temperature on the floor, potentially enhancing the water vapor supply. But the temperature on the poorly illuminated northern wall did not change substantially, forming increasing frost on the wall. Therefore, the water ice deposit inside the Juling crater could be undergoing a seasonal cycle of sublimation and condensation, and Dawn caught a small part of the cycle.

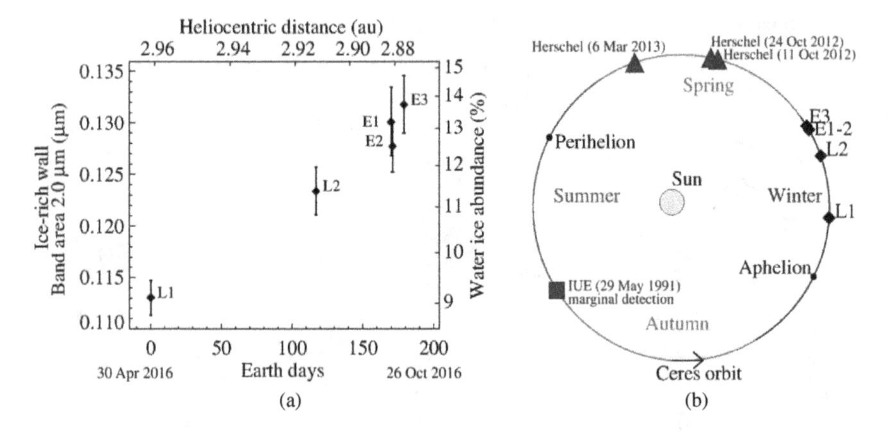

Figure 6.5: Model of ice content change in Juling crater. Left panel shows the 2.0 μm band areas of five epochs with respect to time. Rigth panel shows the locations of Ceres in its heliocentric orbit at the five epochs of observations. Reprinted from Raponi *et al.* (2018).

Although subsurface water ice is ubiquitous on Ceres (Prettyman *et al.*, 2017), exposed ice is rare. Even the largest exposed ice on Ceres cannot be directly detected with remote observations from the Earth (Combe *et al.*, 2019). Similar situation also exists on cometary nuclei (e.g., Sunshine *et al.*, 2006). A thin layer of dry lag deposit on the surface of ice-rich small bodies not only preserves subsurface water ice from sublimation for the age of the solar system, but also masks out any observational signature of water ice from ground-based observations.

6.2 Ice-Related Morphological Features

A wide range of ice-related morphological features have been identified on Ceres, including crater morphology, lobate landslides and ejecta, domes and mounds, pits, depressions, scarps, fractures, grooves, and channels (Sizemore *et al.*, 2019). These features contain information about subsurface ice at depths from meters to tens of kilometers. They could be of cryovolcanic origin, such as large domes, or formed via periglacial processes, like small mounds, or related to impact-produced heating and melting. But all of them require the existence of subsurface ice in various forms and abundances.

6.2.1 *Crater Morphology*

As discussed in Chapter 5, Dawn observations showed that a majority of craters on Ceres are not viscously relaxed (Hiesinger *et al.*, 2016; Schenk *et al.*, 2021), inconsistent with the pre-Dawn prediction (Bland, 2013). The global distribution of unrelaxed craters (Fig. 6.6) indicates a crustal viscosity of at least 1000 times higher than that for pure water ice (Bland *et al.*, 2016). Therefore, ice in Ceres's subsurface cannot exceed 30–40 vol.%, and is mixed with rock, salts, and/or clathrates that provide the required strength to resist viscous relaxation.

However, the large craters > 280 km seem to be missing on Ceres (Marchi *et al.*, 2016; Roig and Nesvorný, 2020). On the other hand, three 500–800-km-wide regions are identified from global topography, composition, and crust density variations as possible relict impact basins. Therefore, craters >300 km could have formed on Ceres but been obliterated, likely due to viscous relaxation. In the existing crater

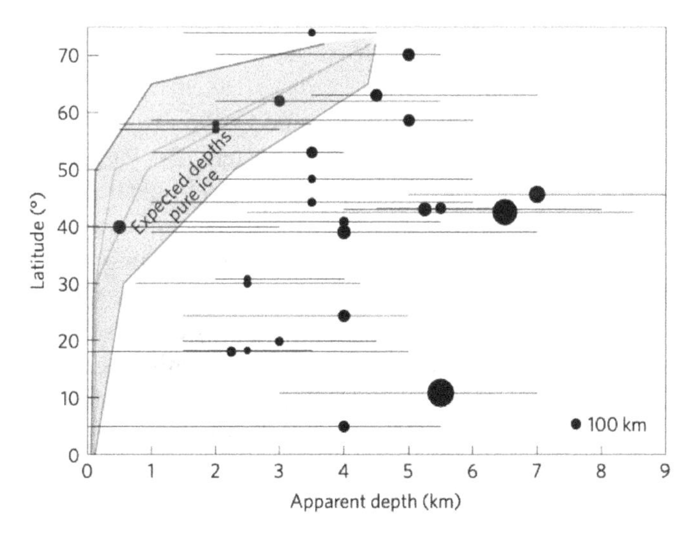

Figure 6.6: Observed depths of Ceres's large craters (black symbols with horizontal error bars) compared with the expected depth for an ice-rich subsurface composition with respect to latitude (gray area and the color lines). The purple, blue, orange, and red lines correspond to different combinations of grain sizes and crater ages: 1 mm and 1 Gyr, 1 mm and 100 Myr, 10 mm and 1 Gyr, and 10 mm and 100 Myr, respectively. Reprinted from Bland *et al.* (2016). Copyright with permission from Springer Nature.

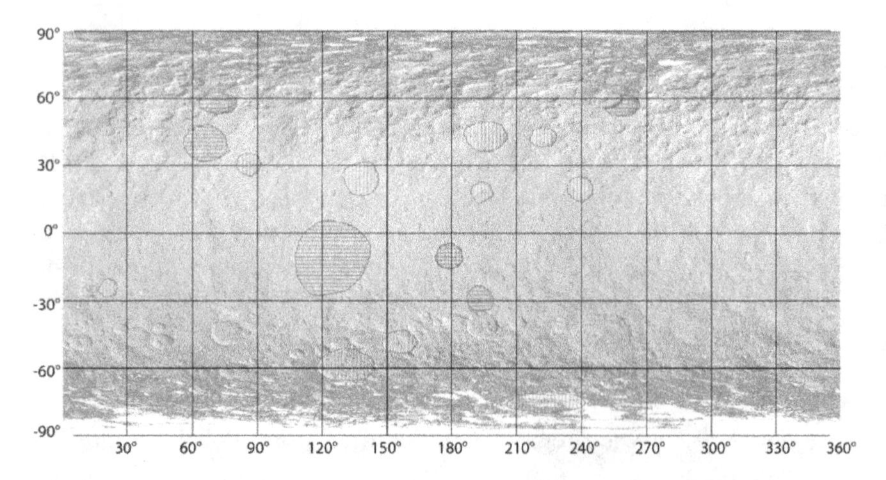

Figure 6.7: Global distribution of relaxed (red horizontal hash) and pitted (blue vertical hash) craters on Ceres overlaid on a LAMO mosaic. Reprinted from Sizemore *et al.* (2019). Copyright with permission from Wiley-VCH Verlag GmbH & Co. KGaA.

populations on Ceres, five large craters show morphology that is consistent with viscous relaxation (Bland *et al.*, 2016; Sizemore *et al.*, 2019): Coniraya, Kumitoga, Kerwan, Omonga, and Geshtin (Fig. 6.7).

In addition to the relaxation of large craters, the various transition sizes of Ceres craters, from simple to complex, to central peak and to central pit, as well as the size at which the depth-to-diameter trend line changes slope, are all consistent with the corresponding trends on icy bodies (Hiesinger *et al.*, 2016; Schenk *et al.*, 2021; See Chapter 5). In particular, the simple to complex transition size of Ceres's craters is consistent with the predicted range of 10–20 km assuming an ice rich shell (Bland, 2013). Therefore, on large spatial scales and under high strain rates during crater formation, Ceres's shell does behave in a similar manner as icy objects. But, on local scales and under low strain rates, Ceres's shell behaves more like rocky material. Based on these characteristics and the low density of Ceres's crust measured from gravity data (about 1.3 g/cm^3), the composition of Ceres's crust was constrained to be <25 vol.% ice, <29 vol.% carbonates and phyllosilicates, and >36 vol.% high-strength hydrated phases, probably clathrates and hydrated salts (Ermakov *et al.*, 2017b; Fu *et al.*, 2017). The coexistence of relaxed and unrelaxed craters of similar size indicates localized enhancement of ice to >40 vol.%.

Another distinctive crater feature that may be related to water ice is the presence of a central pit in a number of craters. Sizemore *et al.* (2019) reported that craters in the 70–150 km range commonly show central depressions, or pits, rather than anticipated central peaks, such as Occator, Gaue, Dantu, Nawish, and Jarimba (Fig. 6.7).

Central pit craters are not expected on Ceres, because of the lack of comparable structures on the similarly sized Saturnian satellites, as well as the difficulty of forming central pits in the 30–60 km range crater on low-gravity bodies based on the Ganymede and Callisto data analysis (Schenk, 1993). The best analogues of Ceres's central pit craters are observed on Ganymede and Callisto, which are much larger than Ceres with radii of 2600 km and 2400 km, respectively, as the dominant crater class in the >25 km range. On Ceres, both central pit and central peak craters were observed. This may be attributed to the higher internal temperatures of Ceres compared to icy satellites, but also possibly to the layering at comparable depths, including a transition to a lower crust enriched in brines (Schenk *et al.*, 2021).

The formation of central pits is poorly understood. Four models involve water or ice: via vapor explosion from rapid heating of subsurface volatiles (Wood *et al.*, 1978; Williams *et al.*, 2014), collapse of mechanically weak icy central peaks (Croft, 1983; Melosh, 1982), uplift of ductile lower layers and displacement of overlying brittle layers, and collapse or draining of a hot plug of liquid water from central uplift (Bray *et al.*, 2012; Croft, 1983; Senft and Steward, 2011). Occator central pit may have involved a hot plug (Scully *et al.*, 2019). Some other models challenge the role of volatiles in central pit formation (Barlow and Tornabene, 2018).

6.2.2 *Lobate Landslides and Ejecta*

Lobate features are widespread on Ceres. Three distinct morphological types of lobate features exist on Ceres (Fig. 6.8; see Buczkowski *et al.*, 2016; Schmidt *et al.*, 2017). Type 1 landslides are characterized as thick, lobate, and steep snouted, and initiating on steep slopes. They are usually as wide as their sources, show longitudinal furrows, and are >100 m thick at their termini. This type of landslide resembles ice-cored and ice-cemented flows on Earth, suggesting abundant ice content. Type 1 flows are typically found on Ceres above 50° latitude (Fig. 6.9).

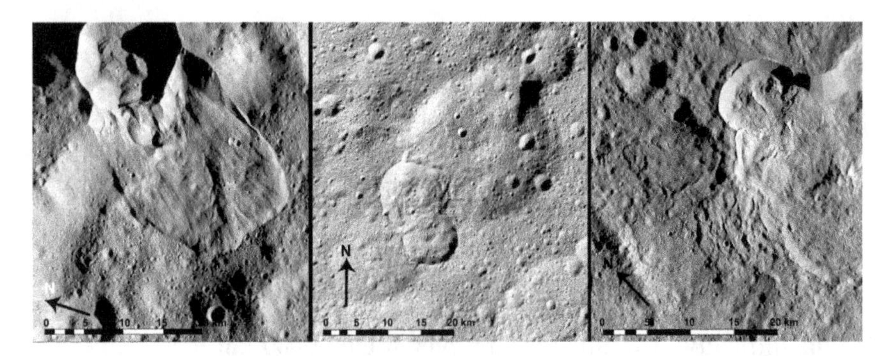

Figure 6.8: Examples of landslides on Ceres. Left panel shows a Type 1 landslide that is similar to rock glaciers and icy landslides on Earth. Middle panel shows a Type 2 landslide that resembles avalanches to the northeast side of the double crater slightly off the center in 7 o'clock direction. This type is the most common type on Ceres. Right panel shows a Type 3 landslide (cuspate/lobate fluidized appearing ejecta) related to craters, possibly impact melt. Based on Dawn Photo Journal PIA21471 (https://photojournal.jpl.nasa.gov/catalog/PIA21471), image credit: NASA/JPL-Caltech/UCLA/MPS/DLR/IDA/PSI.

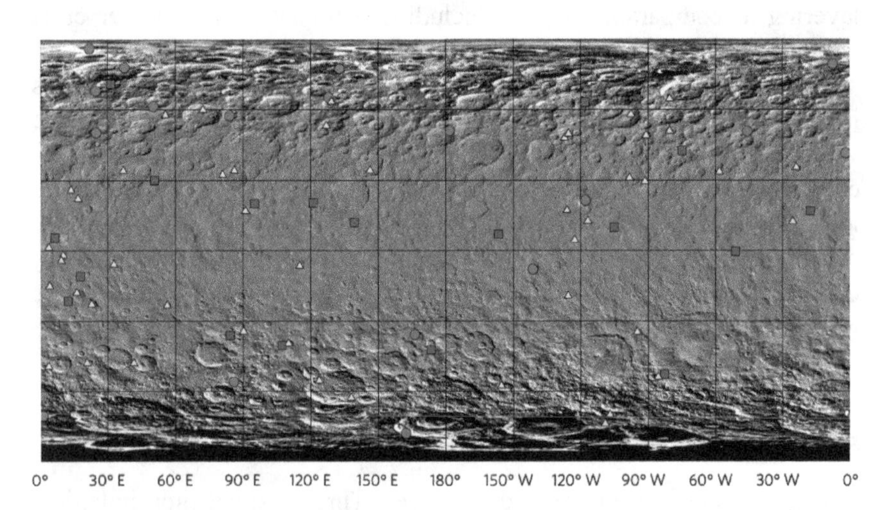

Figure 6.9: Global distribution of lobate features on Ceres. Blue circles represent Type 1 flows, yellow triangles are Type 2 flows, and red squares are Type 3 flows. Reprinted from Schmidt *et al.* (2017). Copyright with permission from Springer Nature.

In contrast, Type 2 landslides are thin (10–100 m thick at termini), long-runout flows, typically fan shaped, spatulate, or channelized, and capable of motion across moderate to shallow slopes. They typically have conical to lobate shapes of a wide range of widths, but always contain platy sheets with rounded tapered toes. The long-runout landslides found on icy satellites such as Iapetus are the best analogues to Type 2 landslides. This type of landslide feature is distributed across Ceres, but mostly in mid- to high-latitude regions (Fig. 6.9). The thin and long-runout morphology of Type 2 landslides indicates lower viscosity and higher mobility compared to Type 1 landslides.

Type 3 flows show broad sheets of smooth materials that are comparable to Type 2 flows, in the crater ejecta field extending out from rims, and terminating in layered sets of lobes or cusps. They show triangular lobes with relatively smooth surfaces interspersed with hummocky regions, and lack of deep furrows and textures. Their morphology is similar to that of fluidized appearing ejecta (FAE) of rampart craters on Mars and Ganymede. Impact into ice-rich ground is considered to be at the origin of this morphological type of flow. They have a wider distribution than Type 2 flows and are mostly concentrated in low- to mid-latitude regions (Fig. 6.9).

Despite these three distinct archetypal feature types, most flow features on Ceres do not clearly fall into those categories based on shape alone, and many coexist or mutually contain one another (Duarte *et al*., 2019). The morphologies of the intermediate landslides' features (Type 1 and 2) include contact crater landslides, multilobed landslides, ejecta-landslide flows, crater rim mass wasting, small flows, and plain-type landslides (between craters and interior of catenae).

The basic mechanical behavior of subsurface ice was inferred from quantitative analysis of these flow features. Chilton *et al.* (2019) measured the height-to-length ratio (H/L) and the volume and area relationship of about 40 Type 1 and Type 2 landslides. The H/L ratios of Ceres Type 1 and Type 2 flows indicate lower effective coefficients of friction than the lowest effective friction in hydrated clays measured in lab experiments, consistent with mobility of these flows on Ceres via warm ice or meltwater.

Between Type 1 and Type 2 flows, H/L values are higher for the former than for the latter, indicating relatively lower mobility of Type 1 flows. In addition, the low-mobility Type 1 landslides show greater depths for the associated failure scarps, which require relatively uniform subsurface properties. On the other hand, the high-mobility Type 2 landslides mostly have depth-limited failures, generally reflecting a layered subsurface structure with relatively weak materials covering strong materials. The morphological variations among flow types reflect vertical and lateral variabilities of ice content in the subsurface, consistent with a layered subsurface.

Combining the geological context and the spatial distribution of Type 1 and Type 2 landslides on Ceres, stratification in ice content in Ceres's subsurface was inferred (Chilton *et al.*, 2019). The top surface is covered by a layer of dry regolith at least a millimeter thick and up to a full annual thermal skin depth of decimeters to meters near the equator. Below the top ice-free layer exists a layer of intermediate ice content that is up to a few hundred meters thick with ~3–14 vol.% ice in possibly the form of lenses and interstitial or fracture-lined films. An ice-rich layer of at least 23 vol.% and up to or greater than 40 vol.% ice lies below the dry and intermediate ice layers. The boundaries of these layers can be diffuse, and latitudinal thickness variations exist. The bottom ice-rich layer is near or exposed at the surface at polar latitudes.

Hughson *et al.* (2019) analyzed the Type 3 flows, i.e., FAEs on Ceres. FAEs are morphologically classified into two subtypes, cuspate/lobate and channelized (Figs. 6.8 and 6.10), and in general the former appear to be thicker than the latter. Cuspate FAEs concentrate in the southern hemisphere, while channelized FAEs do not show any discernible latitudinal

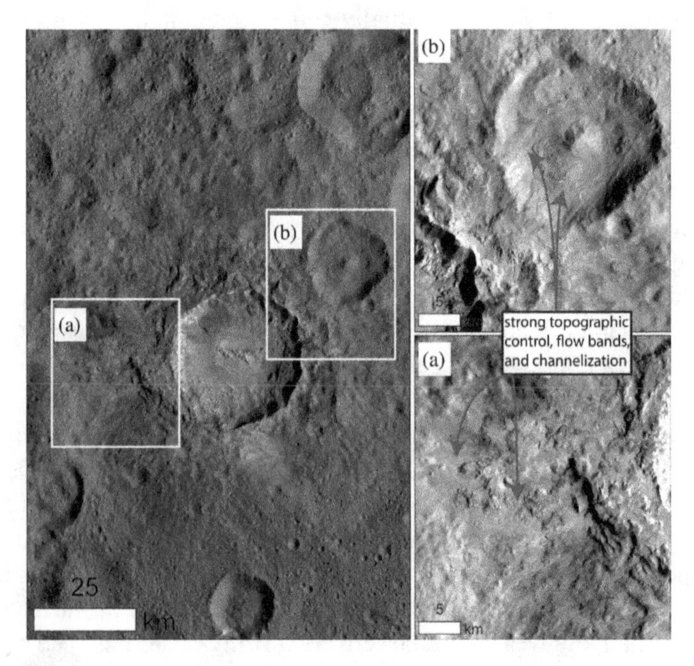

Figure 6.10: Haulani crater shows channelized FAE deposits. Reprinted from Hughson *et al.* (2019). Copyright with permission from Wiley-VCH Verlag GmbH & Co. KGaA.

trend. Through quantitative modeling, the ejecta mobility (EM), strength, and coefficient of sliding friction were measured for all FAEs. The distribution of EM for the two subtypes is similar, although the peak EM is slightly different with values of 1.4 and 1.1 for channelized and cuspate/lobate FAEs, respectively, higher than the values for dry clay minerals. The strength parameter and coefficient of sliding friction values are similar and lower than expected for dry flows, respectively. The low friction of Ceres's FAEs is due likely to a combination of sliding on an intimate mixture of rock and ice, and to friction reduction caused by both fluidization through the incorporation of impact melt fluids and basal lubrication via melted near-surface volatiles.

Of the two subtypes of FAEs, cuspate/lobate FAEs show higher effective viscosities than channelized FAEs. Such a difference may be caused by different interparticle friction due to varying ice content of the material in motion. However, this does not necessarily indicate differences in ice content, but could also be caused by different impact strengths causing different levels of melt. No robust distinction between the physical properties of the two types can be made.

In summary, a vast majority of FAE sources have material strengths more ice-like than rock-like under impact cratering strain rates, consistent with the results of simple-to-complex transition diameter, indicating that Ceres behaves more like icy satellites than terrestrial planets in response to impact. The enhanced mobility of FAEs on Ceres is due to ground ice-rich substrates mediating friction reduction. An upper bound of ~30–50 vol.% of ice at a depth scale of at least 1–5 km proximal to FAE source craters was implied, and it could be reduced by meltwater. The results of Ceres's FAEs imply a modest global reservoir of pore-filling ground ice in the upper few meters to kilometers on Ceres, subject to significant regional enrichment and depletion.

6.2.3 *Domes and Mounds*

Based on size and morphology, the positive topographic features on Ceres were classified into two subclasses, large domes and small mounds (Buczkowski *et al.*, 2016; Sizemore *et al.*, 2019). The large domes class has 33 cataloged domical to conical mountains with reliefs of ~1–6 km and diameters of ~30–120 km. Ahuna Mons is the youngest and the best preserved member of this subclass. Large domes preferentially occur in low-elevation regions (planitiae), and are mostly concentrated in one of

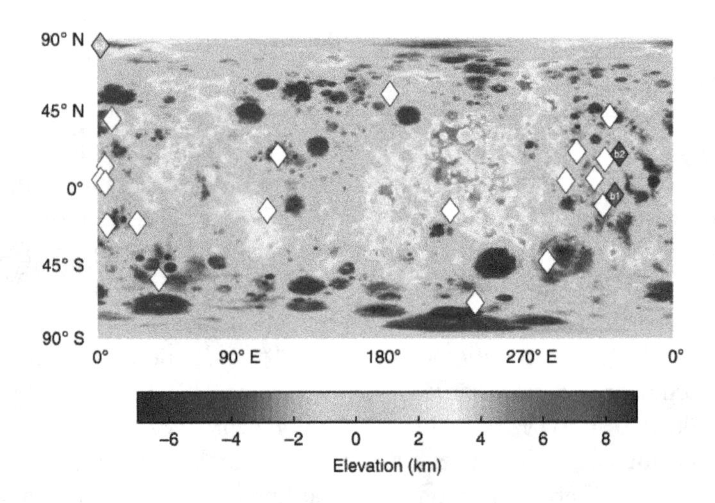

Figure 6.11: Global distribution of large dome features on Ceres, overlaying a topographic map of Ceres. The majority of domes are associated with the old, large basin between −80° and +20° east longitude (Basin B, see Fig. 5.4). Reprinted from Sori *et al.* (2018). Copyright with permission from Springer Nature.

the three potential ancient impact basins identified by Marchi *et al.* (2016) (Fig. 6.11).

The large domes show varying morphological characteristics, and mostly appear to be ancient, displaying heavily cratered appearance with large-scale structures disrupted or modified by large impacts. The relatively well-preserved members with sharply defined peaks and high aspect ratios include Ahuna Mons, Yamor Mons, and two unnamed mountains. Three of them occur at latitudes >55°, while Ahuna Mons at 11° S is an exception. The more rounded and domical features with slightly lower aspect ratios occur widely in the middle to low latitudes. Some members are mostly flattened, including Liberalia Mons and the large dome associated with the fracture system Nar Sulcus inside Yalode basin.

Haulani crater hosts a cluster of relatively small, elongated domes in the large dome class near its west rim. They appear to be blanketed by the bright ejecta material from Haulani crater, suggesting that the impact may have excavated material involved in dome formation. Haulani ejecta material contains more abundant carbonates (De Sanctis *et al.*, 2016) and contains pitted terrains (Sizemore *et al.*, 2017), both evidence of a high volatile content.

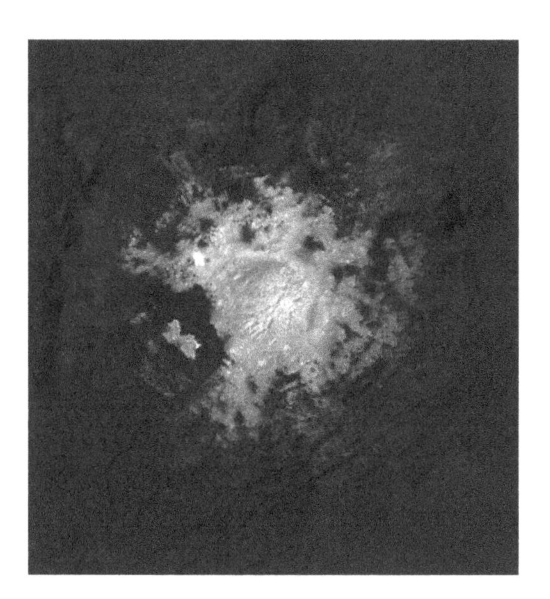

Figure 6.12: Central dome at Cerealia Facula in Occator Crater with fractures both on top of the dome and surrounding it. Based on Dawn Photo Journal PIA21924 (https://photojournal.jpl.nasa.gov/catalog/PIA21924), image credit: NASA/JPL-Caltech/UCLA/MPS/DLR/IDA/PSI.

Unlike the relatively homogenous large domes, small mounds are more morphologically diverse. Sixteen small mounds were identified by Sizemore *et al.* (2019), but mostly distributed inside a few large impact craters, including Kerwan, Gaue, Dantu, Occator, Urvara, and Yolade. They typically exhibit reliefs of 100s of meters and diameters <10 km. The most distinctive feature in this class is the fractured dome inside the central pit of Occator crater (Fig. 6.12). This dome is about 3 km in diameter and has a relief of about 750 m, displaying a complicated fracture network and overlaid by bright deposits, Cerealia Facula.

All hypotheses for the formation of large domes involve upward motion of ice, brines, or slurries of ice, brine, and silicate. The evidence supporting the cryovolcanic origin of large domes, as summarized by Sizemore *et al.* (2019), includes the following: (1) The close association between domes and large impact structures is consistent with cryovolcanic origin. Large impacts could directly access deep layers of volatile materials and produce pockets of melt, and generate fractures that could serve as conduits for mobile materials. (2) The arrangement of the largest concentration of large domes inside the large, ancient impact basin appears to be indicative of a remnant multi-ring structure, within which fractures had developed and were exploited by cryomagmas (Sizemore *et al.*, 2019). A similar association between domes and the fractures in the western Yalode basin (Nar Sulcus) occurs on the inner ring structure of the basin. (3) Some fresh craters located near domes, such as Haulani and Oxo, excavated bright materials that are rich in salt, carbonates, and volatiles (Carrozzo *et al.*, 2018), suggestive of the composition of materials driving dome formation.

The diverse morphology of small mounds, on the other hand, possibly indicates a variety of mechanisms responsible for their formation, with the possibility of cryovolcanic, periglacial, or impact. Cerealia Facula Tholus is the best candidate pingo or cryovolcanic feature among the small mounds class. It could be uplifted by laccolithic intrusion (igneous intrusion that split apart different layers) or formed by volume expansion due to freezing of a reservoir of brines (Schenk *et al.*, 2019). The liquids that were responsible for Cerealia Facula Tholus were mobilized by the Occator crater impact (Raymond *et al.*, 2020). The conical shape of the small mounds inside Yalode and Kerwan basins may suggest a cryovolcanic origin. Other small mounds often coexist with smooth crater material that has been interpreted as impact melt, which would be well suited for pingo development upon refreezing if the contained water exceeds about 30–40 vol.%. The mounds and hummocks on Urvara and Occator crater floors are not distinct in morphology from features in the impact melt sheet of lunar craters, and could be uplifted megablocks or impact debris that entered crater floor materials (Scully *et al.*, 2019; Buczkowski *et al.*, 2016).

6.2.4 *Pits, Depressions, and Scarps*

Pits are rimless depressions with round to irregular shapes, existing in clusters or isolated settings. This type of geological feature has been identified in low- to mid-latitude Martian craters as an indication of shallow subsurface water ice (Tornabene *et al.*, 2012; Boyce *et al.*, 2012). A dedicated search for pits and pitted terrains on Ceres with the Dawn imaging data (Sizemore *et al.*, 2017) unambiguously identified these terrains in four fresh craters (Ikapati, Dantu, Haulani, and Kupalo) and degraded pits

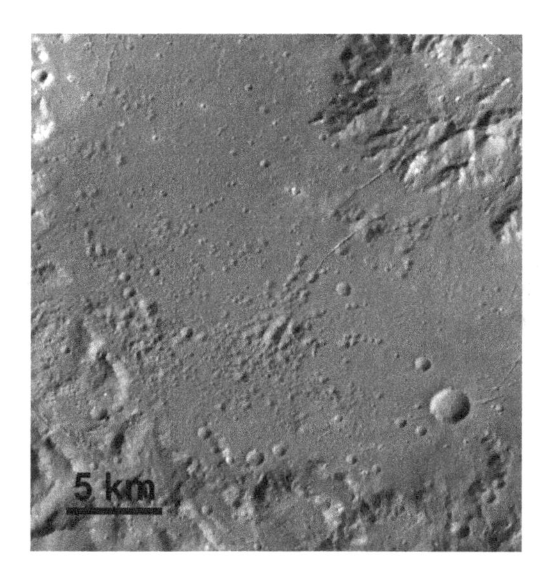

Figure 6.13: Example of pitted terrains on Ceres in Ikapati crater from an FC clear filter LAMO image (35 m/pixel) (image ID: FC21B0064706_16128044942F1B).

in three slightly older craters (Occator, Azacca, and Urvara), as well as a few isolated depressions and scarps (Fig. 6.13).

The Ceres pitted terrains show remarkably similar morphology as those on Mars. The pits have maximum diameters up to 2 km, depending on the sizes of their host craters. The smallest pits that could be identified are about 70 m, which was limited by the resolution of images used in the search. All pitted terrains occur on smooth crater floor materials or ponded ejecta material, or both. A majority of the craters hosting pitted terrains are also associated with lobate flow features. However, not all fresh craters are associated with pitted terrains, notably Juling and Oxo craters, both of which lack flat floors and extensive lobate features, and display exposed surface ice (Combe *et al.*, 2016), although smaller pits <60 m diameter cannot be ruled out. All seven craters showing pitted terrains are distributed in low- to mid-latitude regions.

Sizemore *et al.* (2017, 2019) explored the possible mechanisms that form pits on Ceres. The association of Ceres's pitted terrains with the youngest craters, and the degraded appearance of pitted terrains in slightly older craters indicate that pits formed in a timescale of a few million years, and are quickly erased on timescales of 100s of million years. The quick formation of pits is inconsistent with the sublimation of ground ice on Ceres, because the modeled water sublimation rates are too slow to produce the observed relief of pits during the young age of host craters. In addition, the morphology of pits formed by long-term sublimation of ice is inconsistent with the observed morphology. Although suncups (bowl-shaped open depressions on snow-covered surfaces) show some similarity to Ceres's pits, no evidence suggests extensive, nearly pure surface ice deposits on Ceres. Therefore, quick gas release following the crater-forming impact was considered the most likely formational process for Ceres pits (Sizemore *et al.*, 2017).

Based on a gas-driven pit formation model as applied to Mars pitted terrains (Boyce *et al.*, 2012), the most likely driving material for pit formation on Ceres is molecular water in the regolith. Impact on Ceres is expected to heat the impact site and the ejecta to temperatures sufficient to liberate water, but not sufficient to liberate other species such as CO_2 from carbonates or H_2O from phyllosilicates. The source of water is more likely regolith ice than adsorbed water and water of hydration in salts, because ice has been detected on Ceres's surface and in regolith pores.

The abundance of water ice in pitted material was inferred to be less than ~40–50 vol.% from the models (Sizemore *et al.*, 2017). This value is consistent with that inferred from crater morphology and other modeling. Although the existence of pitted terrains supports the existence of shallow ice, it does not suggest ice as a dominant component in the upper meters to kilometers in the regolith. The preferential distribution of pitted terrains in low- to mid-latitude regions is an indication that surface temperature higher than some threshold is required for pits to form (Sizemore *et al.*, 2017).

In addition to the clustered pits in the pitted terrains, a small number of isolated irregular depressions and scarps in Occator, Azacca, and Yalode have been noticed (Sizemore *et al.*, 2019). Two in Azacca and Occator have a different morphology from clustered pits and are potentially consistent with long-term sublimation. Scarps in the Occator crater ejecta and Yalode floor could be associated with modification of fractures in smooth ejecta, probably through sublimation of water ice. But other processes unrelated to ice or volatiles could also work.

6.2.5 *Fractures, Grooves, Channels, and Troughs*

Linear features on Ceres that could be related to water ice include fractures, grooves, and channels (Buczkowski *et al.*, 2018a, 2018b; Sizemore *et al.*, 2019). Fractures are generally tens of kilometers long, hundreds of meters to >2 km wide, and 10s to ~100 m deep, with a v-shaped depth profile. Grooves are smaller linear features of typically <200 m wide and <10s m deep. Channels are similar to grooves and fractures, but tend to be narrower, shallower, and curvilinear to sinuous, sometimes interconnected, forming network-like features following the local slope direction. Troughs are the largest linear features on Ceres, most notably Nar Sulcus, colocated with a large dome in Yalode basin. Individual troughs >50 km long and with a maximum relief >300 m also exist. These features are primarily localized and associated with impact craters. Linear fractures and grooves are commonly associated with pitted materials on Ceres in the host crater floor material and smooth ejecta outside of the crater rim (Sizemore *et al.*, 2019).

The craters that contain fractures in their floors, termed floor-fractured craters (FFCs), on Ceres, are morphologically similar to lunar FFCs (Schultz, 1976; Jozwiak *et al.*, 2012, 2015), and are characterized by radial, concentric, and/or polygonal fractures cutting the crater floors. A total of 21 FFCs have been identified on Ceres, and categorized into two different types based on the classification of lunar FFCs (Buczkowski *et al.*, 2016). Eight large (>50 km) Ceres FFCs show morphology consistent with the lunar Class 1 FFCs, characterized by central peak complexes, terraced walls, and fractures that can be radial and/or concentric to the central complex and/or the base of the crater wall (Figs. 6.14(a) and 6.14(b)). Thirteen smaller FFCs on Ceres are more consistent with Class 4 lunar FFCs, which are defined by a V-shaped moat separating the wall scarp from the crater interior, and typically have less pronounced floor fractures (Fig. 6.14(c)). In addition, Yalode crater and Urvara crater also host fractures but not classified as FFCs, because their fracture patterns are more consistent with localized fracturing, not systematic fracturing. Of the Class 1 FFCs on Ceres, Dantu is the largest and most significantly fractured, followed by Occator crater.

Similar to lunar FFCs, all Ceres FFCs have anomalously shallow depth-to-diameter (d/D) ratios compared to global average. The models for lunar FFC formation invoked both floor uplift due to magmatic

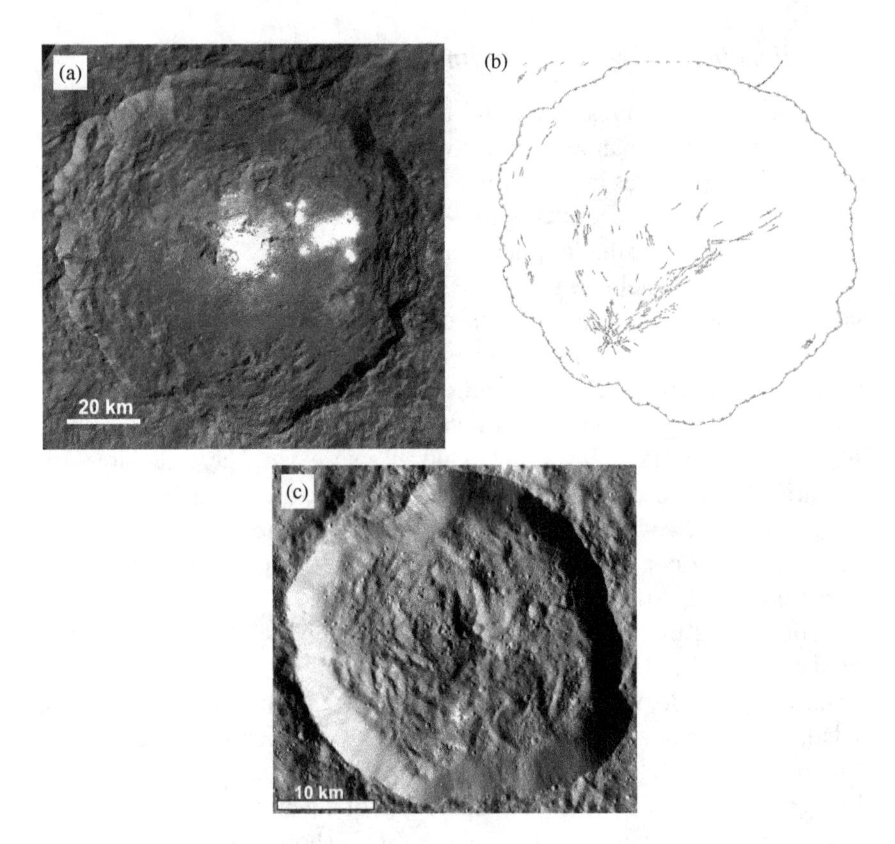

Figure 6.14: Examples of FFCs on Ceres. (a) FC clear filter image of Occator crater from HAMO (137 m/pixel) as an example of Class 1 FFC on Ceres. (b) The fractures on Occator crater floor mapped by Buczkowski *et al.* (2018b). (c) FC clear filter mosaic (35 m/pixel) of Lociyo crater (6.5° S, 228.8° E) as an example of Class 4 FFC on Ceres. Panels (b) and (c) are reprinted from Buczkowski *et al.* (2018b). Copyright with permission from Elsevier.

intrusion beneath the crater (Schultz, 1976; Jozwiak *et al.*, 2012, 2015) and floor shallowing due to viscous relaxation (e.g., Hall *et al.*, 1981). Mars's FFCs have similar morphological characteristics as lunar FFCs, formed due to volcanic activity, but their morphology is heavily influenced by interactions with groundwater and/or ice (Bamberg *et al.*, 2014). Two working models exist to explain the formation of Ceres's FFCs, including cryomagmatic intrusion and solid state flow of low-viscosity and low-density (LV-LD) material driven by differential loading due to uneven impact excavation (Buczkowski *et al.*, 2018a).

Magmatic intrusion similar to the model of lunar FFCs can explain many observed features of FFCs. Fractures at the base of the crater wall occur when tabular uplift of the crater floor occurs, generally 360° around the base of the wall, but fractures in limited areas of the crater floor in the lunar Class 1 FFCs also occur. The magmatic intrusion model has a V-shaped moat, which marks the extent of subsurface intrusion. The low d/D of Ceres's FFCs is also consistent with the magmatic intrusion model. While silicate magma is unlikely for Ceres, evidence exists for cryovolcanic activity on Ceres (Sori *et al.*, 2018; Quick *et al.*, 2019). Therefore, cryomagma is a likely driver for the formation of Ceres's FFCs (Buzckowski *et al.*, 2016).

In the solid state flow model, impact into the edge of the LV-LD material, presumably some mixture of ice, salts, and clathrate, within the heterogeneous crust of Ceres could result in differential loading due to removal of overlaying materials. Such differential loading could cause doming into the crater wall (Bland *et al.*, 2019), consistent with the locations of many large domes (Sizemore *et al.*, 2019) and nearby fractures at the base of the crater wall in some FFCs. This model can also explain the distribution of fractures in a limited area of the crater floor rather than 360° around the base of the wall.

However, the solid state flow model cannot explain V-shaped moat, crater's central structure, or linear fractures crossing crater floor, all of which require cryomagmatic activity either sourced from the deep reservoir or activated by impact melt (e.g., Quick *et al.*, 2019). Additionally, the craters that host the large domes do not have fractured floors. FFCs typically appear to be younger than the large domes. These may indicate different crustal properties between the locations of FFCs and volcanic features.

Other models that have been considered but deemed unlikely for the formation of Ceres's FFCs include viscous relaxation after crater formation and ice diapirism. While numerical modeling showed that post-impact relaxation on a layered subsurface can reproduce the structure of circumferential fractures, it cannot reproduce the relatively low d/D ratios (Otto *et al.*, 2019). Therefore, other processes that cause uplifts of the crater floor have to be invoked. Similarly, ice diapirs would not be able to reach within 10–20 km of Ceres's surface if driven by buoyancy alone (Bland *et al.*, 2019) due to the high viscosity of the near-surface crust (Fu *et al.*, 2017). It is impossible at present to definitively determine the formation mechanisms of FFCs on Ceres and reconcile the formation models of fractures and pits, and detailed modeling in the future is required.

Similar to pitted materials, linear features are mostly confined to low- to mid-latitude regions, possibly suggesting that a threshold temperature also needs to be exceeded to support the formation of Ceres's linear features (Sizemore *et al.*, 2019). The association of linear features with smooth, apparently fluidized materials in the youngest complex craters and a small number of simple craters suggests the involvement of water ice rich materials excavated by impact.

6.3 Exosphere

The existence of shallow buried ice in Ceres's crust (e.g., Prettyman *et al.*, 2017) supports previous model predictions that a tenuous exosphere could exist on Ceres (e.g., Fanale and Salvail, 1989), and provide a source for the observed water vapor around Ceres (A'Hearn and Feldman *et al.*, 1992; Küppers *et al.*, 2014). Dawn's observations put some constraints on the possible origin of the Ceres exosphere and its transient nature, although a full understanding is still lacking.

6.3.1 *Exosphere Detection by Dawn*

An unexpected result from Dawn was the one-time detection of electron bursts at Ceres that were linked to a transient exosphere (Russell *et al.*, 2016). When the Dawn spacecraft was in Survey orbit at an altitude of 4400 km, GRaND detected bursts of electrons of many tens of keV following a solar energetic particle (SEP) event by the electromagnetic radiation emitted when they impinged on the spacecraft (Fig. 6.15). These electron bursts all happened at a particular orientation with respect to the direction of the Sun, but not tied to a particular longitude at Ceres. While energetic particle events were regularly detected by Dawn during the course of the mission, this particular event was the only one accompanied by electron bursts. These electron bursts were similar to those detected in high-Earth orbit in the solar wind when the magnetic field at the spacecraft lies tangent to the surface of the bow shock, where electrons are accelerated along the magnetic field line. Therefore, these electron bursts likely indicated the existence of a bow shock near Ceres.

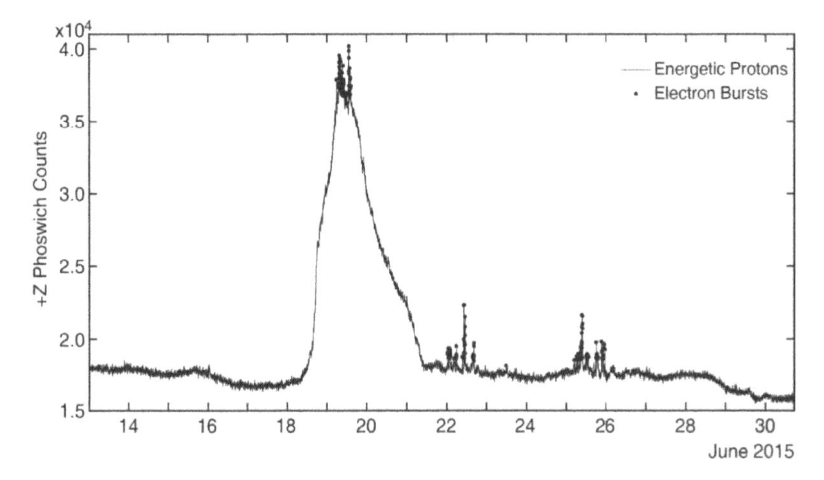

Figure 6.15: GRaND detection of electron bursts around Ceres. The large peak around June 19, 2015 is a solar energetic proton event, and the small peaks on top of the solid line from June 19 to 26 are the electron bursts detected by GRaND. Reprinted from Russell *et al.* (2016). Copyright with permission from AAAS.

Two possible scenarios can generate a bow shock around Ceres, an exosphere and an internal electrically conductive layer. Analysis of the timescale of such a bow shock favored the exosphere hypothesis. The possible electrically conductive layer inside Ceres, while theoretically plausible given the ice-rich and salty nature of Ceres's crust, would be too thin and have an electrical conductivity too low to generate electron bursts consistent with the GRaND observations.

Based on the exosphere hypothesis, a water production rate of about 3×10^{26} molecules/s (9 kg/s; Villarreal *et al.*, 2017) with a lower limit of 6×10^{25} molecules/s (1.8 kg/s; Jia *et al.*, 2017) is required to support a bow shock consistent with the observed electron burst. The origin of such a transient exosphere is unclear. Villarreal *et al.* (2017) examined the previous searches for water vapor around Ceres, and found that the water vapor production on Ceres might be correlated with SEP flux (Fig. 6.16). They hypothesized that solar wind sputtering might be at least partially responsible for water vapor release from Ceres. It is unclear, though, quantitatively how much the exposed surface water and subsurface water can contribute to such a process, or whether that mechanism is capable of producing the observed water vapor production rate.

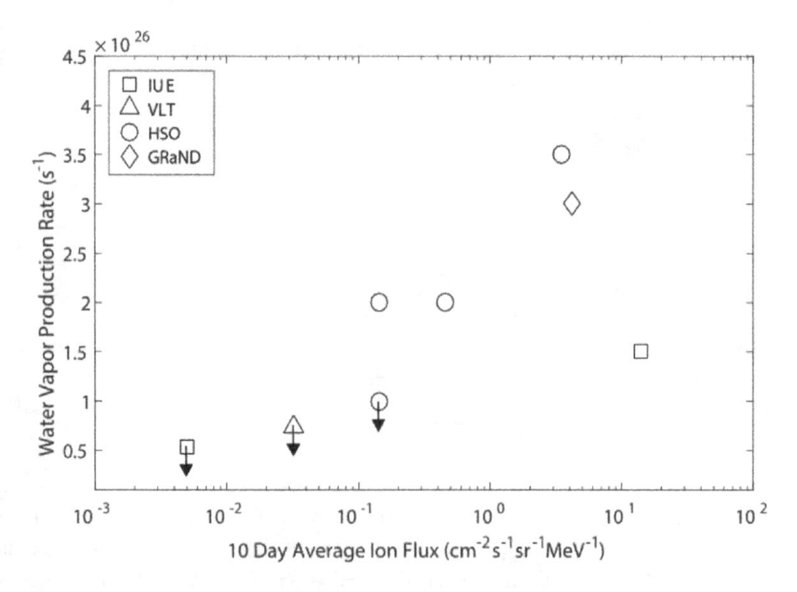

Figure 6.16: Correlation between SEP flux and water production rate observed at Ceres. The SEP fluxes are averaged at 1 au over 10 days prior to the corresponding observations. Reprinted from Villarreal *et al.* (2017). Copyright with permission from IOP Publishing.

6.3.2 *Ground-Based Observations*

Rousselot *et al.* (2019) continued the search for the OH 309-nm emission line off the limb of Ceres near its perihelion in February 2018 with the goal of determining the baseline water sublimation rate of Ceres under solar insolation, and reported a negative detection. The upper-limit production rate for this observation was estimated to be 2×10^{26} molecules/s.

Effort was also made to search for other volatile species around Ceres. Li *et al.* (2020) reported a negative result for their observations of the HCN J = 3-2 emission line at a rest frequency of 265.886 GHz using ALMA. Their upper-limit production rate for HCN was 2×10^{24} molecules/s. The relative abundance of HCN to water for Ceres is completely unconstrained, but the values from comets of about 0.06 to 0.2 (Mumma and Charnley, 2011) would result in a corresponding upper limit of water production rate of up to 3×10^{25} molecules/s. An archival study of the ALMA data did not find evidence of an exosphere (Parks *et al.*, 2019). However, a dedicated search of volatiles around Ceres in the radio wavelengths with ALMA and the James Clerk Maxwell Telescope showed possible evidence for a few volatile species including O_3, NaCl, and KCl (Chuang *et al.*, 2019; Chiang *et al.*, 2019).

Table 6.1 lists all previous efforts to search for water vapor around Ceres, and Fig. 6.17 shows the positions of Ceres in its orbit during those searches. No correlation between the detection/non-detection of water outgassing and the heliocentric distance of Ceres is evident. Although the positive detections all had Ceres in the perihelion half of the orbit, two negative detections interspersed between them, especially the one near perihelion, strongly suggesting that the observed Ceres outgassing activity is episodic. Therefore, even if solar heating is one factor contributing to the outgassing from Ceres, other factors yet to be identified or confirmed, including the SEP sputtering, must also contribute. Those contributors may include impacts that expose subsurface water ice deposits that either slowly deplete ice or are covered by a lag deposit after a period of sublimation, intermittent transportation of underground ice to the surface via thermal processes, or even ongoing geothermal activity.

Table 6.1: Summary of all attempts to detect water vapor around Ceres. Based on Rosselot *et al.* (2019), Astronomy and Astrophysics, vol. 628, id. 22. Reproduced with permission from Astronomy & Astrophysics, © ESO.

No.	Date	Instrument	Water production rate (10^{26} molecules^{-1})	Heliocentric distance (au)	References
1	1990 Jan 14	IUE+LWP	<0.53	2.64	A'Hearn & Feldman (1992)
2	1991 May 29	IUE+LWP	1.4	2.66	A'Hearn & Feldman (1992)
3	2007 Oct 24	VLT+UVES	<0.7	2.83	Rousselot *et al.* (2011)
4	2011 Nov 23	HSO+HIFI	<1.0	2.94	Küppers *et al.* (2014)
5	2012 Oct 11	HSO+HIFI	3–4	2.72	Küppers *et al.* (2014)
6	2012 Oct 24	HSO+HIFI	2.0	2.71	Küppers *et al.* (2014)
7	2013 Mar 6	HSO+HIFI	2.0	2.62	Küppers *et al.* (2014)
8	2015 Jun 19	Dawn+GRaND	3.0	2.93	Villarreal *et al.* (2017)
9	2015 Aug 26	HST+COS	<4	2.95	Roth *et al.* (2016)
10	2015 Sep 3–7	HST+STIS	<2.2	2.96	Roth (2018)
11	2016 Oct 26	HST+COS	<1.8	2.88	Roth (2018)
12	2018 Feb 16	VLT+UVES	<2	2.57	Rousselot *et al.* (2019)

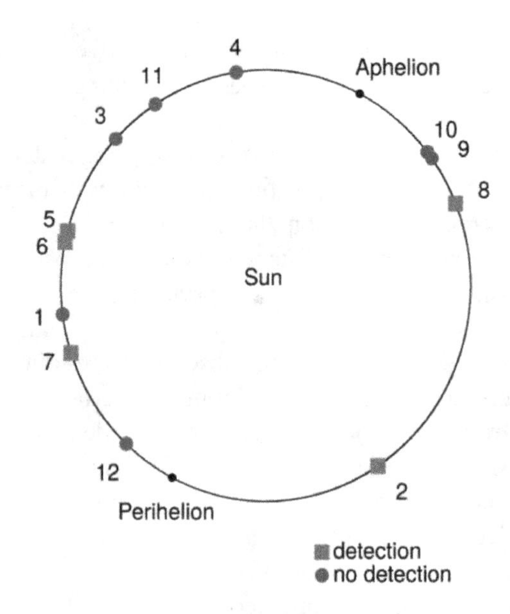

Figure 6.17: Locations of Ceres in its orbit corresponding to the previous searches of water vapor. The numbers correspond to the observations in Table 6.1. Reprinted from Rousselot *et al.* (2019). Copyright with permission from Astronomy & Astrophysics, ESO.

6.3.3 *Source of Water Outgassing*

Dawn observed about ten patches of exposed water ice on the surface of Ceres. The subsurface water ice content that could contribute to the outgassing from Ceres has also been constrained by the GRaND observations (Prettyman *et al.*, 2017). Based on these results, theoretical modeling has been performed to explore the possible sources and mechanisms forming Ceres's exosphere.

Due to the low gravity of Ceres and relatively warm surface temperature, its exosphere has a short dissipation timescale of hours to days (Schörghofer *et al.*, 2017). Active sources must exist to replenish Ceres's water exosphere, either continuously or intermittently. Both exposed surface ice and buried ice could potentially supply the water vapor to Ceres's exosphere.

Based on the GRaND observations, ice is expected to be within 0.5–1 m from the surface at about 45° latitude or higher on both hemispheres, and within a centimeter of the surface at the poles. Modeling of subsurface ice retreating on asteroids including the effect of surface thermal mantling and impact gardening (Schörghofer, 2016) suggested that water outgassing from sublimation would be primarily produced in the equatorial region, and half of the output would occur within ±20° of the equator. The modeled sublimation rate is about 6×10^{24} molecules/s, one order and a half magnitude less than that observed by the Herschel Space Observatory (HSO). The results depend on porosity, structure, and vapor diffusivity of the upper tens of meters in the equatorial region. A higher ice content and a smaller fraction of non-volatile material are required to match the HSO results.

Landis *et al.* (2017) used the observational constraints of the depth of buried ice to model subsurface sublimation with a wide range of ice contents in the regolith, and reached a similar conclusion (Fig. 6.18). In particular, they found that the modeled water production rate could match the HSO observations only when the ice fraction is close to 100%. However, such a high ice fraction would result in an extremely slow development of a sublimation lag, resulting in an ice table at a shallow depth everywhere on Ceres that would have been detectable by GRaND. On the other hand, assuming an ice fraction consistent with the GRaND measurements would result in a water production rate more than one order of magnitude lower than the HSO measurements. Landis *et al.* (2017) modeling results are grossly consistent with Fanale and Salvail (1989) in terms of the total water production rate and the long-term evolution.

For the case of locally exposed water ice patches, when the condition is right (i.e., dark ice with albedo <0.1–0.15 at latitude <50°), the calculation by Landis *et al.* (2017) showed that a 1–10 km^2 area could reproduce the water vapor production rate observed by the HSO (Fig. 6.19). But, such a patch would rapidly fade in a few years in both albedo and water production due to lag build up. The ice covering the pole-facing wall of Oxo crater, the largest area of exposed ice on Ceres, could only generate one order of magnitude lower water production rate than the HSO observations. Formisano *et al.* (2018) reached a similar conclusion. Studies about the exposed ice in Juling crater (Formisano *et al.*, 2016, 2018) suggested that if the whole floor and wall are sublimating, then it could supply water molecules at a rate observed by the HSO. But, in this case, the subsurface ice lifetime would only be about 50 years, unless replenished in some way.

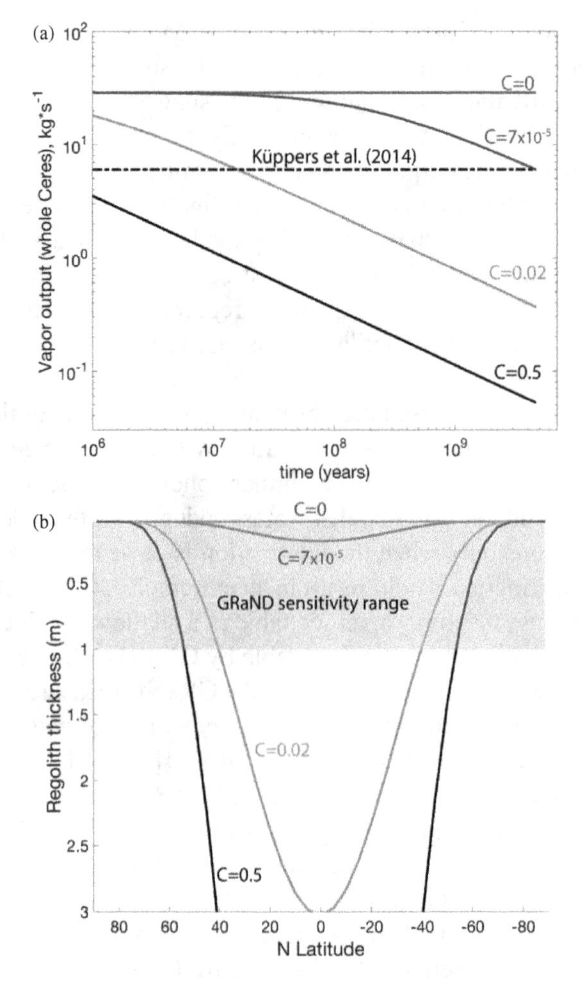

Figure 6.18: (a) Long-term evolution of the water production rate of Ceres for different fractions of water ice in the regolith. C quantifies the fraction of refractory materials, where C = 0 means pure ice. Calculation assumed ice is initially buried at 3 cm beneath a dry layer. Dashed line is the water production rate measured by the Herschel Space Observatory. (b) The depth of ice table with respect to latitude for various ice fractions. The gray shaded area is the sensitivity depth of GRaND. Reprinted from Landis *et al.* (2017). Copyright with permission from Wiley-VCH Verlag GmbH & Co. KGaA.

Including all exposed water ice patches identified on Ceres from the Dawn images and using their actual local topography and albedos, the modeled total water production rate is about 0.06 kg/s, which is two

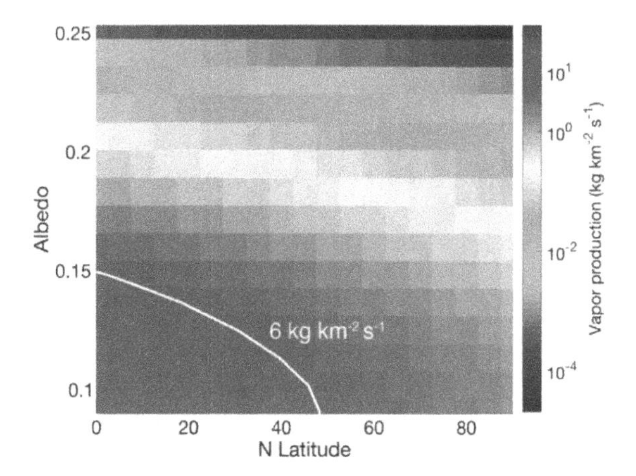

Figure 6.19: Modeled maximum vapor production rates of surface ice on flat terrain with respect to albedo and latitude on Ceres. The white line marks 6 kg/km/s, where a 1 km^2 of exposed ice would generate the vapor production rate observed by the Herschel Space Observatory (Küppers *et al.*, 2014). Reprinted from Landis *et al.* (2017). Copyright with permission from Wiley-VCH Verlag GmbH & Co. KGaA.

orders of magnitude lower than the observed rate (Landis *et al.*, 2019). The possible small ice patches suspected to be present below the Dawn image resolution could supply additional 0.08–0.56 k/s of water vapor, depending on ice fraction, and could remain bright for one Ceres year, based on dynamical models (Landis *et al.*, 2019). Altogether, this is still an order of magnitude lower than the HSO results.

One possible mechanism for slowing down the sublimation lag build up is via self-cleaning through the lofting of refractory particles. However, the size of particles to be lofted by outgassing on Ceres is typically a few microns or less for the possible parameters of Ceres ice patches (Fig. 6.20). Particles could rise and fall during diurnal cycles, but self-cleaning is not likely to be a significant effect.

Finally, an additional mechanism for supplying the transient exosphere is via the obliteration of the optically thin ice caps near Ceres's poles (Schörghofer *et al.*, 2017). The idea is that water vapor could be cold trapped near the polar areas, forming optically thin seasonal ice caps that cannot be detected from imaging or spectroscopic data. A minimum of 2×10^3 kg and a maximum of two orders of magnitude more water ice could be stored in an optically thin polar caps on Ceres. Once the seasonal

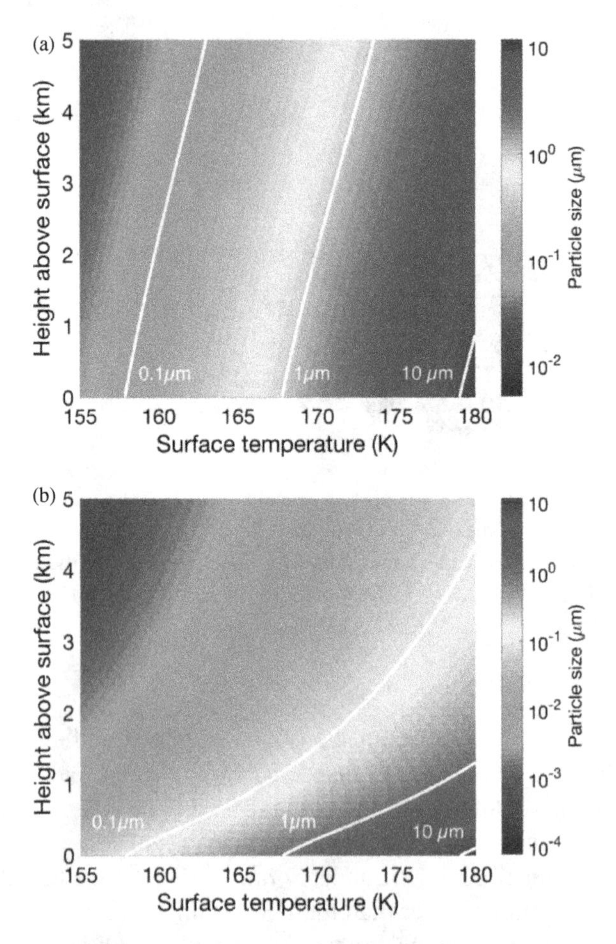

Figure 6.20: Maximum radius of particles that can be lofted by sublimation from (a) a 5-km-radius circular ice patch and (b) a 1 km^2 area ice patch, with respect to ice temperature and lofting particle altitude. Reprinted from Landis *et al.* (2017). Copyright with permission from Wiley-VCH Verlag GmbH & Co. KGaA.

ice caps are suddenly obliterated by, for example, an SEP event, it could match the density of the observed exosphere. However, the exosphere originating from the one-time use of all polar cap ice would only last for a few hours to days. Half of a Ceres year is needed to fully rebuild the ice cap, which does not match the timescale of observed exosphere activity. In addition to water, CO_2 and SO_2 molecules could also be trapped and stored in the perennially shadowed regions at the current obliquity of Ceres (Schörghofer *et al.*, 2017).

6.4 Implications on Ceres Cryosphere

The global distribution of all types of ice-related features (Fig. 6.21) reveals both lateral heterogeneity and stratigraphy (vertical heterogeneity) of subsurface ice at multiple length scales and depth scales on Ceres.

Latitudinally, the Type 1 flow features are confined at high latitude, whereas Type 2 flow features and other small features (pits, fractures, grooves, and channels) are distributed in mid- to low-latitude regions, although it is unclear whether observational bias exists. Longitudinally,

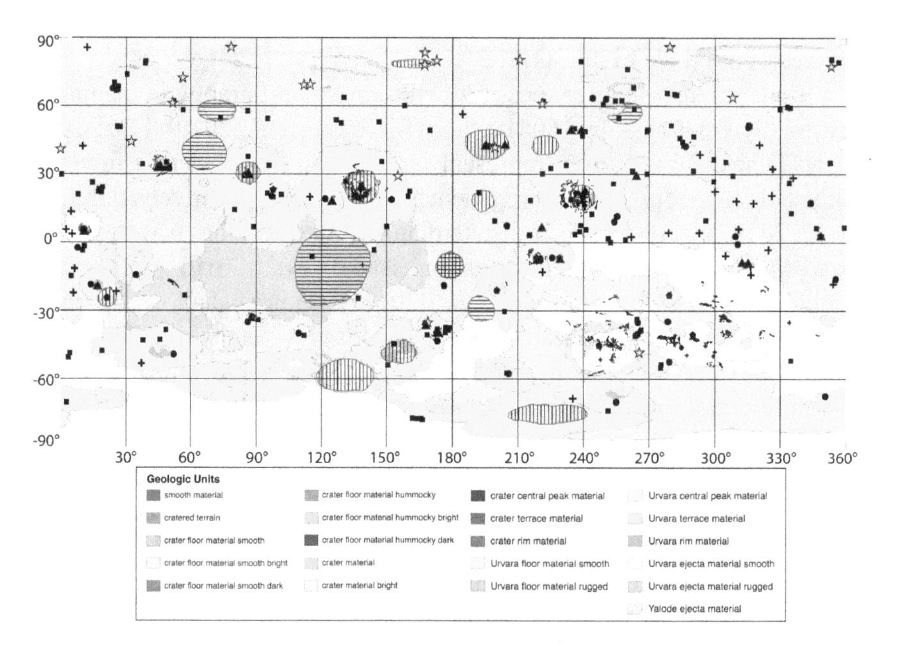

Figure 6.21: Global inventory of cataloged ice-related features on Ceres superposed on the HAMO-based geologic map of Mest *et al.* (2017). Polygons indicate relaxed craters (horizontal hash) or central pit craters (vertical hash). Black squares represent all landslide features (types 1, 2, and intermediate). Black circles indicate fluidized appearing ejecta. Large black diamonds indicate craters hosting pitted materials. Small black diamonds represent depressions and scarps. Black polylines indicate the extent of fractures, grooves, and channels. Black triangles indicate Floor-Fractured Craters (classes 1 and 4). Black pentagons represent craters with circumferential fractures. Small black crosses represent small mounds. Large black crosses represent large mounds. Yellow stars show surface ice exposures, including both directly dected by VIR (Combe *et al.*, 2019) and those in permanently shadowed regions (Platz *et al.*, 2016). Reprinted from Sizemore *et al.* (2019). Copyright with permission from Wiley-VCH Verlag GmbH & Co. KGaA.

large domes are primarily distributed in basin B (see Fig. 5.4) in the eastern hemisphere, and a deficit of ice-related features appears near Kerwan, indicating hemispherical variation in ice content, possibly driven by ancient impacts.

Heterogeneity is also apparent at 1–100s km scale length. The coexistence of relaxed craters and non-relaxed craters of similar ages that exhibit well-preserved topography suggests variations in local ice content. Localized enrichment of shallow ice close to large craters could be due to large impacts that excavated deep, ice-rich material and deposited it on the surface. Impact could also have played an important role by both devolatilizing ice-rich material through impact heating and excavating and moving deep buried ice to the surface.

Evidence also suggests possibly widespread stratigraphy in the upper few to <20 km at less than 60° latitude (Sizemore *et al.*, 2019). First, Type 1 and Type 2 flow features represent failures at different depths in vertically homogeneous and heterogeneous substrates, respectively (Chilton *et al.*, 2019). Second, the solid state diapirism process that was hypothesized to explain large dome formation (Bland *et al.*, 2019) and fracture patterns in FFCs (Buczkowski *et al.*, 2018a) requires shallow layering. The distribution of these features suggests possibly patchy distribution in subsurface layering. Finally, numerical modeling for the formation of circumferential fractures (Otto *et al.*, 2019) requires a low-viscosity layer (10^{20} Pa s) at depths <10 km.

There still exists some ambiguity in the low-density phase material required to explain the ice-related morphologies on Ceres. The crust of Ceres was modeled to be composed of <25 vol.% water ice, <29 vol.% carbonates and phyllosilicates, and >36 vol.% high-strength hydrated phases, e.g., clathrates and hydrated salts, based on the gravity measurements (Ermakov *et al.*, 2017b; Fu *et al.*, 2017). Geochemical modeling suggested that Ceres's crust could contain <20 vol.% salts, of which 2/3 is hydrohalite, and the rest is anhydrous chlorides such as NH_4Cl (Castillo-Rogez *et al.*, 2018). Hydrated salts are too dense and more viscous than ice at the same temperature. Anhydrous chlorides soften ice at low temperature and lower the melting temperature in response to impact heating. Therefore, impact heat, salts, and ice are possibly critical for the formation of ice-related features on Ceres.

Another potentially important low-density, high-strength material is clathrate hydrates. Clathrate hydrates are crystalline compounds where gas molecules are trapped in hydrogen-bonded water molecule cages.

They can only exist under a certain pressure, and are generally unstable above about 3 km depth on Ceres. Upon impact, they are destabilized and release trapped gas, and the constituent water is converted to liquid, vapor, or ice. Clathrates melt at the same temperature as ice, and act like ice in the formation of many ice-related features. They can also be converted to water ice at shallow depth. Therefore, ice and clathrates are the best candidate materials for low-viscosity and/or low-density layers.

Based on the analysis of ice-related features, a broad picture of Ceres's cryosphere emerges (Sizemore *et al.*, 2019). The crust of Ceres was initially ice-rich and globally uniform in composition. Early large impacts established large-scale compositional heterogeneity, and subsequent impacts progressively modified the crust. In particular, impacts excavated ice-rich ejecta from depths and redeposited them on the surface. This would have both created shallow ice-rich layers and facilitated depletion of ice on regional scales. Impacts have also facilitated cryomagmatic and/or cryovolcanic activity via fracturing, transient melt production, and differential loading in the subsurface.

Still, many key questions about Ceres's ice remain to be answered. These include the following: What is the primary driver of H_2O loss at the present epoch? What is the role of deep endogenic activity in the production of cryovolcanic features? Are extrusive or intrusive processes responsible for the formation of individual large domes, or do both types contribute to various extents (Sori *et al.*, 2018)? Are mobile materials sourced from deep brine reservoirs near the crust-mantle boundary, or melt chambers created by large impacts? What is the time scale of ice-related activity? The answers to these questions require further long-term monitoring of Ceres's surface, water vapor production, and more importantly, high-resolution images of regions associated with ice-related features.

Ample evidence of subsurface water ice on Ceres exists in a large variety of ice-related morphological features from tens of meters to hundreds of kilometers in size, indicating a global distribution of subsurface ice from just beneath the top surface to tens of kilometers deep. The global and local heterogeneities of the distribution of subsurface water ice in both lateral and vertical dimensions are likely formed and continuously modified by large impacts, and are also affected by solar heating at the surface and by other geological processes. Ceres's crust appears to be weak at scale lengths of greater than hundreds of kilometers and in response to impacting, but strong at shorter scale lengths and low strain rates. Clathrate hydrates are a likely component that could account for these properties while also explaining the low density of Ceres's crust. However, the sources and mechanisms that generate the water exosphere of Ceres are still unclear.

References

A'Hearn, M. F. and Feldman, P. D. (1992). Water vaporization on Ceres. *Icarus*, **98**, 54–60.

Bamberg, M., Jaumann, R., Asche, H., Kneissl, T. and Michael, G. G. (2014). Floor-fractured craters on Mars—Observations and origin. *Planet. Space Sci.*, **98**, 146–162.

Barlow, N. G. and Tornabene, L. L. (2018). Comparison of central pit craters across the solar system and implications for pit formation models. 49th LPSC, 1687.

Bray, V., Schenk, P., Melosh, H. J., Morgan, J. and Collins, G. (2012). Ganymede crater dimensions—Implications for central peak and central pit formation and development. *Icarus*, **217**, 115–129.

Bland, M. T. (2013). Predicted crater morphologies on Ceres: Probing internal structure and evolution. *Icarus*, **226**, 510–521.

Bland, M. T., *et al.* (2016). Composition and structure of the shallow subsurface of Ceres revealed by crater morphology. *Nat. Geosci.*, **9**, 538–542.

Bland, M. T., *et al.* (2019). Dome formation on Ceres by solid-state flow analogous to terrestrial salt tectonics. *Nat. Comm.*, **12**, 797–801.

Boyce, J. M., *et al.* (2012). Origin of small pits in Martian impact craters. *Icarus*, **221**, 262–275.

Buczkowski, D., *et al.* (2016). The geomorphology of Ceres. *Science*, **353**, aaf4332.

Buczkowski, D., *et al.* (2018a). Floor-fractured craters on Ceres and implications for interior processes. *J. Geophys. Res. Planets.*, **123**, 3188–3204.

Buczkowski, D., *et al.* (2018b). The geology of the occator quadrangle of dwarf planet Ceres: Floor-fractured craters and other geomorphic evidence of cyomagmatism. *Icarus*, **316**, 128–139.

Carrozzo, F. G., *et al.* (2018). Nature, formation, and distribution of carbonates on Ceres. *Sci. Adv.*, **4**, e1701645.

Castillo-Rogez, J. C. and McCord, T. B. (2010). Ceres' evolution and present state constrained by shape data. *Icarus,* **205**, 443–459.

Castillo-Rogez, J., *et al.* (2018). Insights into Ceres's evolution from surface composition. *Meteorit. Planet. Sci.*, **53**, 1820–1843.

Chabot, N. L., *et al.* (2012). Areas of permanent shadow in Mercury's south polar region ascertained by MESSENGER orbital imaging. *Geophys. Res. Lett.*, **39**, L09204.

Chiang, C.-C., Kuan, Y.-J. and Chuang, Y.-L. (2019). ACA observations of Ceres' molecular exosphere. 16th Asia Oceania Geosciences Society Annual Meeting, Singapore, July 28–August 2, 2019, Abstract # PS16-A023.
Chilton, H. T., *et al.* (2019). Landslides on Ceres: Inferences into ice content and layering in the upper crust. *J. Geophys. Res. Planet.*, **124**, 1512–1524.
Chuang, Y.-L., Kuan, Y.-J., Charnley, S., Chuang, M.-C. and Yeh, Y.-F. (2019). Submillimeter spectral observations of molecular exospheres of the Ceres icy world. 16th Asia Oceania Geosciences Society Annual Meeting, Singapore, July 28–August 2, 2019, Abstract # PS16-A025.
Croft, S. (1983). A proposed origin for palimpsests and anomalous pit craters on Ganymede and Callisto. Proc. Lunar Planet. Sci. Conf., 14th, Part I, *J. Geophys. Res.*, **88**, suppl., B71–B89.
Combe, J.-P., *et al.* (2016). Detection of local H_2O exposed at the surface of Ceres. *Science*, **353**, aaf3010.
Combe, J.-P., *et al.* (2019). Exposed H_2O-rich areas detected on Ceres with the Dawn visible and infrared mapping spectrometer. *Icarus*, **318**, 22–41.
De Sanctis, M. C., *et al.* (2016). Bright carbonate deposits as evidence of aqueous alteration on (1) Ceres. *Nature*, **536**, 54–57.
Duarte, K. D., *et al.* (2019). Landslides on Ceres: Diversity and geologic context. *J. Geophys. Res. Planet.*, **124**, 3329–3343.
Ermakov, A. I., *et al.* (2017a). Ceres's obliquity history and its implications for the permanently shadowed regions. *Geophys. Res. Lett.*, **44**, 2652–2661.
Ermakov, A. I., *et al.* (2017b). Constraints on Ceres' internal structure and evolution from its shape and gravity measured by the Dawn spacecraft. *J. Geophys. Res. Planet.*, **122**, 2267–2293.
Fanale, F. P. and Salvail, J. R. (1989). The water regime of asteroid (1) Ceres. *Icarus*, **82**, 97–110.
Formisano, M., Federico, C., De Angelis, S., De Sanctis, M. C. and Magni, G. (2016). The stability of the crust of the dwarf planet Ceres. *Mon. N. Roy. Astron. Soc.*, **463**, 520–528.
Formisano, M., *et al.* (2018). Thermal stability of water ice in Ceres' craters: The case of Juling crater. *J. Geophys. Res. Planet.*, **123**, 2445–2463.
Fu, R. R., *et al.* (2017). The interior structure of Ceres as revealed by surface topography. *Earth. Planet. Sci. Lett.*, **476**, 153–164.
Hall, J. L., Solomon, S. C. and Head, J. W. (1981). Lunar floor-fractured craters: Evidence for viscous relaxation of crater topography. *J. Geophys. Res.*, **86**, 9537–9552.
Hayne, P. O. and Aharonson, O. (2015). Thermal stability of ice on Ceres with rough topography. *J. Geophys. Res. Planet.*, **120**, 1567–1584.
Hiesinger, H., *et al.* (2016). Cratering on Ceres: Implications for its crust and evolution. *Science*, **353**, aaf4758.

Hughson, K. H. G., *et al.* (2019). Fluidized appearing ejecta on Ceres: Implications for the mechanical properties, frictional properties, and composition of its shallow subsurface. *J. Geophys. Res. Planet.*, **124**, 1819–1839.

Jia, Y.-D., Villarreal, M. N. and Russell, C. T. (2017). Possible Ceres bow shock surfaces based on fluid models. *J. Geophys. Res. Space Phys.*, **122**, 4976–4987.

Jozwiak, L. M., Head, J. W., Zuber, M. T., Smith, D. E. and Neumann, G. A. (2012). Lunar floor-fractured craters: Classification, distribution, origin and implications for magmatism and shallow crustal structure. *J. Geophys. Res.*, **117**, E11005.

Jozwiak, L. M., Head, J. W. and Wilson, L. (2015). Lunar floor-fractured craters as magmatic intrusions: Geometry, modes of emplacement, associated tectonic and volcanic features, and implications for gravity anomalies. *Icarus*, **248**, 424–447.

Küppers, M., *et al.* (2014). Localized sources of water vapour on the dwarf planet (1) Ceres. *Nature*, **505**, 525–527.

Landis, M. E., *et al.* (2017). Conditions for sublimating water ice to supply Ceres' exosphere. *J. Geophys. Res. Planet.*, **122**, 1984–1995.

Landis, M. E., *et al.* (2019). Water vapor contribution to Ceres' exosphere from observed surface ice and postulated ice-exposing impacts. *J. Geophys. Res. Planet.*, **124**, 61–75.

Marchi, S., *et al.* (2016). The missing large impact craters on Ceres. *Nature Comm.*, **7**, 12257.

Mazarico, E., Neumann, G. A., Smith, D. E., Zuber, M. T. and Torrence, M. H. (2011). Illumination conditions of the lunar polar regions using LOLA topography. *Icarus*, **211**, 1066–1081.

McCord, T. B. and Sotin, C. (2005). Ceres: Evolution and current state. *J. Geophys. Res.*, **110**, E05009.

McCord, T. B., Castillo-Rogez, J. and Rivkin, A. (2011). Ceres: Its origin, evolution and structure and Dawn's potential contribution. *Space Sci. Rev.*, **163**, 63–76.

Melosh, H. J. (1982). A schematic model of crater modification by gravity. *J. Geophys. Res.*, **87**, 371–380.

Mest, S. C., *et al.* (2017). The global geologic map of Ceres based on Dawn HAMO observations. 48th Lunar and Planetary Science Conference, LPI Contrib. No. 1964, id.2512.

Mumma, M. J. and Charnley, S. B. (2011). The chemical composition of Comets — Emerging taxonomies and natal heritage. *Ann. Rev. Astron. Astrophys*, **49**, 471–524.

Otto, K. A., Marchi, S., Trowbridge, A., Melosh, H. J. and Sizemore, H. G. (2019). Ceres crater degradation inferred from concentric fracturing. *J. Geophys. Res. Planet.*, **124**, 1188–1203.

Parks, M., *et al.* (2019). Using ALMA Spectra to Investigate a Potential Transient Exosphere of Ceres. 50th Lunar and Planetary Science Conference, held 18–22 March, 2019 at The Woodlands, Texas. LPI Contribution No. 2132, id.2974.

Platz, T., *et al.* (2016). Surface water-ice deposits in the northern shadowed regions of Ceres. *Nat. Astron.*, **1**, 0007.

Prettyman, T. H., *et al.* (2017). Extensive water ice within Ceres' aqueously altered regolith: Evidence from nuclear spectroscopy. *Science,* **355**, 55–59.

Quick, L. C., *et al.* (2019). A possible brine reservoir beneath Occator crater: Thermal and compositional evolution and formation of the Cerealia dome and Vinalia faculae. *Icarus,* **320**, 119–135.

Raponi, A., *et al.* (2018). Variations in the amount of water ice on Ceres' surface suggest a seasonal water cycle. *Sci. Adv.*, **4**, eaao3757.

Raymond, C. A., *et al.* (2020). Impact-driven mobilization of deep crustal brines on dwarf planet Ceres. *Nat. Astron.*, **4**, 741–747.

Roig, F. and Nesvorný, D. (2020). Modeling the Chronologies and Size Distributions of Ceres and Vesta Craters. *Astron. J.*, **160**, 110.

Roth, L., *et al.* (2016). Constraints on an Exosphere at Ceres from Hubble Space Telescope Observations. *Geophys. Res. Lett.*, **43**, 2465–2472.

Roth, L. (2018). Constraints on Water Vapor and Sulfur Dioxide at Ceres: Exploiting the Sensitivity of the Hubble Space Telescope. *Icarus*, **305**, 149–159.

Rousselot, P., *et al.* (2011). A Search for Water Vaporization on Ceres. *Astron. J.*, **142**, 125.

Rousselot, P., *et al.* (2019). Search for Water Outgassing of (1) Ceres near Perihelion. *Astron. Astrophys.*, **628**, A22.

Russell, C. T., *et al.* (2016). Dawn arrives at Ceres: Exploration of a small, volatile-rich world. *Science,* **353**, 1008–1010.

Schenk, P. M. (1993). Central pit and dome craters: Exposing the interiors of Ganymede and Callisto. *J. Geophys. Res.*, **98**, 7475–7498.

Schenk, P., *et al.* (2019). The central pit and dome at Cerealia Facula bright deposit and floor deposits in Occator crater, Ceres: Morphology, Comparisons and Formation. *Icarus,* **320**, 159–187.

Schenk, P., *et al.* (2021). Compositional control on impact crater formation on mid-sized planetary bodies: Dawn at Ceres and Vesta, Cassini at Saturn. *Icarus,* **359**, 114343.

Schmidt, B. E, *et al.* (2017). Geomorphology evidence for ground ice on dwarf planet Ceres. *Nat. Geosci.*, **10**, 338–343.

Schörghofer, N. (2008). The lifetime of ice on main belt asteroids. *Astrophys. J.*, **682**, 697–705.

Schörghofer, N., *et al.* (2016). The permanently shadowed regions of dwarf planet Ceres. *Geophys. Res. Lett.*, **43**, 6783–6789.

Schörghofer, N., *et al.* (2017). The putative Ceres exosphere. *Astrophys. J.*, **850**, 85.

Schultz, P. M. (1976). Floor-fractured lunar craters. *The Moon*, **15**, 241–273.

Scully, J. E. C., *et al.* (2017). Evidence for the interior evolution of Ceres from geologic analysis of fractures. *Geophys. Res. Lett.*, **44**, 9564–9572.

Scully, J. E. C., *et al.* (2019). Ceres' Occator crater and its faculae explored through geologic mapping. *Icarus*, **320**, 7–23.

Senft, L. E. and Steward, S. T. (2011). Modeling the morphological diversity of impact craters on icy satellites. *Icarus*, **214**, 67–81.

Sizemore, H. G., *et al.* (2017). Pitted terrains on (1) Ceres and implications for shallow subsurface volatile distribution. *Geophys. Res. Lett.*, **44**, 6570–6578.

Sizemore, H. G., *et al.* (2019). A global inventory of ice-related morphological features on dwarf planet Ceres: Implications for the evolution and current state of the cryosphere. *J. Geophys. Res. Planet.*, **124**, 1650–1689.

Sori, M. M., *et al.* (2018). Cryovolcanic rates on Ceres revealed by topography. *Nat. Astron.*, **2**, 946–950.

Sunshine, J. M., *et al.* (2006). Exposed water ice deposits on the surface of comet 9P/Tempel 1. *Science*, **311**, 1453–1455.

Thomas, P. C., *et al.* (2005). Differentiation of the asteroid Ceres as revealed by its shape. *Nature*, **437**, 224–226.

Titus, T. N. (2015). Ceres: Predictions for near-surface water ice stability and implications for plume generating processes. *Geophys. Res. Lett.*, **42**, 2130–2136.

Tornabene, L. L., *et al.* (2012). Widespread crater-related pitted materials on Mars: Further evidence for the role of target volatiles during the impact process. *Icarus*, **220**, 348–368.

Villarreal, M. N., *et al.* (2017). The dependence of the cerean exosphere on solar energetic particle events. *Astrophys. J. Lett.*, **838**, 8.

Williams, N., Bell, J., Christiansen, P. and Farmer, J. (2014). Evidence for an explosive origin for central pit craters on Mars. *Eight Intl. Conf. Mars*, 1041.

Wood, C. A., Head, J. and Cintala, M. (1978). Interior morphology of fresh Martian craters—The effects of target characteristics. *Proc. Lunar Plan. Sci. Conf. IX*, 3691–3709.

Chapter 7

Interior Structure

Information on the interior structure of Ceres comes from multiple sources: combined gravity and topography on a global scale, crater morphologies on a regional to local scale, and compositional constraints. This chapter reviews this state of knowledge and interpretation for Ceres's internal evolution.

7.1 Gravity

The Dawn mission measured Ceres's gravity on a global scale to degree 18 (Fig. 7.1) during its prime mission (Park *et al.*, 2016). The global gravity field yields constraints on the average internal structure of Ceres. Under the assumption of hydrostatic equilibrium, the degree-two gravity field yields the mean moment of inertia (MoI) that constraints the extent of mass concentration inside a body. Park *et al.* (2016) derived a mean moment of inertia of 0.37. An MoI of 0.4 indicates the body's density is radially uniform, whereas lower values indicate some mass concentration. This kind of inversion is underconstrained though, and many interior models are possible. An additional constraint comes from admittance, which is described below.

During its extended mission at Ceres, Dawn also obtained Ceres's gravity locally up to degree 50 along a swath that encompasses Occator and Urvara craters (Park *et al.*, 2020).

The higher-resolution gravity brought another degree of granularity by revealing a density gradient in the crust (Park *et al.*, 2020). The density

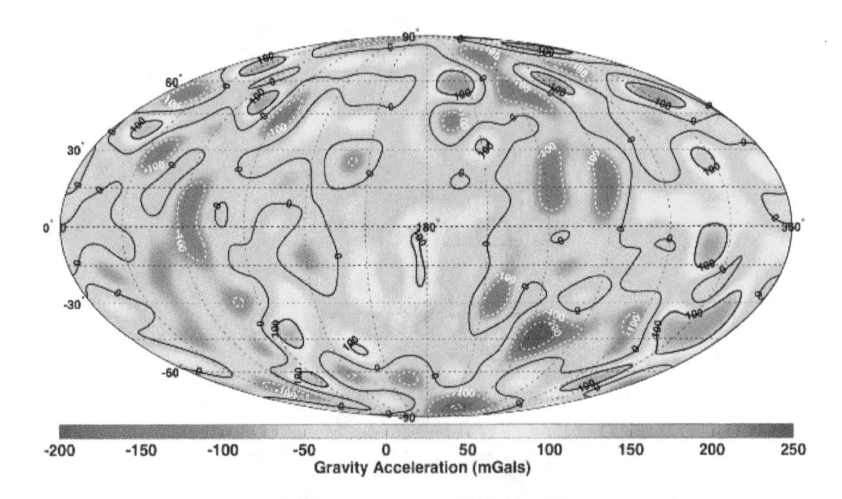

Figure 7.1: Observed radial gravity accelerations at the end of the Dawn prime mission. The accelerations are mapped to a 482.0 × 445.9 km ellipsoid for degree $n = 2$ to 16, but with the large hydrostatic zonal gravity coefficients J_2 and J_4 removed. The maximum and minimum gravity amplitudes are 186 and −282 mGals, respectively. Reprinted from Konopliv *et al.* (2018). Copyright with permission from Elsevier.

increase with depth suggests the incorporation of dense material that could be rock particles and brines concentrating in the ocean.

7.2 Inferences from Admittance

Dawn also achieved global mapping of Ceres under multiple illumination angles, yielding a global digital topography model (DTM) (Park *et al.*, 2019). The DTM presented in Fig. 7.2 allows identifying highlands from lowlands, with about 11 km topography difference between the two (Frigeri *et al.*, 2018). The lowlands were interpreted as basins (Marchi *et al.*, 2016), whereas the main highland (Hanami Planum) was interpreted as original crustal material that has not been disrupted by large impacts (Castillo-Rogez *et al.*, 2019).

The topography also revealed a scarcity of craters in the 100–300 km range (Marchi *et al.*, 2016). The origin of this gap in size frequency lacks explanation at this time. It may indicate partial resurfacing due to a heat pulse or basin formation in an ice-rich crust (Marchi *et al.*, 2016) (see Chapters 4 and 5).

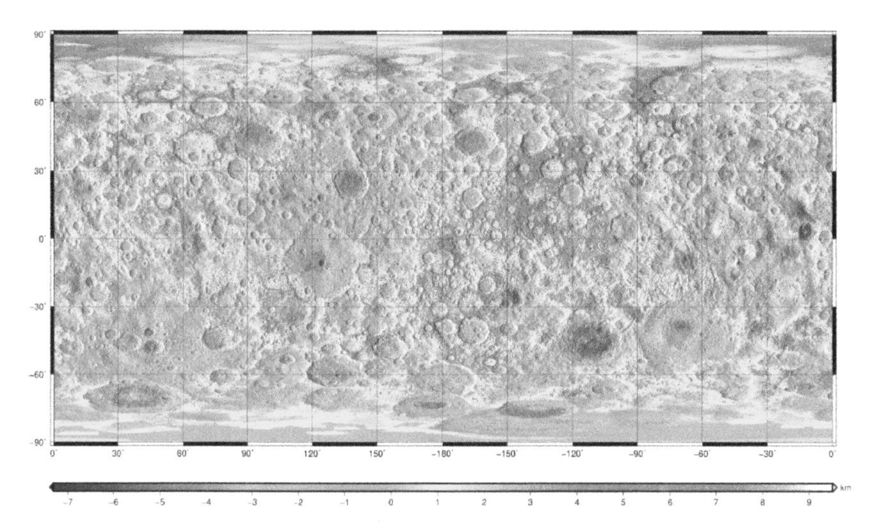

Figure 7.2: Cylindrical equidistant projection of topography based on the stereophotoclinometry technique. The horizontal map resolution is 100 m. The topography is computed relative to a (482 km, 482 km, 446 km) mean ellipsoid. Reprinted from Park *et al.* (2019). Copyright with permission from Elsevier.

The admittance, which is the ratio of the topography and gravity data, provides additional constraints on the interior structure under the assumption of isostatic equilibrium, i.e., the absence of lateral gradients in hydrostatic pressure. From admittance data, Ermakov *et al.* (2017) described Ceres with a two-layer structure: an outer layer (crust) with a density of about 1.25 g/cm^3 and a deeper layer (mantle) with a density of about 2.43 g/cm^3. Assuming a three-layer model, it is not possible to rule out the presence of a core rich in metal (King *et al.*, 2018).

The admittance analysis by Ermakov *et al.* (2017) revealed variations in crustal thickness, from ~25 km in the center of large craters like Yalode and Kerwan to 55 km in Hanami Planum (Fig. 7.3). The latter is more cratered than the surrounding areas, which may have been resurfaced due to basin formation. Variations in crustal thickness by a factor of two have potential implications for basal temperatures. Castillo-Rogez *et al.* (2019) suggested that the temperature below Hanami Planum may approach the water eutectic since heat transfer through the thick crust is slower than in the thin crust regions. In the latter, the temperature at the base of the crust may be as low as 220 K. However, two- or three-dimensional transfer modeling is required to get more accurate estimates. At Kerwan, Bland

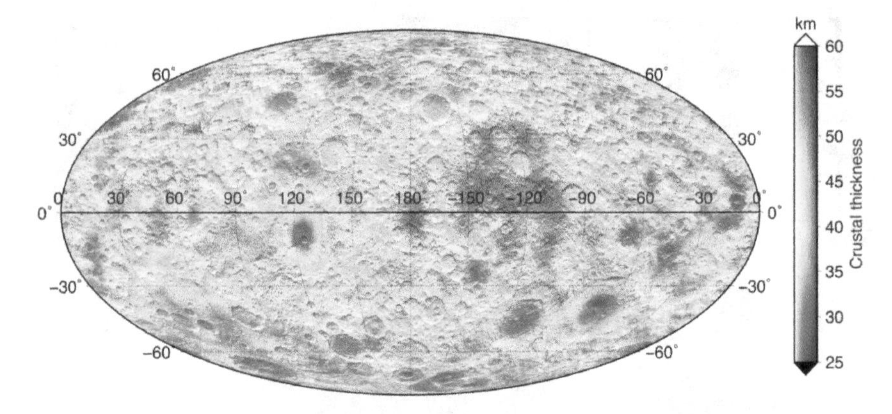

Figure 7.3: Variations of Ceres's crustal thickness inferred from admittance analysis, assuming isostasy. Crustal thinning is found in association with large craters. The region with a thick crust is associated with a highland called Hanami Planum. Reprinted from Ermakov *et al.* (2017). Copyright with permission from Wiley-VCH Verlag GmbH & Co. KGaA.

et al. (2018) inferred the presence of a mass concentration (or mascon) below the crater, similar to observations of large lunar craters (e.g., Zuber *et al.*, 2016). This structure has been interpreted by Bland *et al.* as evidence for mantle uplift or rock dehydration as a consequence of the large impact that created the 280-km-large crater.

A major caveat in the analysis of the Dawn gravity data is the presence of small, non-hydrostatic anomalies in the shape in the order of ~2 km at the equator (Park *et al.*, 2016). This means Ceres's shape does not exactly match the theoretical shape it would acquire, driven by rotational forces, if its viscosity was infinitely small (i.e., a liquid). The current leading hypothesis is that this departure of hydrostaticity reflects a fossil shape acquired when Ceres was spinning about 30 minutes faster than at present (Mao and McKinnon, 2018). During despinning, that shape could have remained frozen, at least partially, if Ceres's crust was strong enough. Mao and McKinnon (2018) suggested that despinning could have been driven by large impacts. By inversion of the gravity and shape data assuming the fossil shape, these authors inferred a slightly different density profile for Ceres's interior. The crustal density is about the same as inferred by Ermakov *et al.* (2017), but the rocky mantle could be about 2.7–2.9 g/cm^3.

7.3 Constraints from Geological Observations

The low crustal density indicates a high content of water. Additional constraints from topography relaxation on a global scale by Fu *et al.* (2017) and local (crater) scale by Bland *et al.* (2016) suggest water ice is not a major component of the crust. Indeed, the crust's mechanical strength is at least three orders of magnitude greater than water ice for Ceres's temperatures. It suggests no more than 40 vol.% of a weak phase, which Bland *et al.* (2016) interpreted as an upper bound on the water ice fraction. That fraction could be less if the crust also contains void porosity. Bland *et al.* (2016) further found lateral variations of crater morphologies on a scale of tens of kilometers that these authors interpreted as evidence for regional variations of ice content in the crust. The overall high strength and low density of the crust were attributed to a large fraction of hydrates (e.g., gas and salt hydrates), which were predicted by geochemical models (Castillo-Rogez *et al.*, 2018, see below). Gas hydrates, also called clathrate hydrates, are cages of water surrounding gas molecules (Fig. 7.4).

Fu *et al.* (2017) suggested the crust is a mixture of 10 vol.% silicates, 20 vol.% hydrated salts, 30 vol.% ice, and 40 vol.% clathrates in order to match the average crustal density derived by Ermakov *et al.* (2017) and be consistent with the strength estimates from Bland *et al.* (2016) and Fu *et al.* (2017). The extent of porosity is not constrained and might show lateral variations, as indicated by the distribution of surface fractures (Scully *et al.*, 2017). Ceres's crust relaxes on scales greater than ~250 km,

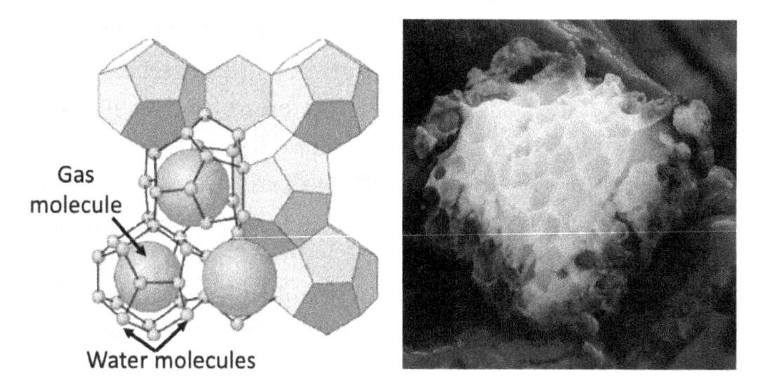

Figure 7.4: Left: Illustration of gas hydrate structure (Reprinted from World Ocean Review). Right: Gas hydrates as found on ocean floors. (Credit: Wikipedia).

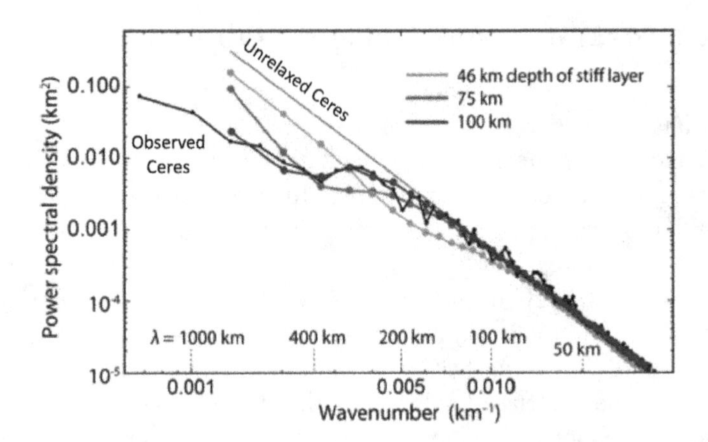

Figure 7.5: Power spectrum of Ceres's topography (black curve) compared against the topography modeled assuming a strong crust with viscosity decaying by one decade per 10 km depth. The different curves cover a range of depths for a strong lower rocky mantle. An interior with a strong mantle starting at 100 km depth matches the observations best. Updated from Fu *et al.* (2017). Copyright with permission from Elsevier.

which Fu *et al.* (2017) interpreted with a crustal viscosity profile decreasing by about one order of magnitude every 10 km (Fig. 7.5).

7.4 Current Understanding of Ceres's Interior

Various structures have been suggested for Ceres's interior, as summarized in Fig. 7.6. Some of them include a water-rich crust (Ermakov *et al.*, 2017; Travis *et al.*, 2018) with different types of impurities. The density of 1.25 g/cm^3 indicates no more than 20% of rock and/or salts in volume. Salts found at Ceres have generally high densities, greater than 2 g/cm^3 (e.g., sodium carbonate: 2.54 g/cm^3). A different kind of model assumes that the low density inferred for Ceres's outer region indicates a high content in organic matter (Zolotov, 2020). Indeed, organics generally have low densities. The most abundant kind found in carbonaceous meteorites, called insoluble organic matter, has a density of about 1.3 g/cm^3. Hence, Zolotov (2020) suggested that the crust could be composed of carbonaceous material and some porosity, and reproduced the density gradient inferred by Ermakov *et al.* (2017).

Although these models can match Ceres's mean moment of inertia of 0.37 as inferred by Park *et al.* (2016), some of them cannot reproduce

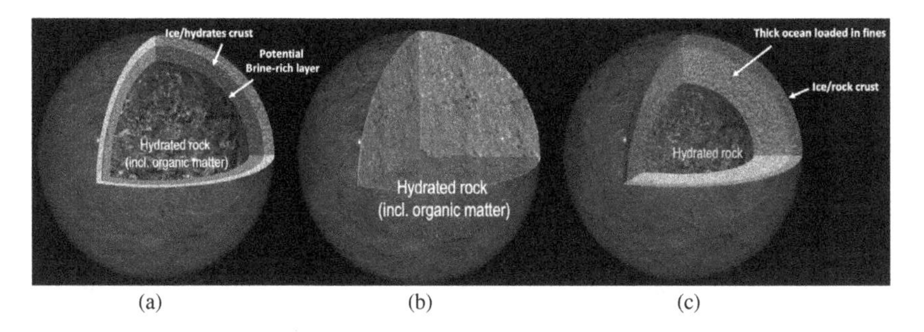

(a) (b) (c)

Figure 7.6: Three interpretations of Ceres's internal structure inferred from integrated analysis of the Dawn observations. Below a regolith a few 100s meters thick, a water-dominated crust contains the bulk of the original ocean that formed shortly after Ceres's formation. Residual liquid at the interface between the water-rich crust and the rocky mantle may be responsible for topography relaxation observed on a global scale (Fu *et al.*, 2017). All models match the mean moment of inertia inferred by Park *et al.* (2016).

other observations returned by Dawn. In particular, the model by Zolotov (2020) does not account for the widespread expression of ice directly on the surface and subsurface (Chapter 6). The model by Travis *et al.* (2018) does not account for Ceres's chemical evolution and thus does not provide a viable framework for explaining the salt deposits found throughout Ceres's surface (Stein *et al.*, 2017), as well as the crust's high strength.

High-resolution gravity data returned by the Dawn XM2 led to the discovery of a positive density gradient in the crust (Park *et al.*, 2020). This suggests that the crust accreted material from the deep ocean upon freezing (e.g., rock particles, salts). Park *et al.* (2020) proposed that this may indicate a concentration of the ocean in impurities as a consequence of advanced freezing. At the time of writing, the density contrast between the top and bottom of the crust is unknown.

7.5 Evolution of a Differentiated Ceres

7.5.1 *Early Evolution*

Here, we consider possible evolutionary pathways for Ceres, assuming its interior is differentiated in a volatile-rich crust and rocky mantle. This kind of interior structure is typical of ice-rich bodies in which early heating led to melting of the volatile phase and to the formation of a global ocean, such as Europa or Enceladus. Short-lived radioisotopes, and especially aluminum-26 (^{26}Al), are believed to be responsible for global ice melting in carbonaceous chondrite parent bodies. Similarly, short-lived radioisotopes likely played a role in Ceres's early history (Castillo-Rogez and McCord, 2010) if it formed within 5 million years after the production of calcium-aluminum inclusions (CAIs) taken as a reference for the original concentration of ^{26}Al (Schramm *et al.*, 1970).

The globally homogenous surface mineralogy at Ceres is consistent with pervasive alteration under a relatively high fugacity of hydrogen (Chapter 4) in a global ocean, a conclusion that is consistent with predictions for, and observations of, large ice-rich bodies (Castillo-Rogez *et al.*, 2018). In these conditions, rocky particles could sink and settle to form a rock-dominated mantle while volatiles migrated to the surface. This density-driven fractionation of water and rock can reproduce the averaged density profile inferred by Ermakov *et al.* (2017). However, this evolution model needs to account for additional observations. One is the high strength of the crust mentioned above. Geochemical modeling indicates that clathrate hydrates can form under low pressure in Ceres's early ocean and they become the dominant form of water at pressures of >10 MPa (Fig. 7.7).

Localized occurrences of natrite (sodium carbonate) at the surface of Ceres provide key constraints on the composition of fluids that are alkaline in nature (i.e., pH greater than 9). Simulation of the freezing of Ceres's ocean formed the various compounds found on Ceres's surface so far (Chapter 4, Fig. 4.2), plus additional species that have not been detected either because they are in low abundances or they do not display absorption features as detectable by Dawn. These simulations also reproduced the conditions for abundant ammonium in the ocean that can be exchanged with cations in clay interlayers at low temperatures (<50°C).

The state of Ceres's rocky mantle is also partially understood. The gravity data inversion is mostly sensitive to the density contrast between crust and upper mantle. A more complex interior model with additional layers includes too many parameters with respect to the observational constraints available. The deficit of iron with respect to carbonaceous chondrite composition potentially points to the fast settling of iron-rich particles during the differentiation phase (Prettyman *et al.*, 2017). Overall, the density of Ceres's mantle, between 2.4 and 2.9 g/cm^3, is low in comparison to the rock density inferred from geochemical modeling, which is >3 g/cm^3 (Castillo-Rogez *et al.*, 2018). This difference may be

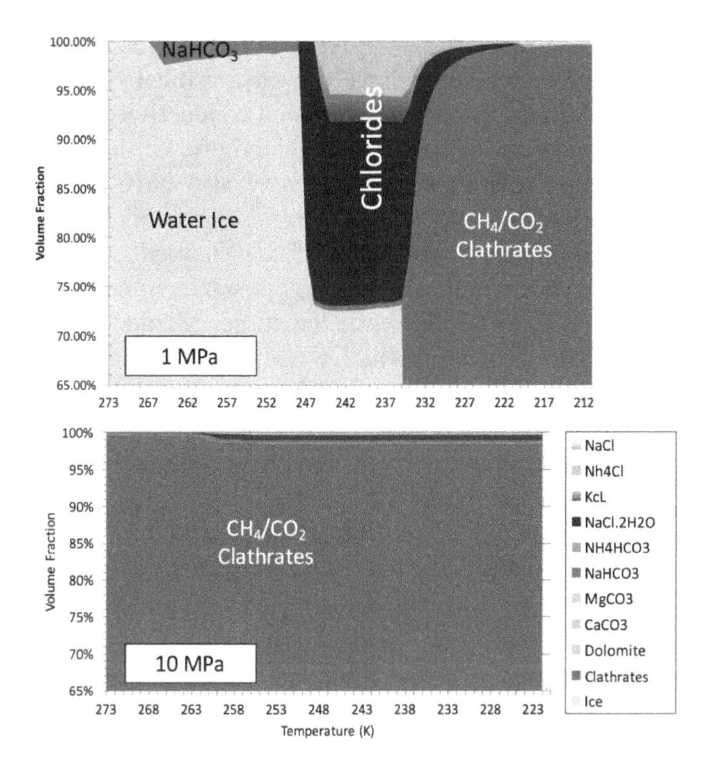

Figure 7.7: Freezing evolution of Ceres's early ocean assuming a starting fluid composition in equilibrium with the mineralogy reported by De Sanctis *et al.* (2015). Top: equilibrium volume fractions of compounds frozen as temperature decreases, starting from 273 K for a pressure of 1 MPa; Bottom: same, for a pressure of 10 MPa. The freezing sequence does not necessarily reflect the final stratification of the ocean as these species significantly differ in densities and Ceres's early ocean might have been convecting. Reprinted from Castillo-Rogez *et al.* (2018). Copyright with permission from Wiley-VCH Verlag GmbH & Co. KGaA.

ascribed to the presence of porosity in the mantle. In this case, porosity refers to pores in the silicate structure that is occupied by a low-density material such as brines.

7.5.2 *Long-Term Evolution*

Thermal evolution models of Ceres suggested that the bulk of the ocean froze within the first 100 to 200 million years after formation (e.g.,

Castillo-Rogez and McCord, 2010; Neveu *et al*., 2015). Over the long term, clathrate hydrates could have played a critical role in slowing down heat loss because of their low thermal conductivity, which is five to ten times lower than ice's thermal conductivity. Furthermore, due to their high strength, clathrate hydrates may also have prevented the onset of convection in Ceres's crust. Formisano *et al*. (2020) studied this question using a two-dimensional finite element numerical code. They found that no thermal convection is possible, assuming less than 40 vol.% of weak material in the crust per Bland *et al*. (2016). Convection may be possible if the ice content is slightly greater than 40% and the temperature at the base of the crust ranges from 250 to 300 K. However, as shown in Fig. 7.8, the modeled temperatures at the base of the crust are expected to be colder than required for convection to be initiated throughout Ceres's history.

The residual liquid for the temperatures expected at the base of Ceres's crust at present (>220 K) is a saturated brine dominated by chlorides (Castillo-Rogez *et al*., 2019) (Fig. 7.9). It is not clear if local

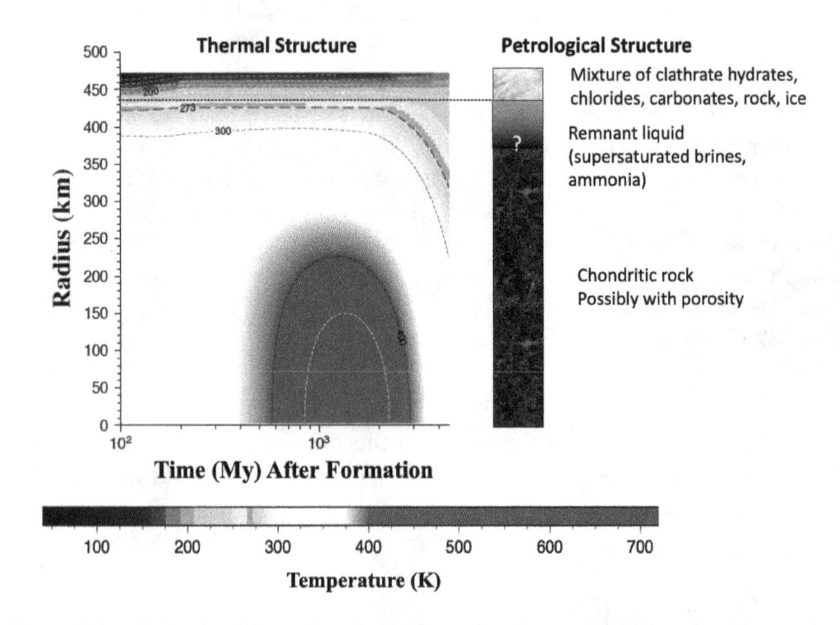

Figure 7.8: Example of thermal evolution for an interior model differentiated into an icy crust and rocky mantle. Based on the modeling approach by Castillo-Rogez *et al*. (2019).

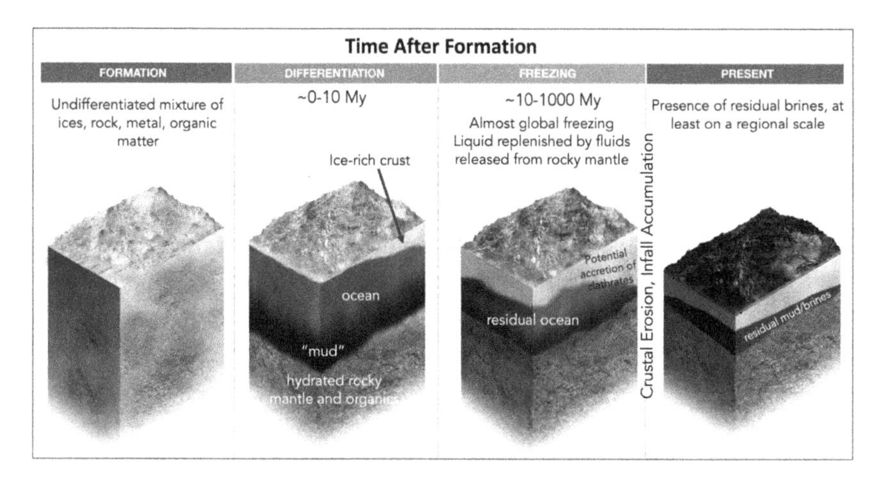

Figure 7.9: Schematic summary of Ceres's evolution.

heterogeneities associated with impact craters and landslides indicate that sodium bicarbonate and other salts are accessible in the shallow subsurface or if they are sourced from the lower part of the crust or below the crust (see Chapter 8). Based on terrestrial analogs (e.g., lake Vostok) and theoretical considerations, slow freezing should lead to a mostly pure ice layer. Indeed, rock particles cannot be accommodated at the ice grain boundaries. Salt is also rejected upon slow freezing, as observed in marine ice (Buffo *et al.*, 2021). The fraction of soluble impurities that may be trapped at the grain boundaries is of the order of tens of micromols (Christner *et al.*, 2006).

The evolution of the rocky mantle is even less understood. It depends in part on its state of consolidation. Neveu and Desch (2015) and Travis *et al.* (2018) suggested that the bulk of the large (millimeter-sized) particles settled early on in a stable inner mantle, while fine (tens of microns) particles remained in suspension in the ocean. Neveu *et al.* (2015) further suggested that brines trapped in the early rocky mantle could precipitate and seal porosity, acting as cement. The long-term fate of the fines is difficult to model. On Earth, fines tend to become electrically charged from adsorbing ions. As a result, the fines tend to agglomerate and sink, a process called "flocculation".

Due to the heat from long-lived radioisotope decay, the mantle temperature could potentially reach the dehydration temperature of silicates

(Castillo-Rogez and McCord, 2010). However, it has also been suggested that sustained hydrothermal convection could keep the mantle cool, less than 100°C (Travis *et al.*, 2018). The low mantle density does suggest that temperatures remained below silicate dehydration (~600–750 K) (Fu *et al.* 2017).

In any case, thermal models showed that the heat lost from the mantle is greater than the heat transferred through the crust if the latter is rich in gas and salt hydrates (Castillo-Rogez *et al.*, 2019). As a result, a residual brine layer could remain until present. However, the radial and lateral extent of that layer is not understood. Available observational constraints are addressed in Chapter 8.

In summary, Ceres's internal structure is partially differentiated in a water-rich crust and rocky mantle with some porosity occupied by brines. The strong crust is likely dominated by hydrates that prevent the onset of convection. The slow heat transfer can explain the presence of brines until the present. Many questions remain, such as the extent and geometry of a deep brine reservoir, the fate of salts precipitated from the ocean, and the partitioning of organic matter between the crust and the deep interior.

References

Bland, M. T., *et al.* (2016). Composition and structure of the shallow subsurface of Ceres revealed by crater morphology. *Nat. Geosci.,* **9**, 538–542.

Bland, M. T., *et al.* (2018). Morphological indicators of a mascon beneath Ceres's largest crater, Kerwan. *Geophys. Res. Lett.*, **45**, 1297–1304.

Buffo, J. J., Schmidt, Huber, C. and Meyer, C. R. (2021). Characterizing the ice-ocean interface of icy worlds: A theoretical approach. *Icarus*, **360**, 114318.

Castillo-Rogez, J. C. and McCord, T. B. (2010). Ceres' evolution and present state constrained by shape data. *Icarus*, **205**, 443–459.

Castillo-Rogez, J. C., Neveu, M., McSween, H. Y., Fu R. R., Toplis, M. J. and Prettyman, T. (2018). Insights into Ceres' evolution from surface composition. *Meteorit. Planet. Sci.*, **53**, 1820–1843.

Castillo-Rogez, J. C., *et al.* (2019). Conditions for the long-term preservation of a deep brine reservoir in Ceres. *Geophys. Res. Lett.*, **46**, 1963–1972.

Christner, B. C., *et al.* (2006). Limnological conditions in Subglacial Lake Vostok, Antarctica. *Limnol. Oceanogr.,* **51**(6), 2485–2501.

De Sanctis, M. C., *et al.* (2015). Ammoniated phyllosilicates with a likely outer Solar system origin on (1) Ceres. *Nature,* **528**, 241–244.
Ermakov, A. I., *et al.* (2017). Constraints on Ceres' internal structure and evolution from its shape and gravity measured by the Dawn spacecraft. *J. Geophys. Res. Planets*, **122**, 2267–2293.
Formisano, M., Federico, C., Castillo-Rogez, J., De Sanctis, M. C. and Magni, G. (2020). Thermal convection in the crust of the dwarf planet—I. Ceres. *Mon. Not. R. Astron. Soc.*, **494**, 5704–5712.
Frigeri, A., *et al.* (2018). The geology of the Nawish quadrangle of Ceres: The rim of an ancient basin. *Icarus*, **316**, 114–127.
Fu, R., *et al.* (2017). The interior structure of Ceres as revealed by surface topography. *Earth Planet. Sci. Lett.*, **476**, 153–164.
King, S. D., Castillo-Rogez, J. C., Toplis, M. J., Bland, M. T., Raymond, C. A. and Russell, C. T. (2018). Ceres internal structure from geophysical constraints. Meteorit. *Planet. Sci.*, **53**, 1999–2007.
Konopliv, *et al.* (2018). The Ceres gravity field, spin pole, rotation period and orbit from the Dawn radiometric tracking and optical data. *Icarus*, **299**, 411–429.
Mao, X. and McKinnon, W. B. (2018). Faster paleospin and deep-seated uncompensated mass as possible explanations for Ceres' present-day shape and gravity. *Icarus*, **299**, 430–442.
Marchi, S., *et al.* (2016). The missing large impact craters on Ceres. *Nat. Comm.*, **7**, 12257.
Neveu, M. and Desch, S. J. (2015). Geochemistry, thermal evolution, and cryovolcanism on Ceres with a muddy mantle. *Geophys. Res. Lett.*, **42**, 10,197–10,206.
Neveu M., Desch, S. and Castillo-Rogez, J. C. (2015). Core cracking and hydrothermal circulation can profoundly affect Ceres' geophysical evolution. *J. Geophys. Res.*, **120**, 123–154.
Park, R., *et al.* (2016). Interior structure of dwarf planet Ceres from measured gravity and shape. *Nature*, **537**, 515–517.
Park, R. S., *et al.* (2019). High-resolution shape model of Ceres from stereophotoclinometry using Dawn imaging data. *Icarus*, **319**, 812–817.
Park, R. S., *et al.* (2020). Evidence of non-uniform crust of Ceres from Dawn's high-resolution gravity data. *Nat. Astron*, **4**, 748–755.
Prettyman, T. H., *et al.* (2017). Extensive water ice within Ceres' aqueously altered regolith: Evidence from nuclear spectroscopy. *Science*, **355**, 55–59.
Scully, J. E. C., *et al.* (2017). Evidence for the Interior Evolution of Ceres from Geologic Analysis of Fractures. *Geophys. Res. Lett.*, **44**, 9564–9572.
Schramm, D. N., Tera, F. and Wasserburg, G. J. (1970). The isotopic abundance of 26Mg and limits on 26Al in the early solar system. *Earth Planet. Sci. Lett.*, **10**, 44–59.

Stein, N. T., *et al*. (2017). The formation and evolution of bright spots on Ceres. *Icarus*, **320**, 188–201.

Travis, B. J., Bland, P. A., Feldman, W. C. and Sykes, M. (2018). Hydrothermal dynamics in a CM-based model of Ceres. *Meteorit. Planet. Sci.,* **53**, 2008–2032.

Zuber, M. T., *et al*. (2016). Gravity field of the Orientale basin from the Gravity Recovery and Interior Laboratory mission. *Science*, **354**(6311), 438–441.

Zolotov, M. Y. (2020). The composition and structure of Ceres' interior. *Icarus*, **335**, 113404.

Chapter 8

Recent Activity

Ceres shows expressions of recent activity in a couple of places: Ahuna Mons and Occator crater (Fig. 8.1). In both cases, the newly emplaced material has been traced to a source in the upper mantle, based on geophysical observations. Hence, the study of these geological landmarks, described in turn below, can provide key information about the nature of Ceres's interior. Ceres also displays several older sites that have been interpreted as evidence for past activity.

8.1 Ahuna Mons and Other Large Domes

Ahuna Mons is a mountain located near the equator. It is about 4 to 5 km tall and 17 km at its base's longest dimension (Fig. 8.2). The mons shows bright streaks rich in Na-carbonate (Zambon *et al.*, 2017). Crater-based chronology indicates that this feature was emplaced less than 250 million years ago and, depending on the reference chronology model used for interpreting the crater count, it could be younger than 70 million years (Ruesch *et al.*, 2016).

It was identified early on that the emplacement of Ahuna Mons should require a low-viscosity source, suggesting the presence of subsurface brines (Ruesch *et al.*, 2016). This was confirmed with the analysis of the gravity anomaly associated with Ahuna Mons, the largest positive gravity anomaly on Ceres. Ruesch *et al.* (2019) derived from this observation that the mons is a mud dome with a source located below Ceres's crust, at about 35 km depth (Fig. 8.3). These authors further inferred that the dome

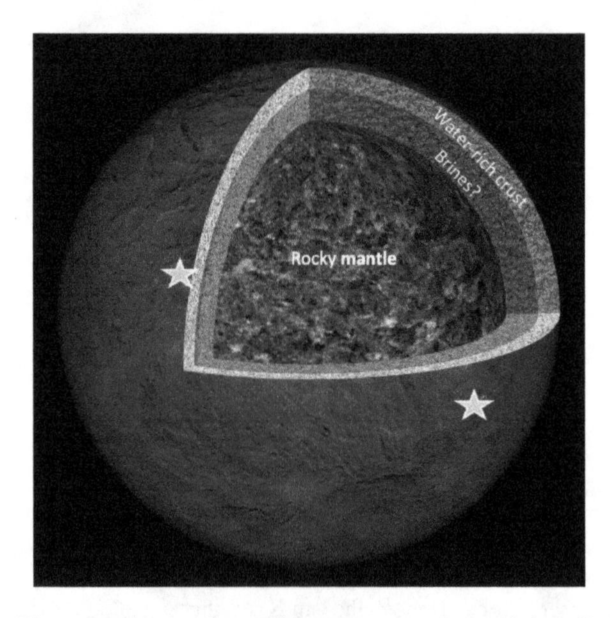

Figure 8.1: The two regions on Ceres with recent expressions of brine effusion, Occator crater (19.86° N, 238.85° E) and Ahuna mons (10.46° S, 315.8° E), are separated by about 620 km. This, combined with topography analysis, suggests a deep brine reservoir may extend on a global scale. Based on Dawn Photo journal PIA22660 https://photojournal.jpl.nasa.gov/catalog/PIA22660, credit: NASA/JPL-Caltech/UCLA/MPS/DLR/IDA.

must have formed from the convective upwelling of mantle material. The presence of sodium carbonate identified at a level of 5–10 vol.% (Zambon *et al.*, 2017) brings additional constraints on the properties of its source. Based on preliminary geochemical modeling, it should have a temperature in excess of 255 K (Castillo-Rogez *et al.*, 2019). This is consistent with the inference of a weak rheological response of the upper mantle to topographic loading, which Fu *et al.* (2017) interpreted as evidence of a few percent of fluids mixed with the rock (pore fluids), although there is no robust constraint on the fraction of fluid abundance.

Brine-driven emplacement of material is not the only form of volcanism suggested at Ceres. The surface exhibits other large domes whose shapes can be explained by the relaxation of features that originally looked like Ahuna Mons (Fig. 8.4) (Sori *et al.*, 2018). These are explained by cryovolcanism, i.e., the extrusion of ice-rich material. The age estimates for these features cover a wide range, suggesting cryovolcanic

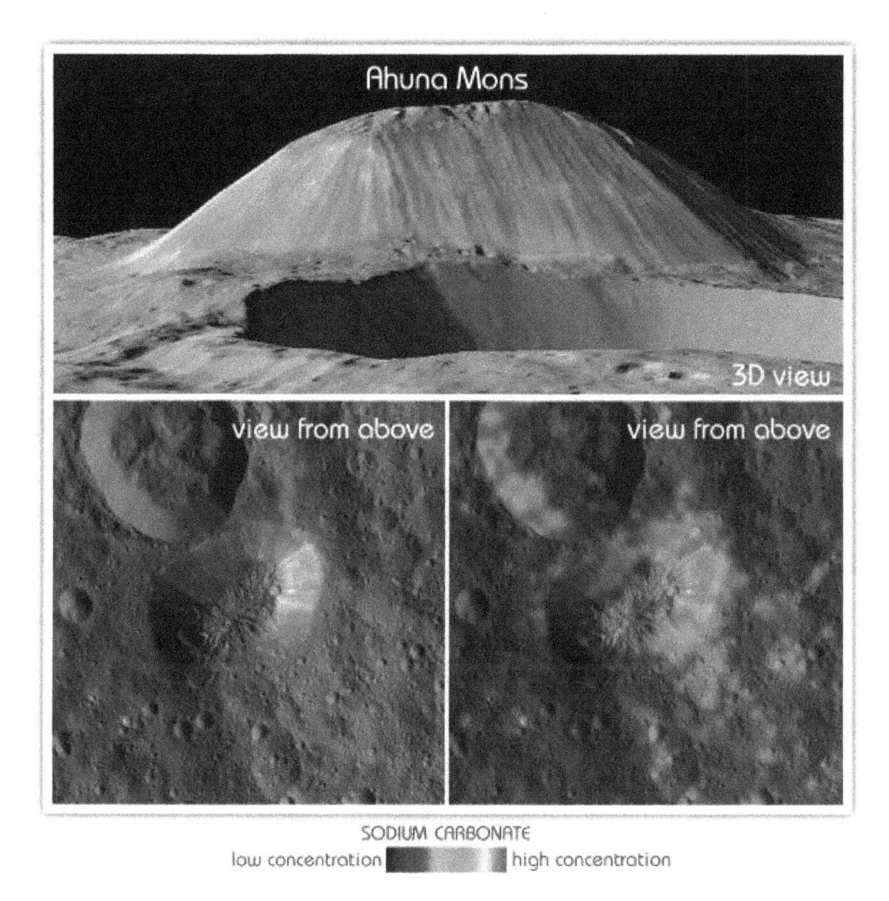

Figure 8.2: Ahuna Mons is a 17-km-wide, 4- to 5-km-tall mountain whose flanks display sodium carbonate. The crater found right next to the mons is much older and is not related to its emplacement. Ahuna Mons is located at 10.46° S, 315.8° E. Credit: NASA/JPL-Caltech/UCLA/MPS/DLR/IDA/ASI/INAF, PIA21919 https://photojournal.jpl.nasa.gov/catalog/PIA21919.

activity has been ongoing throughout the dwarf planet's history. The inferred average extrusion rate (10^4 m^3/yr) is significant, but still orders of magnitude less than the silicate volcanism rates inferred for terrestrial planets. An alternative explanation for the dome formation is via differential loading, that is, the redistribution of material heterogeneities (density, strength) in the crust following impact produced heating (Bland *et al.*, 2019). Based on analogy with salt diapirs on Earth, this mechanism could

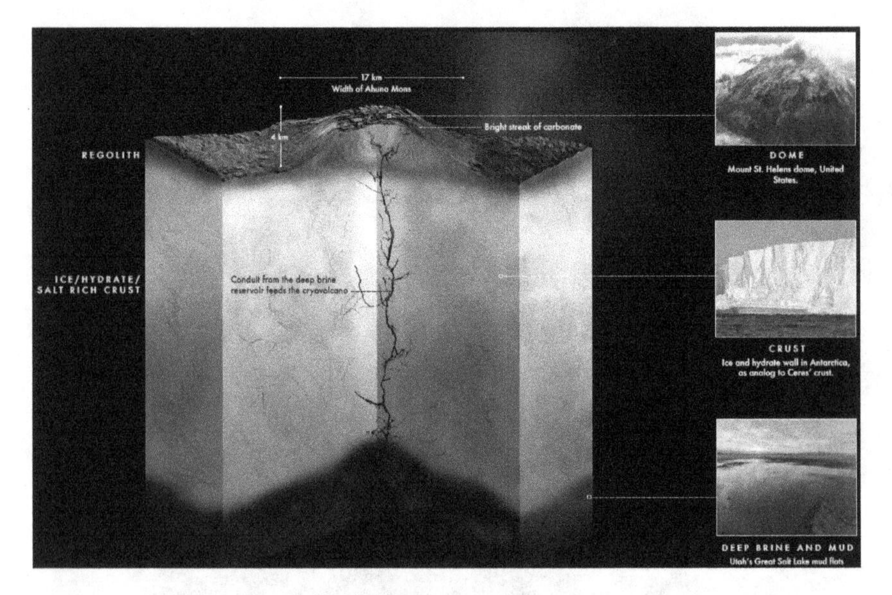

Figure 8.3: Subsurface structure inferred for Ahuna Mons from combining geology, composition, and gravity data. Credit: Raoul Ranoa.

explain why geological activity persisted on Ceres despite limited internal heat sources.

8.2 Occator Crater

Ceres exhibits one geological region where brine effusion occurred recently, less than 20 million years and potentially less than 2 million years ago: the Cerealia, Pasola, and Vinalia Faculae in Occator crater (Fig. 8.5). These features are dominated by sodium carbonate, with evidence for ammonium chlorides (Raponi *et al.*, 2019). Hydrohalite (hydrate sodium chloride $NaCl.2H_2O$) was also found at the top of the central dome in Cerealia Facula, called Cerealia Tholus (De Sanctis *et al.*, 2020).

Cerealia Facula is a ~12-km-diameter evaporite site located in a ~900-m-deep pit at the center of Occator crater. The center of the facula is occupied by a ~600-m-high mountain, Cerealia Tholus. The tholus is dominated by sodium carbonate, but shows a compositional gradient with increasing amounts of chlorides toward its summit (De Sanctis *et al.*, 2020). The facula is encompassed by a network of concentric fractures.

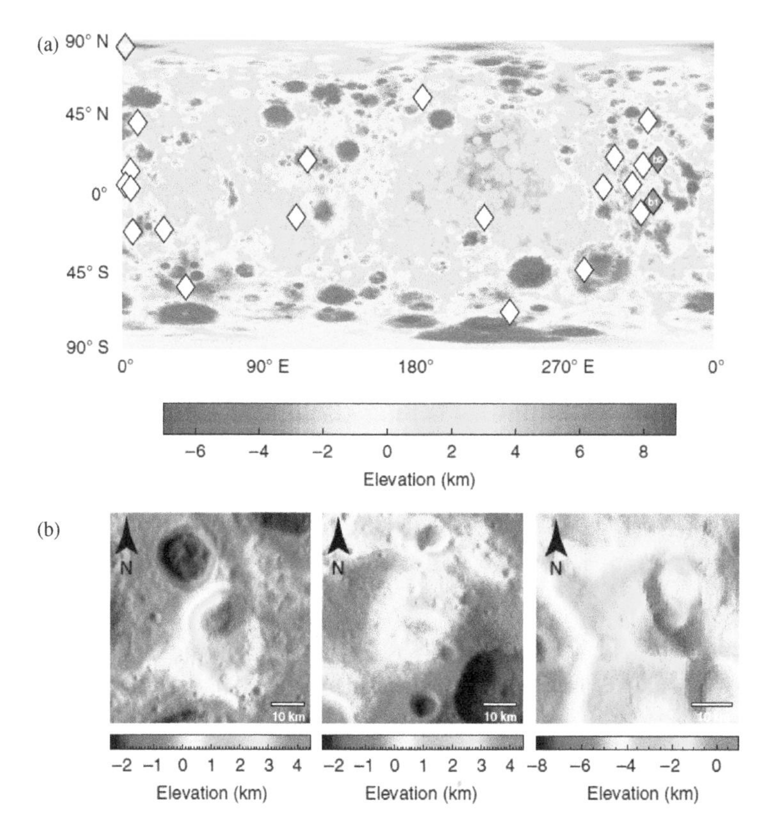

Figure 8.4: (a) Locations of large domes identified by Sori *et al.* (2018) (b) Elevation for Ahuna Mons (left, red diamond in a), a dome in Begbalel crater (violet diamond in a), Yamor Mons (right, blue diamond in a). Reprinted from Sori *et al.* (2018). Copyright with permission from Springer Nature.

Pasola Facula is a ~3-kilometer-large bright area that overlooks the center of Occator crater (Figs. 8.5 and 8.6) from about 400 m altitude. The top of Cerealia Tholus displays extension fractures that are likely the expression of volume increase as a result of the freezing of the impact melt (Scully *et al.*, 2019; Quick *et al.*, 2019). The origin of Pasola Facula is not understood, but it could be the local expression of a brine channel connected to the deep source common to Cerealia and Vinalia Faculae (Scully *et al.*, 2020).

The Vinalia Faculae are a dozen or so bright deposits found on the eastern side of Occator's floor (Fig. 8.5). Some are found on top of the

Figure 8.5: Occator crater is 92 km in diameter. It is located at center latitude of 19.82° N and center longitude of 239.33° E. This picture shows the various faculae found on its floor: Cerealia Facula and Pasola Facula in the center and Vinalia Faculae on the east side. Credit: NASA/JPL-Caltech/UCLA/MPS/DLR/IDA, PIA19889 https://photojournal.jpl.nasa.gov/catalog/PIA19889.

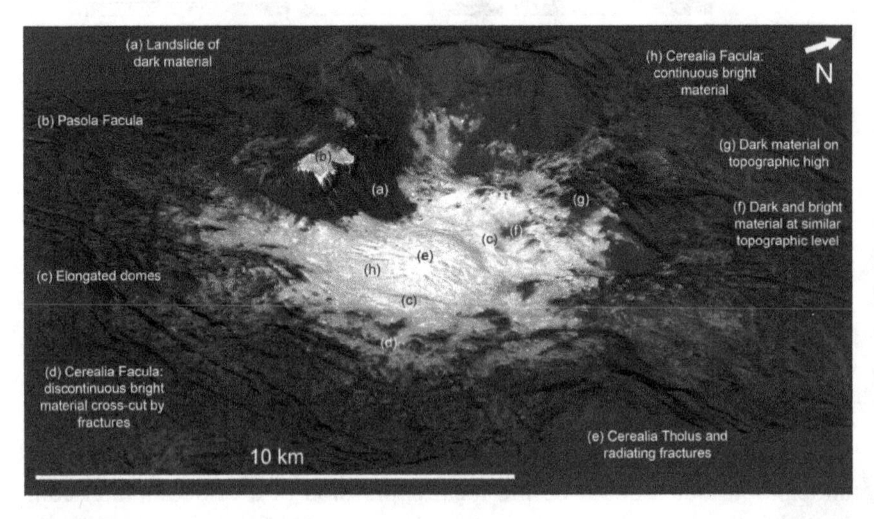

Figure 8.6: Cerealia Facula is a ~12-km-large feature at the center of Occator crater surrounded by concentric fractures. Pasola Facula is perched on the western side of Cerealia Facula. Reprinted from Scully *et al.* (2020). Copyright with permission from Springer Nature.

lobate deposits, while the largest salt deposits in that region extend along the major fractures crossing the floor of Occator (Fig. 8.7). At least one vent has been suggested to be at the source of ballistic deposits (Ruesch *et al.*, 2019) (Fig. 8.7). However, it has also been suggested that the evaporite was exposed following impact-produced melting (Schenk *et al.*, 2019, 2020). The thin salt layers found in this region, in comparison to the thick layers found in Cerealia Facula, indicate that the source of the Vinalia Faculae was limited in extent or more difficult to access than the source of Cerealia Facula (Scully *et al.*, 2020).

While the detailed history of the emplacement of the faculae is a work in progress and might not be entirely resolved with available data, key findings have emerged from the extensive dataset returned in the course of the Dawn mission. First, Cerealia Facula sits in a central pit that is expected to form shortly following the crater formation in an ice-rich target (Schenk *et al.*, 2019a, 2020). Hence, the Dawn observations offered the first up-close characterization of a type of feature expected on icy moons. Also, combined observations and modeling established the role of an impact-produced melt chamber in driving activity, at least in the first stage of the facula emplacement (Scully *et al.*, 2019; Hesse and Castillo-Rogez, 2019). The chamber's lifetime is unknown and it is likely that it

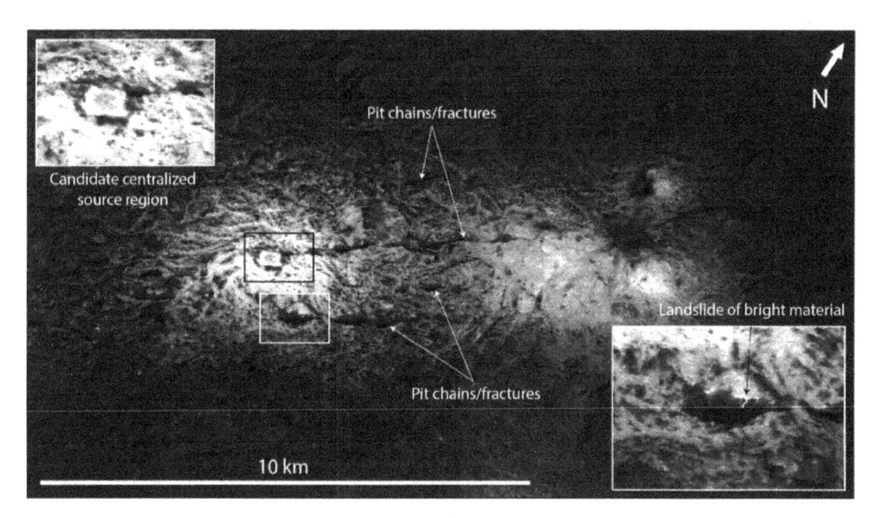

Figure 8.7: Characteristics of the main Vinalia Faculae located along large fractures on the eastern size of Occator crater's floor. Reprinted from Scully *et al.* (2020). Copyright with permission from Springer Nature.

mostly froze <10 million years after crater formation. However, Hesse and Castillo-Rogez (2019) pointed out that this chamber could potentially connect with the deep brine reservoir depending on the thermophysical properties of the crust, the original chamber size, and the temperature at the base of the crust. Considering the aforementioned constraints on a basal temperature of 255 K in recent history, the melt chamber likely reached the deep brine reservoir shortly after formation (Raymond *et al.*, 2020). These findings establish the role of impact-produced heat in providing energy to a body with an otherwise limited energy supply, with implications for many other bodies in the outer solar system.

The origin of the faculae, from a deep brine reservoir or impact-produced chamber, remained debated until the Dawn XM2 phase returned high-resolution images, gravity data, and compositional information of Occator crater's floor. In particular, the discovery of hydrohalite on Cerealia Tholus was interpreted as evidence for recent or even ongoing activity as that material is expected to dehydrate on Ceres's airless and relatively warm surface on a 1000 year timescale (De Sanctis *et al.*, 2020). Furthermore, the Vinalia Faculae are too far from the impact melt chamber, limited in extent to about ~10 km diameter below Cerealia Facula, to feed from that source (Scully *et al.*, 2020). In the nearby Cerealia Facula, Raymond *et al.* (2020) identified the occurrence of mounds in association with extensional fractures, which suggests a deep fracture network connected to a deep brine reservoir. Lastly, gravity data up to degree 45 (Park *et al.*, 2020) resolved fine lateral density variations between the crater region and its surrounding, which have been interpreted as variations in the geometry of a brine-rich region in the lower region of Ceres's crust (Raymond *et al.*, 2020). Integrating pieces of information acquired throughout the Dawn mission led to the subsurface structure sketched in Fig. 8.8.

8.3 Origin of Bright Deposits Across Ceres

Sodium carbonate is frequently found on Ceres, concentrated in a dozen sites on the surface (Carrozzo *et al.*, 2018) (Fig. 8.9). These are generally associated with recent impact craters, such as Oxo, Haulani, and Occator (see Chapter 4). The carbonate composition varies between sites: it is mainly sodium carbonate, but a few places, like Kupalo, exhibit Ca/Mg carbonates instead. These variations in composition likely reflect heterogeneities in the source of the carbonates or they may result from local

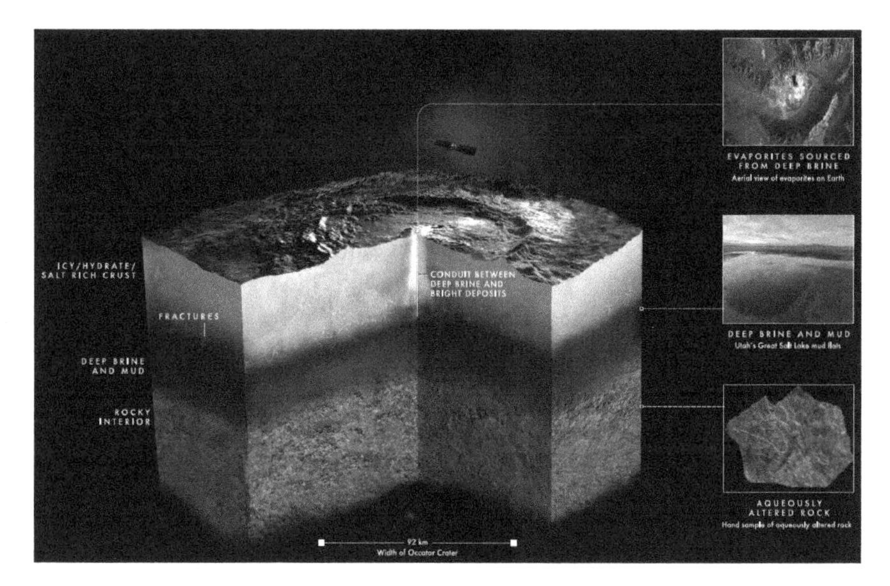

Figure 8.8: Subsurface structure of Occator crater inferred from the Dawn XM2 observations. This sketch shows an impact-produced melt chamber (now frozen) whose geometry is based on the numerical simulations by Bowling *et al.* (2019) and is expected to thermally connect with a deep brine reservoir (Hesse and Castillo-Rogez, 2019). Fractures introduced by the impact created channels between the deep brine reservoir and the surface that fed the faculae over the long term (Quick *et al.* 2019). From Castillo-Rogez *et al.* (2020).

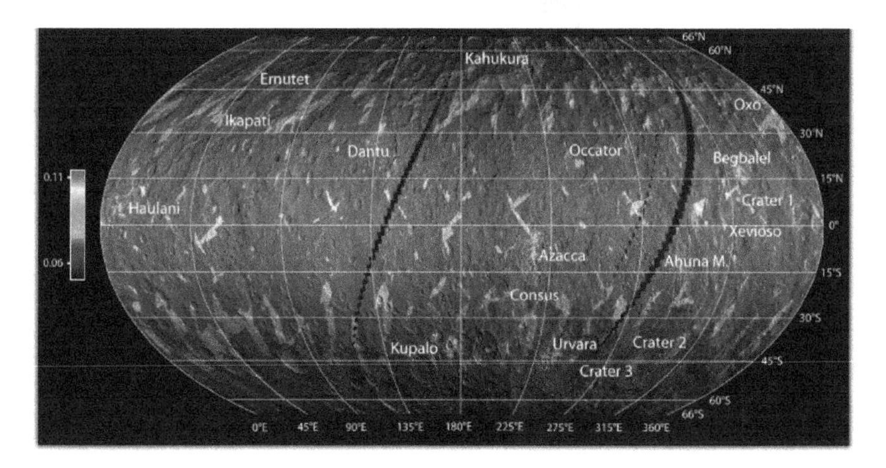

Figure 8.9: Distribution and intensity of the carbonate absorption in VIR data obtained with a ground sampling distance of 1.86 km globally. The carbonate-rich sites are primarily associated with large craters and recent craters. Ahuna mons is the only carbonate-rich landform whose emplacement does not appear related to an impact. Reprinted from Carrozzo *et al.* (2018). Copyright with permission from AAAS.

chemical processing triggered by specific crater formation circumstances. While this is still a work in progress, explaining these variations has the potential to bring important constraints on Ceres's crustal and upper mantle composition.

Besides the large bright regions that show a strong carbonate signature in the VIR data, Stein *et al.* (2017) also reported about 300 bright areas on Ceres at the resolution of the low-altitude mapping orbit (35 m/pixel). Although compositional interpretation is missing for most of these features, they are likely made of carbonates as well, or at least of salts. These areas are generally associated with impact craters, either on the floor and ejecta, or on crater walls, exposed via mass wasting (e.g., landslides). Bright regions against the dark background must have been emplaced relatively recently (tens of million years); otherwise, lateral mixing with dark material scattered via micrometeorites leads to the darkening of these features and eventual disappearance (Thangjam *et al.*, 2018). Hence, exposure of bright material, either via impacts or mass wasting, is an ongoing process on Ceres (Fig. 8.10).

The amount of carbonates found on Ceres's surface suggests this material is abundant in the subsurface, for example, in the form of lenses in the shallow subsurface. However, Stein *et al.* (2017) pointed out that shallow carbonate lenses were likely erased by gardening and lateral mixing over a timescale of a few 100 million years. Hence, recent exposures of carbonate outcrops, which can be tens of km long, require a mechanism for carbonate to be replenished in the shallow subsurface in recent time. Two general explanations have been suggested by Stein *et al.* (2017) (Fig. 8.11): (a) impacts generated melt that locally mobilized salts trapped in the crust and concentrated them upon freezing; (b) subsurface brines represent a long-term source of material transferred following the creation

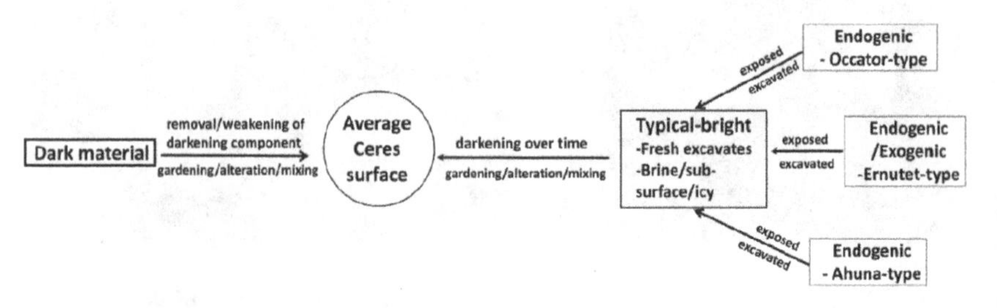

Figure 8.10: Summary of how lateral mixing alters material brightness over time. Reprinted from Thangjam *et al.* (2018). Copyright with permission from Wiley-VCH Verlag GmbH & Co. KGaA.

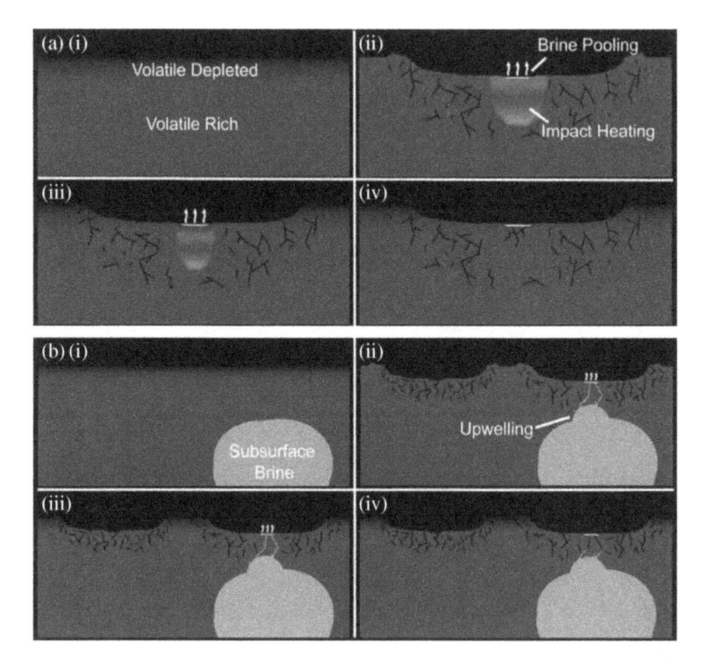

Figure 8.11: The two mechanisms proposed by Stein *et al.* (2019) for explaining the exposure of concentrated salt-rich material on Ceres's surface. Top panels (a) heating generated by an impact produces a local pocket of melt that is a mixture of water, salts, and rock particles. Following exposure, the water ice sublimates, leaving an evaporite. Bottom panels (b) brine pockets present in the crust upwell material either as a consequence of freezing-induced stresses and/or the opening of fractures generated by an impact. Reprinted from Stein *et al.* (2017). Copyright with permission from Elsevier.

of fractures. As shown at Occator crater, it is possible that the two mechanisms acted simultaneously and sequentially, at least in large craters. Stresses generated by the freezing of the melt chamber could drive the exposure of material up to the surface (Neveu and Desch 2015; Quick *et al.*, 2019).

In summary, the above observations have led to the startling conclusion that the dwarf planet Ceres is a geologically active world. The quest for identifying a mechanism capable of mobilizing subsurface material is stimulating a whole new class of interior evolution models (e.g., convecting muddy ocean, Travis *et al.*, 2018) that seek to explain physiochemical conditions within the interior, and their expression on the surface in the form of carbonates and other salts.

References

Bland, M. T., *et al.* (2019). Dome formation on Ceres by solid-state flow analogous to terrestrial salt tectonics, *Nat. Geosci.* **12**, 797–801.

Bowling, T. J., Ciesla, F. J., Davison, T. M., Scully, J. E. C., Castillo-Rogez, J. C. and Marchi, S. (2019). Post-impact thermal structure and cooling timescales of Occator crater on asteroid 1 Ceres. *Icarus*, **320**, 110–118.

Carrozzo, F. G., *et al.* (2018). Nature, formation, and distribution of carbonates on Ceres. *Sci. Adv.*, **4**, e1701645.

Castillo-Rogez, J. C., *et al.* (2019). Conditions for the long-term preservation of a deep brine reservoir in Ceres. *Geophys. Res. Lett.*, **46**, 1963–1972.

De Sanctis, M. C., *et al.* (2020). Recent fresh emplacement of hydrated sodium chloride on Ceres from ascending salty fluids. *Nat. Astron*, **4**, 786–793.

Ermakov, A. I., *et al.* (2017). Constraints on Ceres' internal structure and evolution from its shape and gravity measured by the Dawn spacecraft. *J. Geophys. Res. Planets*, **122**, 2267–2293.

Fu, R., *et al.* (2017). The interior structure of Ceres as revealed by surface topography. *Earth Planet. Sci. Lett.*, **476**, 153–164.

Hesse, M. and Castillo-Rogez, J. C. (2019). Thermal evolution of the impact-induced cryomagma chamber beneath occator crater on Ceres. *Geophys. Res. Lett.*, **46**, 1213–1221.

Neveu, M. and Desch, S. J. (2015). Geochemistry, thermal evolution, and cryovolcanism on Ceres with a muddy mantle. *Geophys. Res. Lett.*, **42**, 10,197. 10,206.

Park, R. S., *et al.* (2020). Evidence of non-uniform crust of Ceres from Dawn's high-resolution gravity data. *Nat. Astron*, **4**, 748–755.

Quick, L., *et al.* (2019). A possible brine reservoir below Occator Crater: Thermal and compositional evolution and formation of the Cerealia Dome and Vinalia Faculae. *Ceres Occator Special Issue of Icarus*, **320**, 119–135.

Raponi, A., *et al.* (2019). Mineralogy of Occator crater on Ceres and insight into its evolution from the properties of carbonates, phyllosilicates, and chlorides. *Icarus*, **320**, 83–96.

Raymond, C. A., *et al.* (2020). Impact-driven mobilization of deep crustal brines on dwarf planet Ceres. *Nat. Astron*, **4**, 741–747.

Ruesch, O., *et al.* (2016). Cryovolcanism on Ceres. *Science*, **353**, aaf4286.

Ruesch, O., *et al.* (2019). Slurry extrusion on Ceres from a convective mud-bearing mantle. *Nat. Geosci.*, **12**, 505–509.

Scully, J. E. C., *et al.* (2019). Synthesis of the special issue: The formation and evolution of Ceres' Occator crater. *Icarus*, **320**, 213–225.

Scully, J. E. C., *et al.* (2020). Formation of the bright faculae in Ceres' Occator crater via long-lived brine effusion in a hydrothermal system. *Nat. Comm*, **11**, 3680.

Schenk, P., *et al.* (2019). The central pit and dome at Cerealia Facula bright deposit and floor deposits in Occator crater, Ceres: Morphology, comparisons and formation. *Icarus*, **320**, 159–187.
Schenk, P., *et al.* (2020). Impact heat driven volatile redistribution at Occator crater on Ceres as a comparative planetary process. *Nat. Commun.*, **11**, article id. 3679.
Sori, M. M., *et al.* (2018). Cryovolcanic rates on Ceres revealed by topography. *Nat. Astron.*, **2**, 946–950.
Stein, N. T., *et al.* (2017). The formation and evolution of bright spots on Ceres. *Icarus*, **320**, 188–201.
Thangjam, G., *et al.* (2018). Spectral properties and geology of bright and dark material on dwarf planet Ceres. *Meteorit. Planet. Sci.*, **53**, 1961–1982.
Travis, B. J., Bland, P. A., Feldman, W. C. and Sykes, M. (2018). Hydrothermal dynamics in a CM-based model of Ceres. *Meteorit. Planet. Sci.*, **53**, 2008–2032.
Zambon, F., *et al.* (2017). Spectral analysis of Ahuna Mons mission's visible-infrared spectrometer. *Geophys. Res. Lett.*, **44**, 97–104.

Chapter 9

Astrobiological Significance

The Dawn mission has revolutionized our understanding of Ceres in the same decade that has also seen the rise of ocean worlds as a research focus. The most significant findings from the Dawn mission are unambiguous evidence for oceanic material exhibited on Ceres's surface, evidence for high concentrations of organics (Ernutet region; De Sanctis *et al.*, 2017, 2019), as well as features indicative of recent brine effusion. Dawn's observations confirmed earlier predictions for a volatile-rich crust encompassing the bulk of the frozen ocean, and a warm and liquid-bearing interior, akin to the icy moons of the outer solar system (Fig. 9.1). The prospect that a relict ocean may have survived into the present led to Ceres's classification as a "candidate" ocean world in the Roadmap to Ocean Worlds (Hendrix *et al.*, 2019). Past and ongoing material transfer from the deep interior to the surface makes Ceres very interesting for astrobiology-driven exploration. The recent exposure of deep material provides a window into the conditions in Ceres's deep brine and allows testing hypotheses of importance to ocean worlds (e.g., evolution of organics and long-term preservation of chemical gradients).

9.1 Ceres's Past Habitability Potential

Current knowledge indicates that Ceres once had water, organic building blocks for life, energy sources, and gradients in redox (which determines the exchange of electrons between species), and perhaps still does at present (Fig. 9.2). Castillo-Rogez *et al.* (2020) explored the constraints obtained on Ceres's habitability potential from the Dawn observations. Upon comparison with other water-rich bodies, these authors concluded

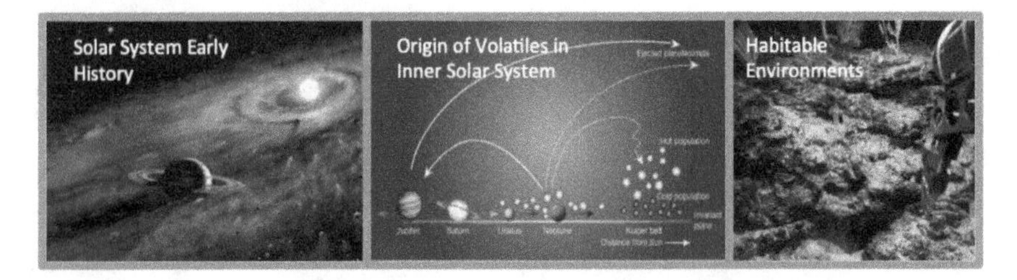

Figure 9.1: Ceres bears multiple connections to astrobiology themes. The dwarf planet is representative of large planetesimals that became involved in planetary formation. Hence, processes that occurred early on Ceres-like bodies, e.g., organic matter processing in a hydrothermal environment, could influence the composition of planets. Ceres is a likely representative of the population of planetesimals that supplied water and organic matter to the inner solar system. Lastly, Ceres likely harbored habitable conditions throughout its history and potentially at present.

Figure 9.2: Ceres's surface displays pervasive evidence for indicators of the occurrence of habitable conditions in Ceres's past and at present: (a) global internal differentiation, (b) diverse salt composition at many sites throughout the surface, (c) local abundance of organic compounds, (d) ice-rich crust, (e) recent cryovolcanic activity, (f) potentially ongoing extrusion of brines in Occator crater. Reprinted from Castillo-Rogez *et al.* (2020). Copyright with permission from Mary Ann Liebert, Inc.

that Ceres was potentially habitable throughout its history, commencing directly after accretion with a global ocean in which advanced chemistry could develop. This global ocean could have been maintained for billions of years (Travis *et al.*, 2018). Most of Ceres's surface properties record the consequences of that early period, while contemporary activity is evident in a few places. Lastly, impacts likely played a major role in creating transient melt chambers in Ceres's water-rich crust, as is currently demonstrated by the faculae in Occator Crater (Fig. 8.9), which require access to a vast chamber of brines (Hesse and Castillo-Rogez, 2019). Similarly, large impacts could bring into solution organics present in the regolith and introduce chemical (redox) gradients, producing potentially habitable environments evolving over a few million years.

Conditions in the early ocean, detailed in Chapter 4, indicate Ceres's surface material formed in an alkaline environment, with a pH between 7 and 11. Temperature had to be less than 50°C in the ocean for the exchange of ammonium and cations in clay interlayers to proceed (Neveu *et al.*, 2017). These conditions are of interest when searching for habitable environments (e.g., Hand *et al.*, 2017 and references therein). Ceres also displays evidence for carbon, nitrogen, hydrogen, and oxygen (Chapter 4), and the presence of sulfur is inferred from ultraviolet observations (Hendrix *et al.*, 2016). Carbon is present in multiple forms: carbonates, organic compounds (aliphatic chains, at least), and amorphous carbon (Marchi *et al.*, 2019). It is also suggested to be present in the form of CO_2 and potentially CH_4 in gas hydrates (Castillo-Rogez *et al.*, 2018). This diversity likely reflects some geochemical cycle inside Ceres. Ceres likely accreted CO_2 and CO ices, which are abundant in the outer solar system and were suggested as the basis for the formation of carbonates inside Ceres (Castillo-Rogez *et al.*, 2018). A fraction of CO_2 could be trapped in clathrate forms since the conditions were met inside Ceres (Chapter 7). The destabilization of clathrate hydrates upon impacting could release gas driving cryovolcanic activity (Quick *et al.*, 2019). It is also likely that Ceres accreted a large fraction of organics that were subject to processing in hydrothermal conditions, as has been inferred from the observations of carbonaceous chondrites (e.g., Vinogradoff *et al.*, 2017; Oba *et al.*, 2020). A part of the soluble organic compounds was likely associated with silicates during the differentiation of a rocky mantle, based on observations of carbonaceous chondrites (e.g., Le Guillou *et al.*, 2014). Furthermore, nitrogen-rich organics (e.g., amino acids) could represent a source of ammonia as a result of desorption under pressures of the order of 100 MPa and a few 100 degrees C (e.g., Pizzarello *et al.*, 2012), conditions that are relevant to Ceres. Whether or not organics are the source of the ammonium found on Ceres's surface is an open question at this time. It is not known if organic compounds could form from smaller molecules inside Ceres, an important question for a future mission to address. In summary, available observations suggest Ceres's geodynamical evolution, even if it was limited in time, could lead to the redistribution and potentially the processing of carbon-based ices and organic compounds.

9.2 Ceres's Current Habitability Potential

As described in Chapter 8, Ceres displays evidence for ongoing exposure of material on its surface (De Sanctis *et al.*, 2020). This suggests the existence of deep-seated brines, at least locally. The mineralogy found at Occator crater suggests an alkaline environment, likely a residual layer evolved from the global ocean inferred in its early history. The temperature of that brine is unknown though. The mineralogy points to at least 245 K and it could be in excess of 255 K (Castillo-Rogez *et al.*, 2019). The exposure of Ahuna Mons, some 100–200 million years ago, in a region far from Occator crater, supports the idea introduced by Fu *et al.* (2017) that a deep brine layer may be present on a global scale. A major difference between Occator faculae and Ahuna Mons is that in the former case, brine effusion is directly associated with fractures. That is, the fractures likely provided a pathway for the deep-seated brines, the latter being under pressure as a result of crustal freezing (Neveu and Desch, 2015). On the other hand, Ahuna Mons is not associated with any apparent fractures, which suggests a more active mechanism for its emplacement. The possibility that fractures in that region have been concealed as a consequence of lateral mixing is unclear considering billion-year-old fractures are found in other places on Ceres (Scully *et al.*, 2017). Higher spatial resolution gravity data might be able to resolve this conundrum.

The nature of the residual fluid in the upper mantle is partially constrained; it could include sodium and potassium chloride brines as suggested by geochemical modeling (Neveu and Desch, 2015; Castillo-Rogez *et al.*, 2018). The brines likely correspond to residual liquid from the freezing of the global ocean. The eutectic temperature of that brine could be as low as about 220 K (Castillo-Rogez *et al.*, 2018). Ammonia could also be present and decrease the eutectic further. However, the widespread occurrence of ammonium both in the form of clays and salts on Ceres's surface indicates that these formed in an environment where ammonia was a minor component. Following Le Chatelier's Principle, a large part of the ammonia could be turned into ammonium since the latter was removed from the medium, either by exchange with cations in clays or by salt precipitation.

Another important parameter defining habitability is the occurrence of chemical gradients (e.g., redox disequilibrium) expressed in pairs of electron donors and receivers in the deep brine (Fig. 9.3). Long-lived oceans are expected to reach chemical equilibrium, i.e., chemical activity stops by lack of compounds that can react with each other. However, Ceres displays chemical species that are oxidizing or reducing in nature, suggesting that chemical gradients in Ceres's brines were long-lived and may still be present.

Several processes could maintain chemical gradients or shift redox conditions throughout Ceres's history (Castillo-Rogez *et al*., 2020). This is emerging work intended to explain how ocean worlds, Europa in particular, could maintain habitable conditions in its deep ocean over the long term. Three processes are under study, detailed below: (1) radiolysis of water by the decay of long-lived radioisotopes; (2) fluids released from thermal metamorphism of the rocky mantle; and (3) introduction of redox gradients into the crust via impacts and mantle intrusions.

The radioactive decay of long-lived radioisotopes in the mantle or potassium-40 in the ocean can produce local redox gradients and form multiple products (Le Caer, 2011) that can act as electron acceptors. These include H_2O_2, and OH, as well as H_2 which can be an electron donor

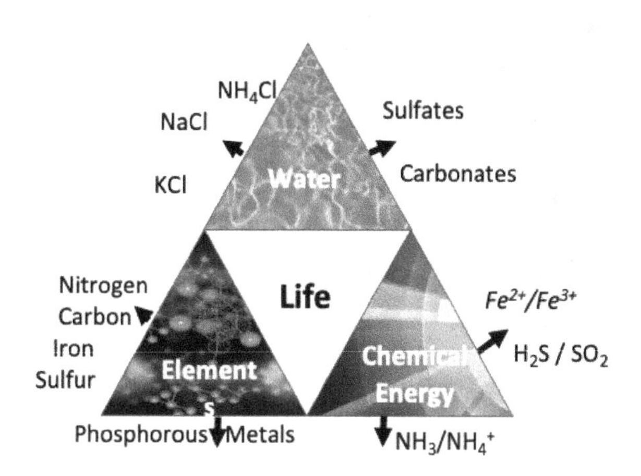

Figure 9.3: Key compounds found on Ceres's surface or suspected to exist based on geochemical modeling and their relationships to the key pillars defining habitability for life.

(see Fig. 9.4). Radiolysis is an important energy source in subsurface environments on Earth, as it maintains redox gradient availability to microbial life (Holland *et al.*, 2013). For example, presently, tens of billions of moles of hydrogen per year are produced globally via radiolysis in the continental shield crust alone (Sherwood Lollar *et al.*, 2014).

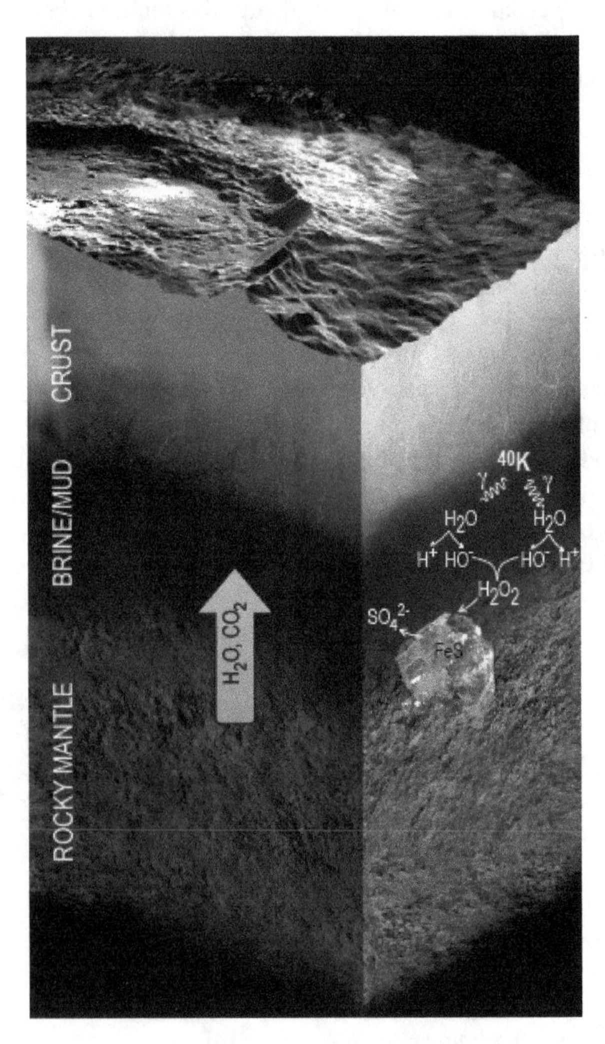

Figure 9.4: Illustration of two processes that may affect the long-term chemistry of covered oceans: water radiolysis by long-lived radioisotope decay and the release of volatiles from the mantle as a consequence of thermal metamorphism (based after Altair *et al.*, 2018). Credit: Raoul Ranoa.

Following the method of Bouquet *et al.* (2017), Castillo-Rogez *et al.* (2020) show that 0.017 nanomoles/yr of H_2 per liter of water, 0.02 nanomoles/yr/l of H_2O_2, and 0.04 nanomoles/yr/l of OH could be produced in Ceres's porous mantle at present. On early Ceres and other bodies, radiolysis could augment other chemical redox reactions and maintain habitability of such an environment long after the initial chemical gradients would have been exhausted (Onstott *et al.*, 1997, 2019; Altair *et al.*, 2018).

Thermal metamorphism is expected to occur in the rocky mantles of large water-rich bodies, including Ceres (e.g., Castillo-Rogez and McCord, 2010). That process has not been properly modeled until recently though. Heating of a mixture of phyllosilicates, carbonates, and organics under moderate pressure leads to a change in petrology and the release of fluids, for example, water released from the structure of clays and serpentine and carbon dioxide produced from the breakdown of carbonates. These fluids are oxidizing and their transfer (partial or total) to the top of the mantle can have two consequences. If a residual ocean is still present during the period of thermal metamorphism, these fluids introduce oxidants into the residual ocean. If the ocean is entirely frozen, then metamorphism contributes to the late formation of a deep ocean. The newly formed ocean might freeze partially or entirely, depending on the timing and duration of the metamorphism event. Melwani Daswani *et al.* (2021) suggested that the ocean of Jupiter's moon Europa could be entirely borne from the thermal evolution of a proto-Europa composed of carbonaceous material. The prospect for Ceres's hydrosphere (i.e., outer volatile-rich layer) to be the product of thermal metamorphism is a work in progress. Lastly, organics trapped in the rocky mantle may break down into smaller molecules or evolve and form oils, depending on their nature, and migrate to the ocean.

The last mechanism known to create chemical gradients is the introduction of exogenic material via impacts. Bowling *et al.* (2019) show that a large fraction of impactor material, up to 70 wt.%, could be retained in the melt chamber generated in Ceres's crust by the impact that created Occator crater. Considering that the reservoir temperature may be well over 0°C (Bowling *et al.*, 2019), aqueous alteration could be ongoing for as long (Hesse and Castillo-Rogez, 2019) (Fig. 9.5). This process could have been occurring throughout Ceres's history (Marchi *et al.*, 2019), resulting in profound changes in the crust chemistry. Moreover, large impactors (tens of kilometers) could introduce fractures that reached the liquid reservoir below the crust, as suggested for Occator crater

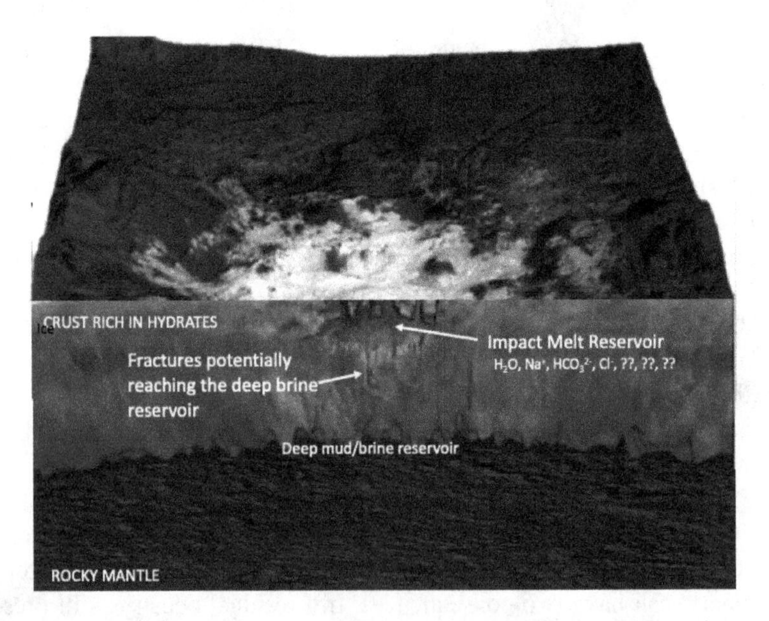

Figure 9.5: State of understanding of the crust below Occator's faculae and potential connection with a deep brine reservoir following the creation of the crater. Reprinted from Castillo-Rogez *et al.* (2020); see also Raymond *et al.* (2020). Copyright with permission from Mary Ann Liebert, Inc.

(Quick *et al.*, 2019; Raymond *et al.*, 2020). Basin-forming impactors could even reach the rocky mantle (Davison *et al.*, 2015). Hence, deep brine material could be regularly injected into the crust in the course of Ceres's history where it could introduce transient liquid pockets that may react with crustal material. The research on this topic is emerging though, so the astrobiological implications of material transfer in Ceres remain to be studied.

9.3 Ceres's Habitability Through Time

Although our knowledge of many aspects of Ceres's history is still uncertain, it is possible to lay out a general timeline of the major events that have shaped Ceres's internal evolution and determined its habitability potential. Early on in its history, Ceres underwent global melting of its volatile phase, leading to the separation and settling of a rocky mantle. During that phase, the rock was subject to aqueous alteration, leading to major changes in its mineralogy, to the enrichment of the ocean in solutes, and to the creation of a habitable environment. The ocean lasted at least ~200 million years, but a small layer could have been preserved until present thanks to the slowing freezing rate brought about by the accretion of clathrate hydrates in the crust. Still, in this evolution trajectory, the brine's eutectic temperature is expected to be <240 K for most of Ceres's history, which might be too cold even for psychrophiles (organisms that are capable of growth and reproduction in low temperatures), and other parameters quantifying habitability have not been studied. Castillo-Rogez *et al.* (2019) suggested that the temperature in the brine reservoir below Hanami Planum could be warmer because of the thicker crust in that region. This seems to be supported by the Dawn gravity data of that region (Raymond *et al.*, 2020), but requires further study.

This internal evolution history may branch to an alternative trajectory resulting from the release of vast amounts of fluids from the rocky mantle. The time frame for that event, if it happened, would probably be about 1 billion years after formation, around the peak of potassium-40 decay, when temperatures could exceed 750 K. The extent of the mineralogical transformation and the volume of material involved depend on many parameters, in particular the thermal conductivity of the rock. Rock dehydration leads to an increase in thermal conductivity by at least a factor of two, but the feedback between rock dehydration and thermal evolution remains to be modeled.

Evidence for brines inside Ceres at present, at least locally, suggests some of the aforementioned processes for slowing down heat loss or replenishing the ocean occurred in Ceres. However, further investigation is needed in order to determine whether that liquid environment survived throughout Ceres's history or was transient, and if its properties changed through time. Lastly, large impacts could create transient melt chambers and introduce pathways from the deep brine to the surface throughout Ceres's history and at present, as illustrated by the Occator faculae. In theory, the composition of material exposed via impact-produced fractures at craters of various ages could inform on the evolution of the brine composition through time. In practice, asteroid surfaces homogenize on short timescales as a consequence of infalls and lateral mixing with impact ejecta. Hence, only a few large craters still display recognizable salt deposits (see Chapters 4 and 5).

The fate of organic compounds with time is also an important topic of consideration, especially as organic compounds are found in the Ernutet crater and in the regolith. While the Ernutet organics were exposed recently (Bowling *et al.*, 2020), the timing of their emplacement in Ceres's shallow subsurface is unknown. As illustrated in Fig. 7.9, organic compounds accreted from the solar nebula were partitioned between the liquid phase and the rocky mantle. It is possible that the Ernutet organics were intrusions of organic-rich brines or oils from the mantle via fractures in the crust. However, one would expect this mechanism to act on a global scale and organics to be found at other freshly excavated sites. It is also possible that organics may be present at different depths in the crust, either due to heterogeneities in the porosity distribution or as a result of heterogeneous accretion during crustal freezing. Organic compounds trapped in the rocky mantle could be degraded as a consequence of heat and could potentially release ammonia when the temperature was a few hundreds degrees celsius (e.g., Pizzarello and Williams, 2012). Whether or not this process contributed to the ammonium salts and ammoniated clays found on Ceres's surface is unknown. Lastly, it is not possible, based on available observations, to conclude that organic synthesis took place in Ceres's long-lived ocean. The transformation of organic compounds is expected based on observations of carbonaceous chondrites and laboratory experiments (e.g., Vinogradoff *et al.*, 2017, 2018). However, the conditions were not necessarily present for large organic chains to evolve from smaller building blocks.

9.4 Relationships to Other Bodies

Examples of Ceres's relationships to other bodies are illustrated in Figs. 9.6 and 9.7. First, Ceres is akin, both in terms of density, and thus water to rock fraction, and of internal structure to some of the giant planet icy moons. Ceres's density is similar to Neptune's moon Triton (~2.06 g/cm^3), believed to be a captured Kuiper Belt Object (Agnor and Hamilton, 2006.) Furthermore, Ceres's high abundance in organic compounds, similar to some comets, has been interpreted as evidence for an origin in the far outer solar system (Marchi *et al.*, 2019).

Ceres shares geophysical similarities with other ice-rich bodies. It is similar in size to Saturn's moon Dione and Pluto's moon Charon. It has been suggested that for mid-sized (100–1000 km) icy bodies, differentiation may be partial (i.e., an iron core does not separate from a rocky mantle). In these bodies, a rocky mantle may be loosely consolidated and porous (Choblet *et al.*, 2017; Travis and Schubert, 2015; Bland and

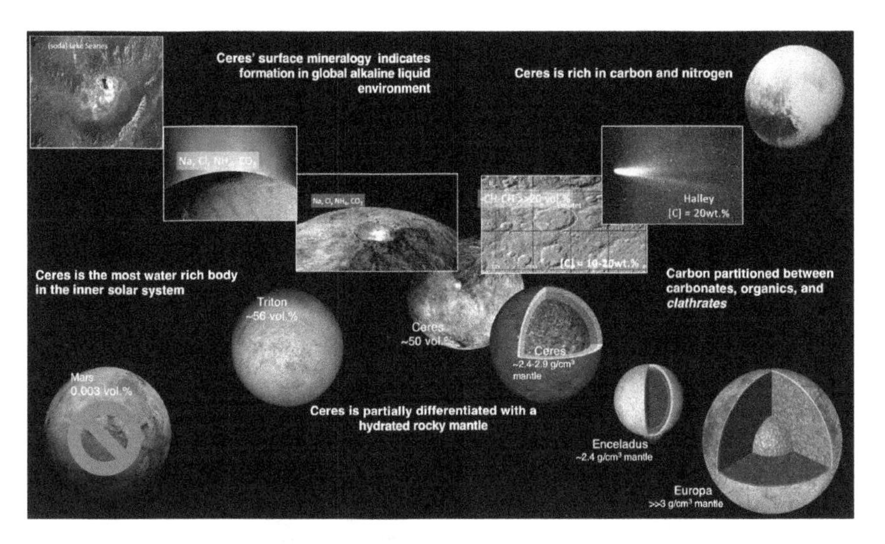

Figure 9.6: Ceres's relationships to various planetary bodies, in terms of density, interior structure, composition in key volatile elements, and alkaline chemistry.

Travis, 2017; Travis *et al.*, 2018). Hydrothermal circulation acts in keeping the interior cool. This would explain why Ceres's mantle density could be as low as 2.4 g/cm^3, similar to the density inferred for Enceladus's mantle from the gravity data returned by the Cassini mission (Iess *et al.*, 2014). Both Ceres and Enceladus show evidence for abundant carbonates (see Postberg *et al.*, 2011; Glein and Waite, 2020), which suggests these two bodies host similar liquid environments. Alkaline, "soda" lakes commonly found on Earth were formed from the injection of carbon dioxide into a liquid body, generally in connection to a volcanic region (e.g., soda lakes, Mono Lake in California's Owens Valley). Lastly, clathrate hydrates have been suggested to be abundant in the crusts of Saturn's moon Titan (Lunine and Stevenson, 1985) and Pluto (Kamata *et al.*, 2019).

Ceres could be a representative endmember for ocean worlds that are not tidally heated, similar to Callisto and potentially also Pluto (Nimmo *et al.*, 2016). Furthermore, according to its size and water abundance, Ceres belongs to a class of objects that could host a high fugacity of hydrogen, organic molecules, and alkaline conditions, as was suggested for Europa (e.g., McKinnon and Zolensky, 2003) and inferred from Cassini observations of Enceladus (Zolotov, 2007; Marion *et al.*, 2012).

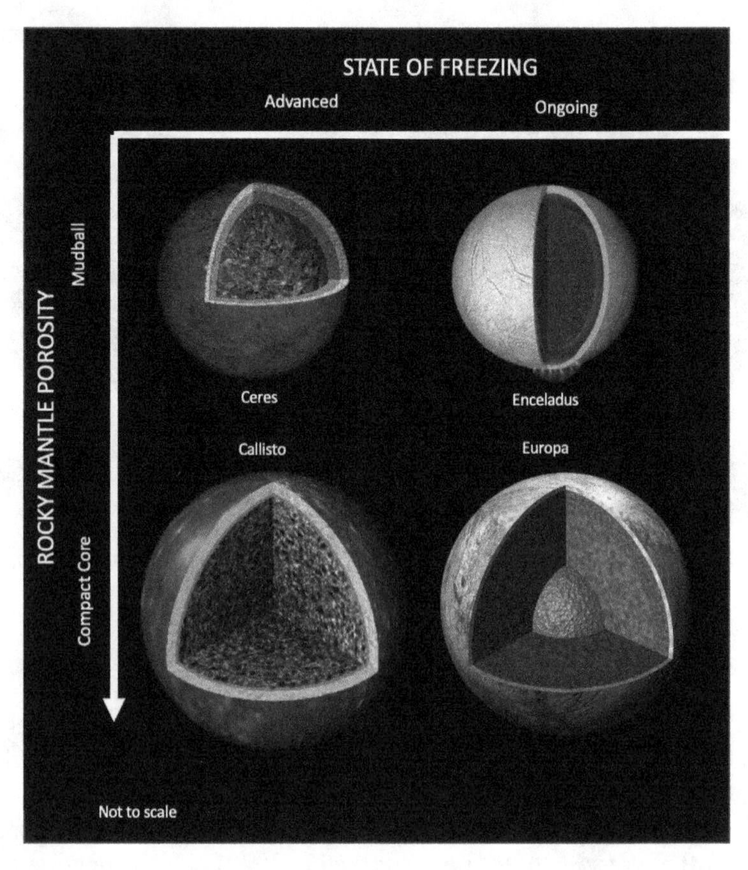

Figure 9.7: In the spectrum of ocean worlds, Ceres shares physical similarities with Enceladus and Callisto, but is radically distinct from Europa. See text for details. Reprinted from Castillo-Rogez *et al.* (2020). Copyright with permission from Springer Nature.

Lastly, Ceres likely represents a class of planetesimals formed in the outer solar system that supplied water and volatiles to the inner solar system. Recent ground-based astronomical observations revealed the existence of several objects in the main belt of asteroids that contain a large fraction of ice, in particular 10 Hygiea (Vernazza *et al.*, 2019) (Fig. 9.8), 31 Euphrosyne (Yang *et al.*, 2020), and 704 Interamnia (Hanus *et al.*, 2020). Hygiea in particular also displays evidence for carbonate on its surface (Vernazza *et al.*, 2017). It is possible these bodies formed in the same accretional environment. Recent models indicate that several Ceres-sized bodies could form in the outer solar system (Johansen *et al.*, 2015)

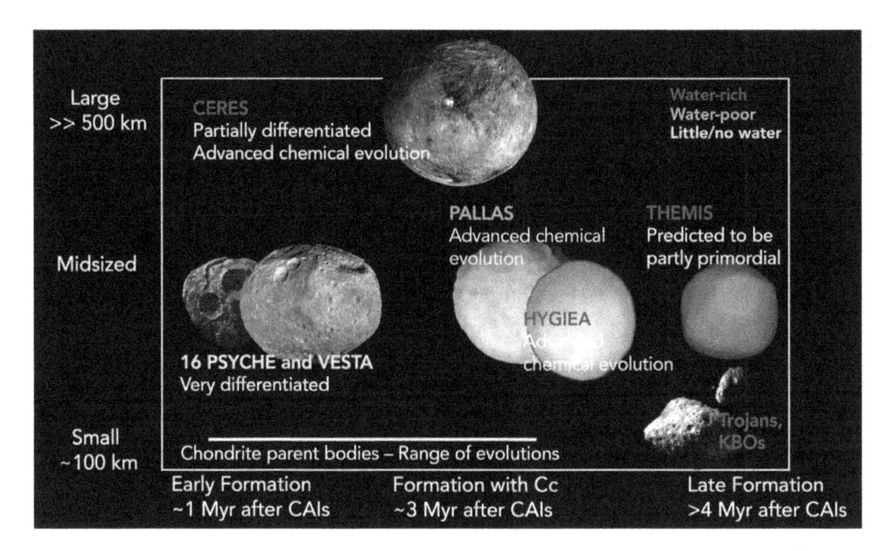

Figure 9.8: Geophysical and compositional observations from space missions and large astronomical facilities have revealed that internal differentiation is a common feature of large asteroids and protoplanets. Reprinted from Neumann *et al.* (2014) for Vesta, Marsset *et al.* (2020) for Pallas, Vernazza *et al.* (2020) for Hygiea.

and could have been involved in bringing volatiles to Earth (Budde *et al.*, 2019) or were involved in catastrophic disruption in the inner solar system (Canup and Salmon, 2018).

As per thermal models, Ceres is likely a "relict" ocean world, i.e., with a residual ocean or regional seas. However, it is also possible that the late release of fluids from the rocky mantle as a result of thermal metamorphism could replenish the residual brine chemistry or even create a late global liquid layer at the base of the crust. The implications of that event, if it happened, remain to be investigated. Processes suggested to take place in mid-sized and large icy moons, like Europa or Triton, could be investigated at Ceres in order to help assess the habitability potential of these bodies.

References

Agnor, C. and Hamilton, D. (2006). Neptune's capture of its moon Triton in a binary–planet gravitational encounter. *Nature*, **441**, 192–194.

Altair, T., de Avellar, M. G. B., Rodrigues, F. and Galante, D. (2018). Microbial habitability of Europa sustained by radioactive sources. *Sci. Rep.*, **8**, 260.

Bland, P. A. and Travis, B. J. (2017). Giant convecting mud balls of the early solar system. *Sci. Adv.*, **3**, e1602514.

Bouquet, A. Glein, C. R., Wyrick, D. and Waite, J. H. (2017). Alternative energy: Production of H_2 by radiolysis of water in the rocky cores of icy bodies. *Astrophys. J. Lett.*, **840**, L8.

Bowling, T. J., Ciesla, F. J., Davison, T. M., Scully, J. E. C., Castillo-Rogez, J. C. and Marchi, S. (2019). Post-impact thermal structure and cooling timescales of Occator Crater on Asteroid 1 Ceres. *Icarus*, **320**, 110–118.

Bowling, T. J., Johnson, B. C., Marchi, S., De Sanctis, M. C., Castillo-Rogez, J. C. and Raymond, C. A. (2020). An endogenic origin of cerean organics. *Earth Planet. Sci. Lett.*, **534**, 116069.

Budde, G., Burkhardt, C. and Kleine, T. (2019). Molybdenum isotopic evidence for the late accretion of outer Solar System material to Earth. *Nat. Astron.*, **3**, 736–741.

Canup, R. and Salmon, J. (2018). Origin of Phobos and Deimos by the impact of a Vesta-to-Ceres sized body with Mars. *Sci. Adv.*, **4**, eaar6887.

Castillo-Rogez, J. C. and McCord, T. B. (2010). Ceres' evolution and present state constrained by shape data. *Icarus*, **205**, 443–459.

Castillo-Rogez, J. C., Neveu, M., McSween, H. Y., Fu R. R., Toplis, M. J. and Prettyman, T. (2018). Insights into Ceres' evolution from surface composition. *Meteorit. Planet. Sci.*, **53**, 1820–1843.

Castillo-Rogez, J. C., *et al.* (2019). Conditions for the long-term preservation of a deep brine reservoir in Ceres. *Geophys. Res. Lett.*, **46**, 1963–1972.

Castillo-Rogez, J. C., *et al.* (2020). Ceres: Astrobiological target and possible ocean world. *Astrobiology*, **20**, 269–291.

Choblet, G., *et al.* (2017). Powering prolonged hydrothermal activity inside Enceladus. *Nat. Astron.*, **1**, 841–847.

Davison, T. M., *et al.* (2015). Impact bombardment of Ceres. 46th Lunar and Planetary Science Conference, LPI contrib. no. 1832, p. 2116.

De Sanctis, M. C., *et al.* (2017). Localized aliphatic organic material on the surface of Ceres. *Science*, **355**, 719–722.

De Sanctis, M. C., *et al.* (2019). Characteristics of organic matter on Ceres from VIR/Dawn high spatial resolution spectra. *Mon. Not. R. Astron. Soc.*, **482**, 2407–2421.

De Sanctis, M. C., *et al.* (2020). Fresh emplacement of hydrated sodium chloride on Ceres from ascending salty fluids. *Nat. Astron.*, **4**, 786–793.

Fu, R., *et al.* (2017). The interior structure of Ceres as revealed by surface topography. *Earth Planet. Sci. Lett.*, **476**, 153–164.

Glein, C. and Waite, J. H. (2020). The carbonate geochemistry of Enceladus' ocean. *Geophys. Res. Lett.*, **47**, e2019GL085885.

Hand, K. P., *et al.* (2017). Europa Lander Study 2016 Report. https://europa.nasa.gov/resources/58/europa-lander-study-2016-report/.

Hanuš, J., *et al.* (2020). (704) Interamnia: A transitional object between a dwarf planet and a typical irregular-shaped minor body. *A&A*, **633**, A65.

Hendrix, A. R., Vilas, F. and Li, J.-Y. (2016). Ceres: Sulfur deposits and graphitized carbon. *Geophys. Res. Lett.*, **43**, 1–8.

Hendrix, A. R., *et al.* (2019). The NASA roadmap to ocean worlds. *Astrobiology*, **19**, 1–27.

Hesse, M. and Castillo-Rogez, J. C. (2019). Conditions for the long-term preservation of a local brine reservoir below Occator Crater on Ceres. *Geophys. Res. Lett.*, **46**, 1213–1221.

Holland, G., Sherwood Lollar, B., Li, L., Lacrampe-Couloume, G., Slater, G. F. and Ballentine, C. (2013). Deep fracture fluids isolated in the crust since the Precambrian era. *Nature*, **497**, 357–360.

Iess, L., *et al.* (2014). The gravity field and interior structure of Enceladus. *Science*, **344**, 78–80.

Johansen, A., Mac Low, M.-M., Lacerda, P. and Bizzarro, M. (2015). Growth of asteroids, planetary embryos, and Kuiper belt objects by chondrule accretion. *Sci. Adv.,* **1**, e1500109, 1–11.

Kamata, S., *et al.* (2019). Pluto's ocean is capped and insulated by gas hydrates. *Nat. Geosci.* **12**, 407–410.

Le Caer, S. (2011). Water radiolysis: Influence of oxide surfaces on H_2 production under ionizing radiation. *Water*, **3**, 235–253.

Le Guillou, C., Bernard, S., Brearley, A. J. and Remusat, L. (2014). Evolution of organic matter in Orgueil, Murchison and Renazzo during parent body aqueous alteration: In situ investigations. *Geochimica et Cosmochimica Acta,* **131**, 368–392.

Lunine, J. I. and Stevenson, D. J. (1985). Thermodynamics of clathrate hydrate at low and high pressures with application to the outer solar system. *Astrophys. J. Supp. Series*, **58**, 493–531, 1985.

Marchi, S., *et al.* (2019). An aqueously altered carbon-rich Ceres. *Nat. Astron.*, **3**, 140–145.

Marsset, M., *et al.* (2020). The violent collisional history of aqueously evolved (2) Pallas. *Nat. Astron.*, **4**, 569–576.

Marion, G. M., Kargel, J. S., Catling, D. C. and Lunine, J. I. (2012). Modeling ammonia-ammonium aqueous chemistries in the solar system's icy bodies. *Icarus*, **220**, 932–946.

McKinnon, W. B. and Zolensky, M. E. (2003). Sulfate content of Europa's ocean and shell: Evolutionary considerations and some geological and astrobiological implications. *Astrobiology*, **3**, 879–897.

Melwani Daswani, M., Vance, S. D., Mayne, M. J. and Glein, C. R. (2021). A metamorphic origin for Europa's ocean. *Geophys. Res. Lett.*, **48**, id.e94143.

Neumann, W., Breuer, D. and Spohn, T. (2014). Differentiation of Vesta: Implications for a shallow magma ocean. *Earth Planet. Sci. Lett.*, **395**, 267–280.

Neveu, M. and Desch, S. J. (2015). Geochemistry, thermal evolution, and cryovolcanism on Ceres with a muddy mantle. *Geophys. Res. Lett.*, **42**, 10,197–10,206.

Neveu, M., Desch, S. J. and Castillo-Rogez, J. C. (2017). Aqueous geochemistry in icy world interiors: Fate of antifreezes and radionuclides. *Cosmochimica et Geochimica Acta*, **212**, 324–371.

Nimmo, F., *et al.* (2016). Reorientation of Sputnik Planitia implies a subsurface ocean on Pluto. *Nature*, **540**, 94–96.

Oba, Y., *et al.*, (2020). Extraterrestrial hexamethylenetetramine in meteorites—a precursor of prebiotic chemistry in the inner solar system. *Nat. Commun.*, **11**, 6243.

Onstott, T. C., *et al.* (1997). The deep gold mines of South Africa: Windows into the subsurface biosphere. *SPIE Proceedings, Instruments, Methods, and Missions for the Investigation of Extraterrestrial Microorganisms*, **3111**, 344–357.

Onstott, T. C., *et al.* (2019). Paleo-rock-hosted life on Earth and the search for life on Mars: A review and strategy for exploration. *Astrobiology*, **19**, 1230–1262.

Pizzarello, S. and Williams, L. B. (2012). Ammonia in the early solar system: An account from carbonaceous meteorites. *Astrophys. J.*, **749**, 161.

Postberg, F., Schmidt, J., Hillier, J., Kempf, S. and Srama, R. (2011). A salt-water reservoir as a source of compositionally stratified plume on Enceladus. *Nature*, **474**, 620–622.

Quick, L., *et al.* (2019). A possible brine reservoir below Occator Crater: Thermal and compositional evolution and formation of the Cerealia Dome and Vinalia Faculae. *Icarus*, **320**, 119–135.

Raymond, C. A., *et al.* (2020). Impact-driven mobilization of deep crustal brines on dwarf planet Ceres. *Nat. Astron.*, **4**, 741–747.

Scully, J. E. C., *et al.* (2017). Evidence for the Interior Evolution of Ceres from Geologic Analysis of Fractures. *Geophys. Res. Lett.*, **44**, 9564–9572.

Sherwood Lollar, B., Onstott, T. C., Lacrampe-Couloume, G. and Ballentine, C. J. (2014). The contribution of the Precambrian continental lithosphere to global H_2 production. *Nature*, **516**, 379–382.

Travis, B. J. and Schubert, G. (2015). Keeping Enceladus warm. *Icarus*, **250**, 32–42.

Travis, B. J., Bland, P. A., Feldman, W. C. and Sykes, M. (2018). Hydrothermal dynamics in a CM-based model of Ceres. *Meteorit. Planet. Sci.*, **53**, 2008–2032.

Vernazza, P., *et al.* (2017). Different origins or different evolutions? Decoding the spectral diversity among C-type asteroids. *Astronom. J.*, **153**, 72.

Vernazza, P., *et al.* (2019). A basin-free spherical shape as an outcome of a giant impact on asteroid Hygiea. *Nat. Astron.*, **4**, 136–141.
Vinogradoff, V., *et al.* (2017). Paris vs. Murchison: Impact of hydrothermal alteration on organic matter in CM chondrites. *Geochimica et Cosmochimica Acta*, **212**, 234–252.
Vinogradoff, V., Bernard, S., Le Guillou, C. and Remusat, L. (2018). Evolution of interstellar organic compounds under asteroidal hydrothermal conditions. *Icarus*, **305**, 358–370.
Yang, B. J., *et al.* (2020). Binary asteroid (31) Euphrosyne: Ice-rich and nearly spherical. *A&A*, **641**, A80.
Zolotov, M. Y. (2007). An oceanic composition on early and today's Enceladus. *Geophys. Res. Lett.*, **34**, L23203.

Chapter 10

Open Questions and Future Exploration

Ceres is a rich target for scientific exploration. The Dawn mission has resolved many questions about Ceres and opened new questions stemming from the discovery of the dwarf planet's potential significance for Astrobiology. Investigations of Ceres can also inform on early solar system evolution and planetary processes. The interest in Ceres has generated several mission concepts that have in common to target the faculae in Occator crater, for in situ exploration and even sample return. Preparing for these missions will require pursuing research on various fronts: for example, continued analysis of the Dawn datasets, theoretical research on the workings of dwarf planets, experimental research on Ceres's analogs as well as fieldwork, and observation with Earth-bound assets.

10.1 Open Questions at the End of the Dawn Mission

10.1.1 *Origin of Ceres*

A fundamental result of the Dawn mission is the realization that Vesta and Ceres formed in different places. Vesta is believed to have formed near or at its current location (Bottke *et al.*, 2006). Pre-Dawn knowledge suggested that the two bodies formed in the same neighborhood but at different times. The resulting contrast in ^{26}Al available in the two bodies would have been responsible for the loss of volatiles at Vesta, whereas Ceres underwent a milder thermal evolution. While it is likely that the formation of the two bodies was separated by a couple of million years, the discovery of ammonium across Ceres's surface (De Sanctis *et al.*, 2015) brought firm evidence for an origin of Ceres's materials in the outer solar system. It has been suggested that Ceres could have accreted small outer solar system planetesimals that migrated via gas drag (Mousis and Alibert, 2005). However, this mechanism is unlikely to lead to the preservation of ammonia in 10-meter-sized planetesimals crossing the gap opened by Jupiter (Turner *et al.*, 2012). It is not possible to narrow down Ceres's origin in the solar system, either between the orbits of the giant planets, as suggested by recent planetary migration models (e.g., Raymond and Izidoro, 2017), or in the Kuiper Belt (McKinnon, 2008). The latter is more difficult to achieve from a dynamical standpoint though, with a capture probability estimated at ~5% (D. O'Brien, personal communication). Leading models for the origin of icy bodies in the main belt of asteroids track the consequences of the growth and migration of giant planets on the scattering of primordial planetesimal belts (Grazier *et al.*, 2014; Raymond and Izidoro, 2017). Combining these two effects provides an efficient means to transfer a large amount of material to the main belt (Raymond and Izidoro, 2017; Fig. 10.1).

Ceres's origin will remain unknown until new observations become available in the form of more detailed mineralogy and isotopic measurements. Processes involving volatiles, such as aqueous alteration and sublimation, likely resulted in isotope fractionation, altering or even erasing the signature of origin. While ^{16}O and ^{18}O show great variations across meteorites and cometary materials, their interpretation into a logical storyline has failed to emerge. Other markers are more stable against internal evolution, in particular isotopes of minor refractory elements such as chromium, cobalt, and titanium. Oxygen-17 is another isotope to remain impervious to aqueous processing (see Fig. 10.2). As these elements occur in very small abundance, their measurement is better approached via sample return.

Are there other main belt asteroids that formed with Ceres?

Ceres is classified as a C-type asteroid, but that complex contains many spectral subclasses. Presumably, the subclasses point to variations in composition and/or different internal evolutions, for example, driven by the object size. Among the large (several hundreds of kilometers) objects that have been extensively observed with astronomical facilities, 10 Hygiea shows strong spectral similarities to Ceres (Fig. 10.3). One cannot rule out that smaller bodies may have formed in the same accretional environment as Ceres, but the extent of aqueous alteration was limited due to their

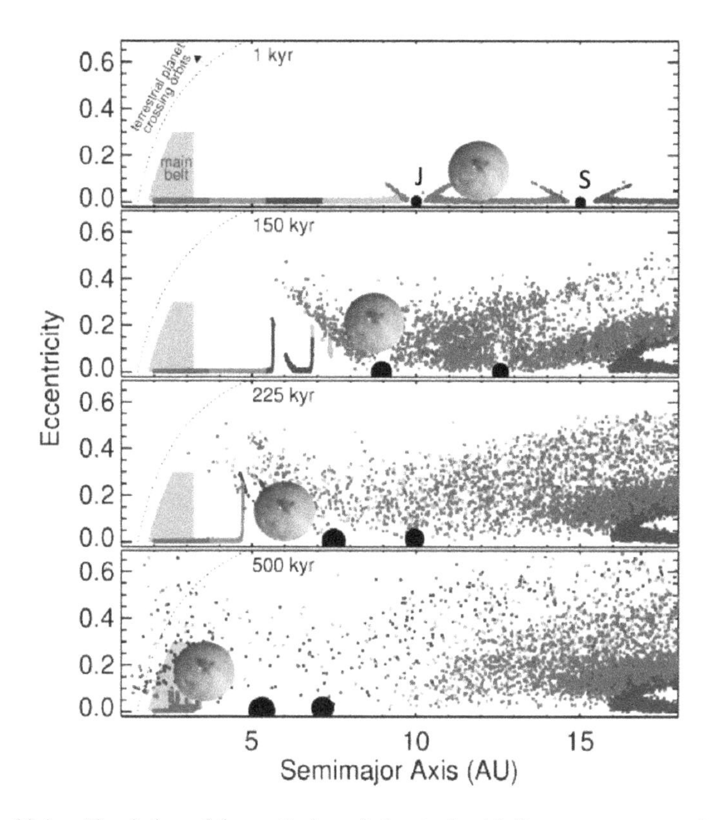

Figure 10.1: Simulation of the scattering of planetesimal belts presents across the giant planet region as a consequence of planetary growth and migration (based after Raymond and Izidoro, 2017.) In this framework, Ceres could have formed somewhere between the orbits of Saturn and Neptune before being scattered with other C-type planetesimals. Reprinted from Raymond and Izidoro (2017). Copyright with permission from Elsevier.

smaller sizes (Young *et al.*, 2003). Spectral bands diagnostic of the presence of ammonium (around 3.1 micron) would help establish a genetic connection between Ceres and other asteroids, but the detection of this band is made difficult by the low albedo (<0.09) of that class of bodies.

10.1.2 *Origin and Formation of Regolith*

The origin of Ceres's surface material is one of the big remaining mysteries at the end of the Dawn mission. If the regolith material comes primarily from Ceres, then the mechanism that can explain the emplacement of tens to hundreds of meters of regolith remains to be elucidated. The two leading

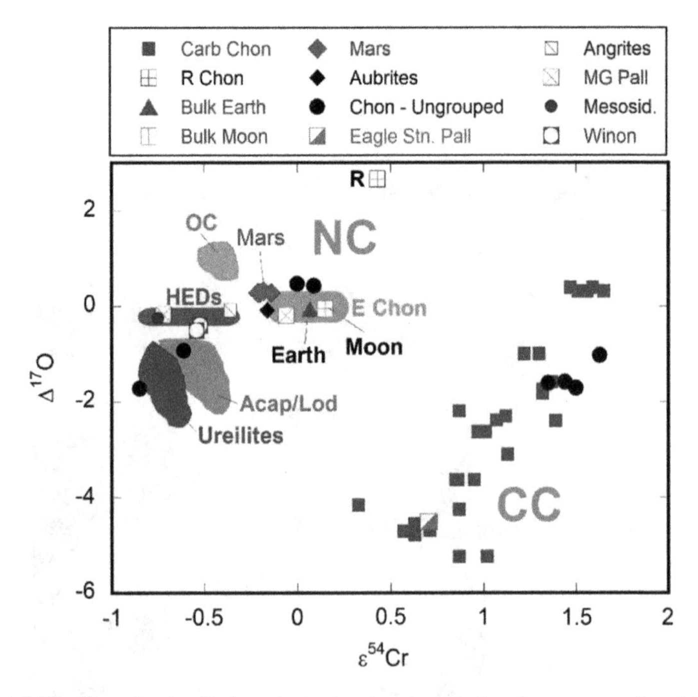

Figure 10.2: The clearly distinct isotopic signatures of carbonaceous chondrites and other meteorites have been attributed to the creation of separate inner and outer solar system reservoirs (Kruijer *et al.*, 2017). This distinction is obvious in this representation of delta-^{17}O against Cr isotope. Reprinted from Burbine and Greenwood (2020) after Warren (2011). Copyright with permission from Springer.

hypotheses, early exposure of oceanic material (Neveu and Desch, 2015) or infalling material (Vernazza *et al.*, 2017; Marchi *et al.*, 2019; Mao and McKinnon, 2020), can be tested via microscopic analyses of mineral relationships and isotopic composition. The high likelihood for a large fraction of exogenic material to be present on Ceres's surface will drive landing site selection for future missions or require a sample return so that endogenic and exogenic phases can be sorted out using highly capable facilities on Earth.

10.1.3 *Interior Structure*

10.1.3.1 *Extent of Differentiation*

Many uncertainties remain about Ceres's interior, in particular whether the radial density increase with depth inferred from the gravity data

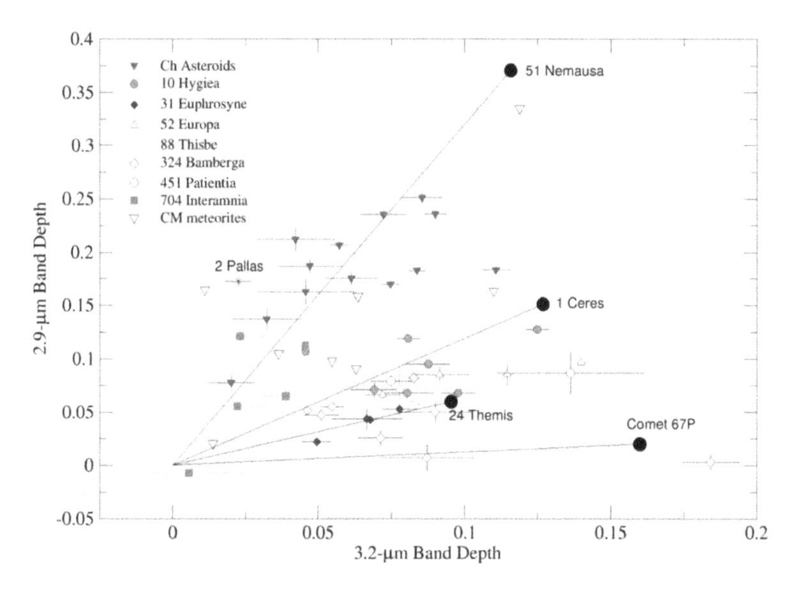

Figure 10.3: Summary of band depth information for several large C-type asteroids and comet 67P. This figure highlights subtle differences among C-type asteroids, pointing to variations in chemical make-up and or internal evolution. Ceres shows strong similarities with 10 Hygiea in particular. Reprinted from Rivkin *et al.* (2019). Copyright with permission from Wiley-VCH Verlag GmbH & Co. KGaA.

reflects a compositional stratification or a decrease in porosity in a homogeneous mixture of hydrated rock, salts, and organic compounds (Zolotov, 2020). Resolving this ambiguity can take multiple approaches. First, the Dawn observations presented widespread evidence for ice, either directly on the surface or as a driver of geological evolution. Hence, models alternative to the differentiated rocky mantle and icy crust model would need to demonstrate that they can reproduce these observations. Second, the thermal stability of the organic-rich model needs to be tested since phyllosilicates, salts, and organic matter have low thermal conductivities and could lead to extensive thermal metamorphism. Also, the mechanical properties of organic compounds in planetary settings are not well understood per lack of relevant experimental measurements. For example, heating could trigger the separation of organic compounds from the rock, leading to the formation of diapirs. However, many parameters are lacking to properly model this potential process.

The global evolution of rocky material in low-gravity ocean worlds is also poorly understood. Bland and Travis (2017) suggested that these objects could sustain long-lived convection in an ocean loaded in fine rock particles. Neveu and Desch (2015) and Travis *et al.* (2018) attempted to model the evolution of that ocean for Ceres. This type of modeling involves a large number of parameters that make the outcome of the simulations highly uncertain. In particular, the role of salts and organics in driving flocculation is not accounted for in these models. Better understanding the fate of particles in large oceans in low-gravity bodies is relevant to many other icy bodies, such as icy moons and dwarf planets in the Kuiper Belt.

10.1.3.2 *Distribution (extent, geometry), and the Nature of Liquid*

Brines have been expected to play a major role in the evolution of icy moons. Ceres is the first target displaying direct evidence for brine-driven activity. The extent of brines, either in the form of pore fluid (Fu *et al.*, 2017), localized brine pockets, or a more extensive body of liquid on a global scale (Travis *et al.*, 2018), is unknown. The viscosity profile inferred from the topography relaxation modeling is not well constrained below the crust: an upper bound of 10^{20} Pa s is provided by Fu *et al.* (2017), but no lower bound can be derived. Additional evidence for deep brines, at least on a regional scale, comes from the observations of recent landforms built from brine extrusion. Constraints on the viscosity of the material effused at Occator crater and Ahuna Mons were offered by Ruesch *et al.* (2019a, 2019b) and Quick *et al.* (2019) based on morphologies. Furthermore, the 5 to 10 vol.% sodium carbonates found at Ahuna Mons (Zambon *et al.*, 2017) point to a liquid temperature greater than 255 K (Castillo-Rogez *et al.*, 2019). Additional compounds should include sodium and potassium chloride brines, as suggested by geochemical modeling (Neveu and Desch, 2015; Castillo-Rogez *et al.*, 2018). The brines likely correspond to residual liquid from the freezing of a global ocean suggested in Ceres's early history (Castillo-Rogez and McCord, 2010; Ammannito *et al.*, 2016).

10.1.3.3 *Crustal Evolution*

The study of Ceres's crust offers a window into the freezing of icy worlds. Indeed, until the Dawn observations, little was known about the crustal properties of these objects by lack of geophysical probing. The inversion of gravity data in terms of density profile is underconstrained and thus the inferred crustal density comes with some large uncertainties or is simply assumed. The Dawn data already returned higher-resolution probing of the crust of an ice-rich body (see Chapter 7) and future exploration could gain additional insights via high-resolution gravity data on a global scale. Electromagnetic sounding might also be used to map the distribution of brines and resolve transfer pathways between a deep brine reservoir and surface landforms such as Ahuna Mons (Grimm *et al.*, 2021). Future geophysical exploration may also confirm, or disprove, the hypothesis that Ceres's crust is rich in clathrate hydrates. A better understanding of an icy world crust structure from physical and chemical observations would help address the following questions: How does the crust of water-rich worlds freeze? How does the evolution of the crust affect the chemical evolution (including organics) of Ocean Worlds?

10.1.4 *Origin of Organic Matter*

The origin of organic matter found at the Ernutet crater and the large abundance of carbon found throughout the surface remain debated. Pieters *et al.* (2018) pointed out that the Ernutet region show no distinct geological features in favor of an exogenic or endogenic origin. Bowling *et al.* (2020) suggested low-probability retention of organics supplied by a cometary impactor, but some of the simulations featured in that paper suggest at least 10% could be preserved and match the VIR-based inference.

This aspect is important because Marchi *et al.* (2019) suggested that the high abundance of carbon (the upper bound derived by GRaND is similar to the carbon abundance observed at 1P/Halley) could be a signature of Ceres's accretional environment hinting at an origin with cometary material. These authors also suggested as an alternative that Ceres could have been hosting the production of new organics in its interior.

10.1.5 *Origin of Exosphere*

The Dawn mission could not verify the origin of the vapor detected by Küppers *et al.* (2014) with the Herschel Space Observatory (HSO). On the one hand, Dawn was not equipped to search for outgassing. On the other hand, the eleven or so ice-rich regions spotted by Dawn (Combe *et al.*, 2018) can account for only 10% of the 6 kg/s vapor production rate derived from the HSO data (Landis *et al.*, 2017). Altogether, Landis *et al.* (2017, 2019) show that accounting for all possible sources of vapor production can explain only 20% of the HSO results. It is possible, as shown by Landis *et al.* (2017), that larger patches of ice created by small impacts were exposed at the time of the HSO observations, but were darkened over a scale of a few years, making them undetectable by the Dawn spacecraft. Two alternative or complementary explanations have been proposed: cryovolcanic activity (Küppers *et al.*, 2014) that might be associated with Occator crater (Nathues *et al.*, 2019) and sputtering of ice by energetic particles (Villarreal *et al.*, 2019).

10.1.6 *Drivers of Long-Term Geology Activity*

The long-term preservation of liquid until recently and possibly at present is not readily explained due to the lack of a long-term heat source inside Ceres. Long-lived radioisotopes are not sufficient to maintain a deep ocean inside Ceres. However, several models pointed out the role of second-phase compounds in decreasing eutectic temperatures (Castillo-Rogez and McCord, 2010) and the role of clathrate hydrates in slowing down heat loss (Castillo-Rogez *et al.*, 2019; Hesse and Castillo-Rogez, 2019). The effect of clathrates in preserving liquid inside dwarf planet Pluto was also suggested by Kamata *et al.*, (2019). Salts have been found on Ceres's surface, in particular, ammonium chloride and hydrohalite that have a eutectic around 245 K. Other salts may be present, such as chloride mixtures that may decrease the eutectic down to 220 K. In these conditions, the amount of liquid is very small, less than 1% of the original ocean volume (Castillo-Rogez *et al.*, 2019). Clathrate hydrates are difficult to identify with remote sensing; in fact, they are not stable on Ceres's surface due to the low pressure and warm temperatures in the main belt of asteroids. Their spectral signature is mostly similar to ice, with an additional absorption band for the encaged gas species.

Large impacts may play a major role in supplying heat in the form of dissipated kinetic energy. Indeed, depending on the nature of the target material, 10 to 20% of the kinetic energy may be turned into heat, the rest being used for fragmentation of the material and production of ejecta. A 10-km impactor in the main belt, suggested to be responsible for the formation of Occator crater, could bring enough heat to increase Ceres's crust temperature up to 300 K (Bowling *et al.*, 2019). Hence, the impacts responsible for the large basins suggested for the formation of the Planitia (Marchi *et al.*, 2016) could have resulted in massive melting, loss of volatiles, crustal thinning, potential alteration of the rocky mantle (Davison *et al.*, 2015), and deep deposition of heat. The consequences of Ceres's integrated collisional history remains to be addressed.

10.1.7 *Characterization of Habitability*

Although there is evidence that Ceres's early ocean met certain habitability criteria and that the dwarf planet may still maintain a liquid layer at present, Ceres's habitability through time remains to be quantified. Important open questions include the following: (a) the extent to which Ceres's deep ocean was an open system benefiting from the addition of volatiles released from the rocky mantle and exogenic material introduced by impacts; (b) the evolution of organic matter exposed to different environmental conditions through time: as part of hydrothermal activity during Ceres's differentiation, mixed with clays in a warming mantle, and potentially in a late hydrothermal system created by the release of volatiles from the mantle.

Ceres is particularly interesting for future exploration because of the recent and potentially ongoing transfer of material from deep brine to the surface. The evaporites evolved from the brine exposure can be investigated in areas that appear accessible to a future landed mission, based on the best images returned by the Dawn mission (Scully *et al.*, 2021) (see below).

10.2 Future Exploration of Ceres on Earth

As highlighted above and in previous chapters, a better understanding of Ceres and other ocean worlds can be gained in laboratories and at terrestrial analogs, as well as with a continuous astronomical observation program. This section is based on input from contributors to a white paper by Castillo-Rogez *et al.* (2021).

10.2.1 *Theoretical Modeling*

(*a*) *Modeling Convection in Extraterrestrial Oceans Loaded in Rock Particles*

Long-lived convection of particles suspended in a deep ocean, in low-gravity conditions, has been suggested for Ceres (Travis *et al.*, 2018). The authors show that slow convection could delay heat loss so that Ceres could preserve a thick ocean at present. This kind of hydrodynamical model involves a large number of parameters and the modeling of various mechanisms. For example, the charging of rock particles by ions (salts) could lead to flocculation, decreasing the fraction of particles in suspension. This mechanism is not incorporated in the Travis *et al.* (2018) model. Organic compounds could play a similar role as salts or change the viscosity of the ocean. Laboratory measurements of the dynamical properties of this kind of complex liquid mixture are necessary in order to progress in this area.

(*b*) *Differentiation in Mid-Sized Bodies* (100–1000 *km*)
Along the same line, the mechanisms driving differentiation in low gravity bodies like Ceres or Enceladus are not well understood. Ceres and Enceladus share a similar rocky mantle density of about 2400 kg/m^3, which indicates a fluid-filled porosity of at least 30%. Choblet *et al.* (2017) proposed that Enceladus's mantle is heavily fractured. In the case of Ceres, the mantle is larger and might be stratified in a solid layer overlain by a highly porous layer. However, the physics of a complex mixture that may involve a large fraction of salts and organic compounds remains to be studied. This topic is also relevant to the parent bodies of carbonaceous chondrites.

(*c*) *Geochemical Cycles in Ocean Worlds*
Geochemical cycles are important ways to predict the fate of major elements and compounds, in particular, organic matter and redox pairs that may be used in metabolism in potentially habitable objects. Of particular importance, carbon-based compounds have been found in various forms on Ceres: carbonates, organic species, graphite/amorphous carbon, and potentially as clathrate hydrates. The connection between these various species remains to be studied in more detail. For example, carbonates and organic compounds are found in close association in Ernutet crater (De Sanctis *et al.*, 2017). Organic compounds present in the subsurface may have degraded into graphite and amorphous carbon (Hendrix *et al.*, 2016; Marchi *et al.*, 2019). Additional work is needed to better understand the fate of these carbon compounds from accretion until the present.

10.2.2 *Laboratory Studies*

Future exploration of Ceres would benefit from investigating terrestrial and laboratory analogs with a focus on better understanding the physics and chemistry of brines, organic matter, and mud mixtures in bodies with low gravity. Examples of experiments of interest in order to advance our understanding of Ceres and other water-rich bodies in the same size range include the following:

(a) Laboratory research on salt clasts present in meteorite collections, which have been suggested to come from Ceres or Ceres-like bodies

Two clasts of halite have been found in H-chondrites named Zag and Monahans (Fig. 10.4). These clasts contain a large number of minerals trapped during freezing of the liquid environments of their parent bodies. Most interestingly, fluids were also found in these clasts that can provide environmental constraints, such as the pH and redox conditions of the source environment (Zolensky *et al.*, 2015). Analyses of these clasts need to be pursued in order to fully decipher their content. That research is particularly important in order to prepare for a future mission to Ceres that would return salts from the Cerealia faculae (e.g., Shi *et al.*, 2020).

(b) Thermophysical properties of brines, hydrated salts, and clathrates

Thermophysical properties of brines in relevant planetary context have been the focus of experimental work with application to Europa (e.g., Prieto-Ballesteros and Kargel, 2005). While that earlier work focused on

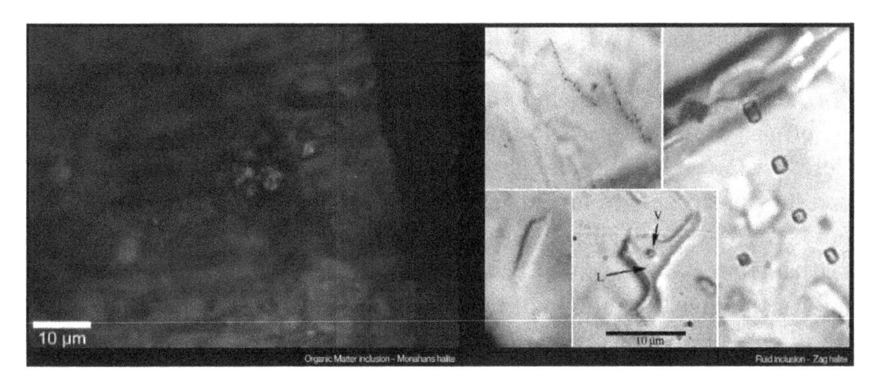

Figure 10.4: Microscopic views of the Monahans (Left) and Zag (Right) salt crystals. Impurities in the crystals represent a variety of minerals (e.g., pyroxene and organic compounds (Left) and fluids (Right). Courtesy of Mike Zolensky, Johnson Space Center; Chan *et al.* (2018).

sulfates and, to a lesser extent, chlorides, future work should target mixtures of carbonates, chlorides, and ammonium compounds that are more relevant to Ceres and Enceladus. Future studies should also explore the properties of clathrates exposed to high concentrations of salts, building on the Mars literature (e.g., Gainey and Elwood Madden, 2012), but in conditions relevant to Ceres.

(c) Thermophysical properties and mechanical behavior of organic matter

As organic matter might be locally present in abundance, its influence on the thermomechanical properties of mixtures needs to be studied in conditions relevant to Ceres and other icy worlds. In particular, the thermophysical properties of insoluble organic matter, which represents about 75 wt.% of carbonaceous chondrite organic matter, are poorly understood.

(d) Effect of radiolysis in the creation of redox gradients in ocean worlds, for example, to understand the efficiency of this process and its potential for creating local habitable zones

Energetic particles released by radioisotope decay (of ^{40}K, ^{232}Th, ^{235}U, and ^{238}U) can locally break down water molecules and create redox gradients (Bouquet *et al.*, 2017; Castillo-Rogez *et al.*, 2020). While this mechanism is expected to increase the habitability of liquid environments, its modalities in a complex mixture of rock and brines are not well understood and would benefit from being studied in laboratory (e.g., yield rate estimation).

(e) Behavior of brine and mud mixtures in low gravity

As brine and silicate particle slurries are involved in various processes on Ceres, we need to gain a better understanding of their behavior in zero-pressure surface environments at Ceres's temperatures, e.g., flow properties such as fluid-rich debris flows and impact ejecta. Furthermore, experimental simulations of brine/organic/rock convection are needed to inform thermal evolution and material transfer in the interiors of Ceres, Enceladus, and other low gravity bodies.

(f) Library of material signatures for various types of instrumentations

In order to prepare for a future mission to Ceres, one needs to investigate the response of relevant surface material analogs to instruments under consideration for future missions (see Section 10.3) as well as ground-based observations (Section 10.2.3), e.g., in the ultraviolet and mid-infrared. Of particular interest, one should estimate the detection limit of organic carbon in mixtures of salt and rock particles, in particular using Raman spectroscopy and infrared spectroscopy. Space weathering can add additional challenges to the interpretation of optical spectra as irradiation processes (e.g., cosmic rays, ultraviolet) tend to modify the absorption signatures of minerals and organics, but these effects have not been studied extensively in laboratory for conditions relevant to Ceres.

10.2.3 *Earth-Based Observations*

Long-term monitoring and fast reaction to possibly transient phenomena, such as variations in exospheric properties (Rousselot *et al.*, 2011, 2019; Küppers *et al.*, 2014) and the changing surface ice (Raponi *et al.*, 2018), are the most important aspects of Earth-based observations of Ceres. A large suite of available facilities and instruments on the ground and in near-Earth space provides full coverage of wavelengths not covered by the Dawn mission, although they will be limited by spatial resolution and sensitivity compared to spacecraft exploration. The questions that can be addressed by telescopic observations from Earth or near-Earth space include the following:

(a) *Origin of Ceres's sporadic outgassing activity*: Given the transient nature and the unpredictability of outgassing from Ceres, long-term, continuous monitoring from the ground is the only way to characterize this phenomenon. Both regular monitoring of the possible outgassing over at least one full orbital period of Ceres and fast-response observations of Ceres, such as following solar energetic proton events, are needed to probe the possible sources and mechanisms of outgassing.
(b) *Search for other volatile species, such as N, C, and S*: These species are commonly observed in cometary comae, and contain important clues about the origin, the chemical composition, and processes of the source objects. The release of these species from the surface into the exosphere increases their detectability from remote sensing observations. Detection and determination of the abundance of these species have significant implications for understanding the chemical evolution of the composition and potential habitability of Ceres.

(c) *Constraints of Ceres's surface roughness and porosity from radar observations*: These properties are important both to understand the evolution of Ceres's regolith and inform a future landed mission. Because a returned radar signal decays with the fourth power of distance, these observations are best performed around the opposition close to Ceres's perihelion.
(d) *High-resolution thermal mapping to determine the thermal properties and thermal environment of the surface and subsurface*: Thermal conditions on the surface and subsurface both provide clues about the thermal state of Ceres, and directly determine the state of water in the subsurface. The near-infrared observations performed by Dawn VIR instrument up to 5.0 μm are sensitive only to the surface temperatures of areas at < 40 to 50° latitude in the midday. Thermal mapping at longer wavelengths covering one full Ceres year would be ideal to probe down to the annual thermal skin depth (~0.5 m).
(e) *Observations of Ceres at wavelengths complementary to the 0.4–5 μm range observed by Dawn, including ultraviolet, mid-infrared, THz frequencies, and radio frequencies*: Ultraviolet wavelengths are sensitive to some surface compounds and processes such as water and graphite (Hendrix *et al*., 2012, 2016) and atomic species in the exosphere. Mid-infrared observations provide additional mineralogical information on the surface, as well as some thermal constraints. THz and radio frequencies can detect volatile species in the exosphere, and probe subsurface dielectric and thermal properties.

The facilities and instruments needed to observe Ceres from the Earth and near-Earth space emphasize high-spatial resolution, high sensitivity, and a wide range of wavelengths. These include the Hubble Space Telescope (HST), James Webb Space Telescope (JWST), various instruments for the Stratospheric Observatory for Infrared Astronomy (SOFIA), Atacama Large Millimeter/submillimeter Array (ALMA), and possibly the Five-hundred-meter Aperture Spherical Telescope (FAST) in China in the future.

The HST is the only facility currently available for observations in the full range of ultraviolet wavelengths in high spatial resolution. It has made significant contributions to studying the surface composition of Ceres and the search for outgassing. The Large UV/Optical/IR Survey (LUVOIR), a multi-wavelength space telescope concept under development as of writing by NASA, will provide critical UV capability after the HST retires.

JWST, currently expected to launch at the end of 2021, will provide high spatial resolution imaging and spectroscopic capability covering 0.6–28 μm with four instruments, Near-Infrared Camera (NIRCam), Near-Infrared Spectrograph (NIRSpec), Near-Infrared Imager and Slitless Spectrograph (NIRISS), and Mid-Infrared Instrument (MIRI) (Milam *et al.*, 2016). The diffraction limited spatial resolution with JWST's 6 meter primary mirror, together with the integrated field unit capability, is capable of supporting compositional and thermal mapping of Ceres inaccessible from Dawn and from the ground. The high sensitivity of JWST's instruments and the coronagraphic imaging capability of NIRCam and MIRI could also contribute to the long-term monitoring of water outgassing and volatile species, although Ceres itself will saturate at the shortest wavelength of MIRI (Rivkin *et al.*, 2016). The Faint Object infraRed CAmera for the SOFIA Telescope (FORCAST) provides mid-infrared capabilities that can be used to provide clues about the surface composition and the state of aqueous alteration inaccessible to Dawn's near-infrared instrument. The GREAT (German Receiver for Astronomy at Terahertz frequencies) instrument for SOFIA has the capability to monitor water outgassing from Ceres at similar frequencies that Herschel Space Observatory utilized to detect localized water vapor near Ceres (Küppers *et al.*, 2014), and can be used for the exosphere monitoring. It also bridges to the frequency coverage of ALMA, which could also search for various volatile species (e.g., Chuang *et al.*, 2019; Chiang *et al.*, 2019; Parks *et al.*, 2019). The high-resolution capability of ALMA makes it ideal for high-resolution thermal mapping of Ceres (e.g., Li *et al.*, 2020).

10.2.4 *Terrestrial Analogs*

The investigation of terrestrial analogs is also an important aspect of the preparation for the future exploration of Ceres. Field testing at terrestrial analogs can help with demonstrating aspects of future sampling systems and other instruments. For example, the Occator evaporites, which appear to be a high-priority target of future missions (see below), represent a unique and new type of material for planetary landers. Sampling that material for return to Earth or for feeding instruments could require the development and testing of a new kind of sampling system.

Examples of landmarks on Earth that share commonalities with Ceres are shown in Fig. 10.5. Analogs can be found for various types of features: chemistry and mineralogy, volcanic activity, tectonic activity, periglacial

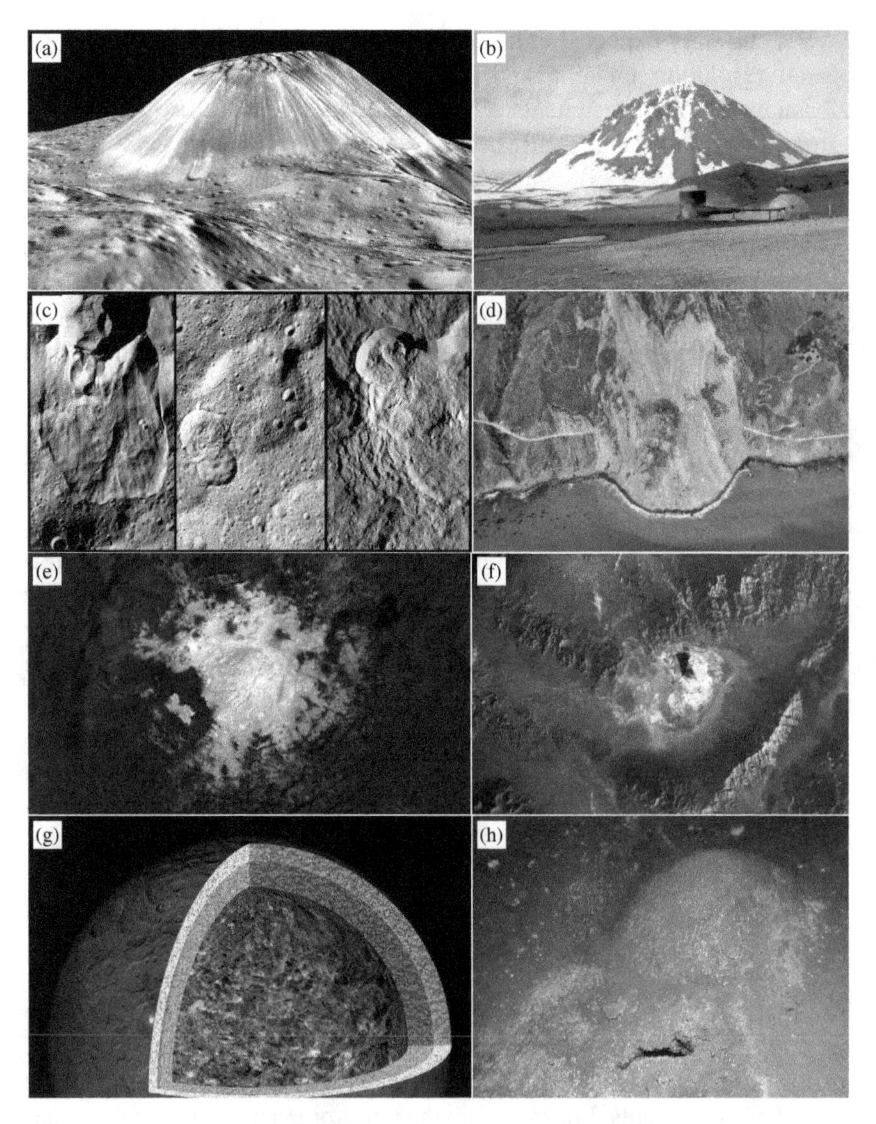

Figure 10.5: Examples of terrestrial analogs to some of Ceres's features: (a) volcanic dome Ahuna Mons and (b) an equivalent, volcanic Hlíðarfjall dome, Iceland; (c) examples of landslides on Ceres and (d) equivalent on Earth; (e) Cerealia Facula, with its main dome (Cerealia Tholus) of salts and (f) Lake Searles evaporites in California; (g) Ceres's crust is enriched in gas hydrates, which are commonly found on Earth's ocean floor (h). Credit: NASA/JPL-Caltech/UCLA/MPS/DLR/IDA, (a) PIA20915 https://photojournal.jpl.nasa.gov/catalog/PIA20915, (b) Hlíðarfjall dome, Iceland, Credit: Hansueli Krapf/Wikimedia Commons contributor Simisa/CC BY-SA 3.0, (c) PIA21471 https://photojournal.jpl.nasa.gov/catalog/PIA21471, (d) The Mud Creek landslide, California, Credit: USGS;

features, mass wasting (e.g., landslides), etc. Many of these landforms present on Earth can be studied to better understand the processes driving Ceres's geology. However, the large difference in gravity (a factor 35) generally drives the outcome of these processes. Other bodies may also offer landmark analogs, in particular Mars's periglacial features (Schenk *et al.*, 2020), icy moon crater morphologies (Hiesinger *et al.*, 2016; Schenk *et al.*, 2021), and lunar fracture floor craters (Buczkowski *et al.*, 2019).

Periglacial Landforms: Impacts into the high ice content in Ceres's upper crust lead to full or partial melting of ice, depending on the energy of the event, which could drive the formation of many geological structures that have analogs on Earth. Indeed, in polar regions, and in particular where the soil is perennially frozen in a permafrost, water melt and refreezing drives volume changes and the formation of frost heaves and pingos. The latter have been suggested as analogs to domes found in Occator crater, which displays fresh features evolved from impact-produced melt (Schmidt *et al.*, 2020).

Volcanic Domes: A handful of tall domes have been found by Dawn on Ceres (Sori *et al.*, 2017), in particular Ahuna Mons. Ahuna Mons was found to be of volcanic origin involving brines and rock particles (Ruesch *et al.*, 2019a). Earth presents many domes of volcanic origin. Although the magma compositions at play significantly differ from each other, the mechanisms driving eruption are similar: partial magma crystallization (formation of slurry), buoyancy driven by gas expansion and accelerated upon depressurization, and development of cracks as a result of volume changes as the magma cools. The Dawn data revealed several expressions of cryovolcanism: brine effusion at Cerealia Facula (Scully *et al.*, 2019) and brine fountaining and scattering at the Vinalia Faculae (Ruesch *et al.*,

Figure 10.5: (*Continued on facing pages*) (e) PIA21924 https://photojournal.jpl.nasa.gov/catalog/PIA21924, (f) Lake Searles, Credit: NASA, (g) PIA22660 https://photojournal.jpl.nasa.gov/catalog/PIA22660, (h) Methane hydrate mound on the Biloxi Salt Dome in the northern Gulf of Mexico, Image courtesy NOAA Okeanos Explorer Program, found at https://www.nationalgeographic.com/news/energy/2013/03/pictures/130328-methane-hydrates-for-energy/.
Based on NASA feature: https://www.nasa.gov/feature/jpl/what-looks-like-ceres-on-earth. Credit Elizabeth Landau.

2019b). On Earth, domes formed from the extrusion of magma are found at volcanoes with a high content of silicon, such as Mount St. Helens in the United States or the Chaitén dome in Chile.

Soda Lakes: The mineralogical assemblage found at Occator faculae, a mixture of sodium carbonates and various chlorides, is also typically found on Earth, for example, in lakes associated with past volcanic activity. The degassing of carbon dioxide from the volcano drives alkaline conditions (pH between 9 and 12) and a high concentration of carbonate and bicarbonate ions. These lakes are generally also rich in chloride. Typical examples include the East African Rift Valley, lakes in the Owens Valley in California (e.g., Mono Lake), and many lakes found in the Himalayas. In arid regions, these lakes form evaporites almost throughout the year. These salt deposits may be analogs to the salt deposits found in the faculae. A major difference is likely the structure of the salt aggregates, the crystal size, and the amount of porosity due to exposure at atmospheric pressure versus vacuum. In particular, exposure in vacuum prevents the formation of hydrates as water is quasi-instantaneously vaporized.

Study of soda lakes as analogs to Ceres is especially interesting for understanding the potential of salt grains to capture organic matter (Benzerara *et al.*, 2006) and fluids representatives of their source. An extreme but particularly compelling example is in the form of two clasts of halite found in the meteorite collections. The Zag and Monahans clasts are millimeter crystals that were found embedded in H-type chondrites (e.g., Rubin *et al.*, 2002). They are of exogenic origin and have been suggested to be extruded from Ceres and scattered in the main belt of asteroids. A connection with Ceres cannot be definitively proven until an in situ mission obtains key markers for comparison. Whatever their source, these clasts are evidence that grain salts on extraterrestrial worlds contain a lot of information on their source brine.

Compacted Sediments: The density of Ceres's mantle, which is lower than rock density by about 10 to 25%, suggests about 15 to 35% of porosity if pores are filled by brines. A similar porosity is expected in sediments under a pressure of about 40 MPa (top of Ceres's mantle) (e.g., Bahr *et al.*, 2001). Furthermore, Ceres's pressure and temperature conditions are favorable to the formation of gas hydrates (clathrates). These are found commonly on Earth's oceanic floor and in permafrost regions. Similarly, these compounds are expected to be abundant in Ceres's crust (Chapter 7).

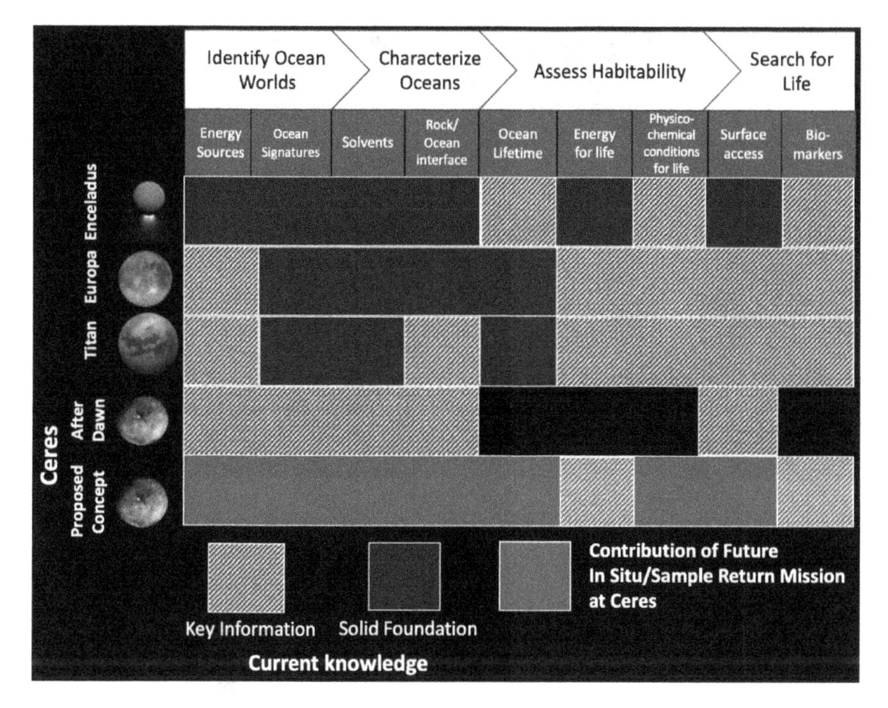

Figure 10.6: Roadmap to Ocean Worlds based on Hendrix *et al.* (2019) describing the state of knowledge of various ocean worlds, including Ceres. Based on the results from the Dawn mission, Ceres has been considered a "candidate" ocean world. The recent discovery of freshly exposed hydrohalite in Occator crater suggests the occurrence of a brine reservoir at least below Hanami Planum.

Hydrothermal Systems: Different hydrothermal environments are relevant to Ceres. In Ceres's early ocean, the environmental conditions, in particular high pH and fugacity of hydrogen, are expected to be similar to the deep seafloor (Kelley *et al.*, 2005). These environments involve the release of abundant hydrogen as part of the serpentinization of mafic material (e.g., freshly exposed basalt on Earth). In more recent times, serpentinization could have been taking place in local melt chambers formed by the conversion of kinetic energy into heat of crater-forming impacts. Depending on its composition, the impactor could contribute anhydrous material subject to serpentinization in the transient melt chamber (Bowling *et al.*, 2019). The cumulated introduction of impactor material into the crust over Ceres's history, potentially up to ~3×10^{19} kg (Marchi *et al.*, 2019), could theoretically represent a major component of Ceres's upper crust and in particular of its regolith.

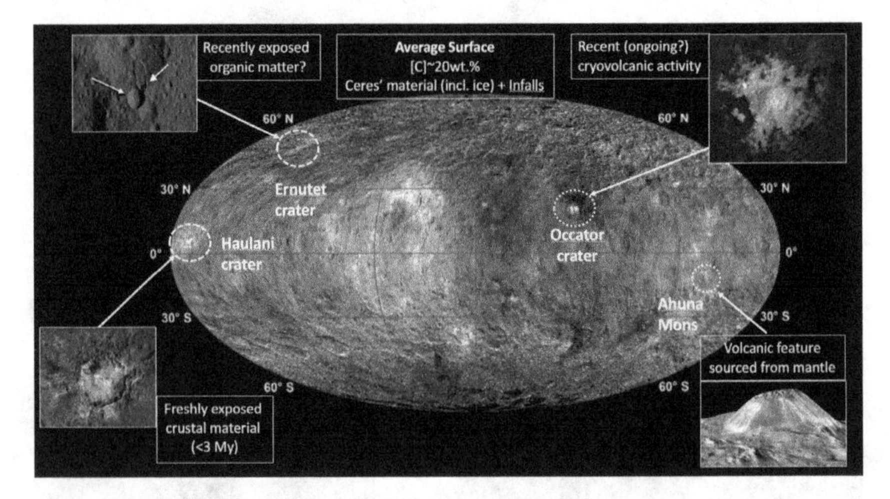

Figure 10.7: Ceres's surface is globally homogeneous, except for a few landmarks where high abundances of organic matter and of oceanic materials have been found. These regions are likely candidates for in situ surface exploration and/or sample return.

Salt Tectonic Structures: These were taken as analog for explaining the association of many domes with impact craters (Bland *et al.*, 2019). The principle is that impact-generated heat decreases material viscosity, which results in solid state flow in a heterogeneous crust. Compositional heterogeneities lead to differential loading between low- and high-density materials. On Earth, low-density and low-strength salt layers captured within rock layers can become mobile along fractures or form diapirs.

10.3 Roadmap to the Future Exploration of Ceres

The general direction of the future exploration of Ceres is to progress along the Roadmap to Ocean Worlds (OW; Hendrix *et al.*, 2019). This roadmap was developed in response to the US congressional mandate to frame the current state of understanding of ocean worlds and advise on future exploration priorities. Figure 10.6 summarizes the state of knowledge for four themes (identify, characterize oceans, assess habitability, search for life). It shows that Ceres was categorized as a candidate ocean world by Hendrix *et al.* (2019). This roadmap indicates that future missions to Ceres should aim to assess key questions posed by the Dawn mission and in particular confirm the presence and composition of a deep liquid inside Ceres.

Figure 10.8: Axel rover developed for extreme terrain access (here shown in the context of the recurring slope lineae on Mars). The deployable Axel rover contains up to 40 kg of payload including a small sampling system. Reproduced from Nesnas and Burdick (2013).

10.3.1 *Possible Sites for Landed and Sample Return Missions*

Following up on the results from the Dawn mission, a pre-decadal study sponsored by NASA sought to design concepts that could address Ceres's past and current habitability potential (Castillo-Rogez *et al.*, 2020). The study identified five major regions on Ceres that would offer compelling opportunities to address these topics from different angles (Fig. 10.7):

(1) Ernutet crater displays organic compounds intimately mixed with carbonates. Although its origin, exogenic (e.g., supplied by a comet or asteroid impact) or endogenic, is debated (Pieters *et al.*, 2018), impact models show that the destruction of a large amount of organic matter upon impact (Bowling *et al.*, 2020) is not consistent with the large

abundances derived by De Sanctis *et al.* (2017) and Kaplan *et al.* (2018). Higher-resolution imaging in color and infrared spectroscopy could help retire uncertainties about the origin of this material by bringing better understanding of its relationship with surface material and geology.

(2) Haulani crater is the freshest crater on Ceres, dated 2.5-3 My (Tosi *et al.*, 2018), that is wider than 30 km. It displays very fresh material with a diverse composition: anhydrous and hydrated sodium carbonate, ammonium chloride, and very dark and bluish material apparently similar in nature to the ejecta found in the northeastern region of Occator crater. This material offers an opportunity to sample the crust of Ceres and thus the composition of Ceres's early ocean (Castillo-Rogez *et al.*, 2020). A mission to Haulani crater would thus return constraints on Ceres's early habitability.

(3) Ahuna Mons is the most impressive expression of recent brine-driven volcanism on Ceres's surface (Ruesch *et al.*, 2016). Likely sourced from the top of Ceres's muddy mantle (Ruesch *et al.*, 2019a), Ahuna is a probe of Ceres's deep interior. Hence, its exploration would bring key constraints on the geochemical conditions of Ceres's residual ocean. Ahuna Mons's material is difficult to access due to steep slopes (40°; Ermakov *et al.*, 2019). Hence, its exploration might require robotic platforms designed for extreme terrains, such as the Axel rover (Nesnas and Burdick, 2013) (see Fig. 10.8).

(4) Occator crater displays evidence for very recent and potentially ongoing brine effusion activity on Ceres's surface at the Cerealia and Vinalia faculae (e.g., Scully *et al.*, 2020). Cerealia Facula was primarily sourced from a melt chamber generated by impact heat into Ceres's crust with a late contribution from the deep brine reservoir (Raymond *et al.*, 2020; Scully *et al.*, 2020). On the other hand, the Vinalia Faculae appear primarily sourced from the deep brine reservoir. The faculae were identified by Castillo-Rogez *et al.* (2020) as the most compelling sites for addressing Ceres's current habitability. A mission capable of exploring a diversity of materials (e.g., faculae, floor material, ejecta) would significantly progress along the Roadmap to Ocean Worlds.

(5) Lastly, Ceres's average surface is also a target of interest to address Ceres's origin and early history. In situ investigation of Ceres's surface would help retire potential uncertainties about the origin (exogenic/infalls or endogenic) of Ceres's surface rocky material (Marchi *et al.*, 2019).

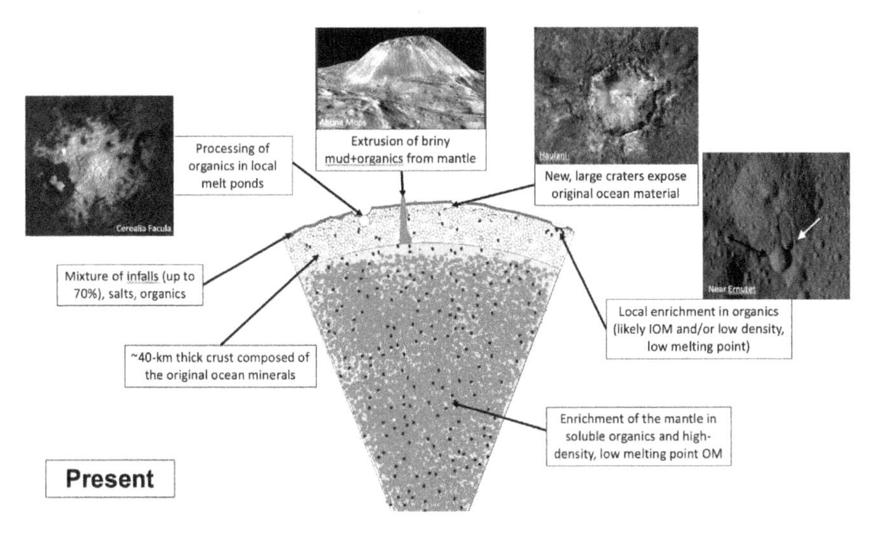

Figure 10.9: Connection between key surface landmarks and interior structure. Figure using PIA20355 https://photojournal.jpl.nasa.gov/catalog/PIA20355, PIA20915 https://photojournal.jpl.nasa.gov/catalog/PIA20915, PIA20358 https://photojournal.jpl.nasa.gov/catalog/PIA20358. Credit: NASA/JPL-Caltech/UCLA/MPS/DLR/IDA/PSI/LPI.

A future mission to Ceres should aim at searching for the presence of brines at present via geophysical techniques. Based on our current understanding of Ceres's current thermal state, low-latitude regions, especially in the region of Hanami Planum, are more likely to present liquid below the crust at least in the form of pockets, and potentially in the form of a vast sea below a ~50 km crust (Raymond *et al*., 2020).

10.3.2 *Possible Mission Architectures*

Different mission architectures have been proposed in the literature that could address key science objectives that in turn address the open science questions presented above. These concepts are all focused on accessing the surface and analyzing material in order to quantify chemical markers such as isotopes, minerals, and elements.

(*a*) *Landed Missions*

Different kinds of landers can be envisioned for a mission to Ceres. Per its low gravity, about 1/35th of Earth's, Ceres's surface is relatively easy to access at low fuel cost. Moreover, Ceres's gravity is several orders of magnitude greater than the gravity of most small bodies. Hence, surface operations are expected to be easier, with a large lander offering sufficient counterweight against the force involved in material sampling, for example. In these conditions, legged landers are viable platforms. Wheeled rovers are also a possibility, for example, the Axel Rover developed by Nesnas and colleagues (e.g., Nesnas and Burdick, 2013) (Fig. 10.8), although the low gravity implies traction may be more limited than on Mars. Instead, thruster-helped hopping has been considered in recent studies (Castillo-Rogez *et al.*, 2020). There are pros and cons to that mobility approach. Hopping on Ceres is relatively propellant intensive if long-range hops are considered (Castillo-Rogez and Brophy, 2020). However, they can allow accessing sites separated by a few tens of kilometers. Ceres's surface presents sufficient diversity (Figs. 10.7 and 10.9) such that this kind of hopper would be able to access different sites of high scientific value. In their study, Castillo-Rogez *et al.* (2020) considered a hopper that would explore one of the Vinalia Faculae and the ejecta (Homowo Regio) North East of Occator crater, the two being separated by about 40 km.

Several different payloads have been suggested for a future lander to Ceres, but they all involve the capability to determine the mineralogy, isotope, and elemental composition of Ceres's faculae. Relevant techniques include Raman spectroscopy or near- and mid-infrared spectroscopy for mineralogy, alpha particle and X-ray spectrometer (APXS) for elements, and mass spectrometry or tunable laser spectroscopy for isotopes (e.g., Castillo-Rogez and Brophy, 2020; Gassot *et al.*, 2021). In terms of geophysical probing of the interior, only magnetotelluric sounding has been demonstrated to probe a few tens of kilometers and detect deep brines (Grimm *et al.*, 2021). Ceres is not expected to host an active seismic source that could be used to probe the deep interior. That is, only micrometeorites may be the source of seismic activity, but it would be too weak to penetrate deep below Ceres's regolith. Lastly, a radar sounder, like the SHAllow RADar on the Mars Reconnaissance Orbiter or the Mars Advanced Radar for Subsurface and Ionosphere Sounding (MARSIS) on Mars Express, could potentially probe below the regolith. However, the large abundance of salts identified in the Dawn data would likely attenuate the radar signal and limit its overall penetration depth.

(*b*) *Sample Return Missions*

Recent studies have advocated for a sample return mission from Occator faculae (e.g., Burbine and Greenwood, 2020; Shi *et al.*, 2020; Castillo-Rogez and Brophy, 2020; Gassot *et al.*, 2021). Castillo-Rogez and Brophy

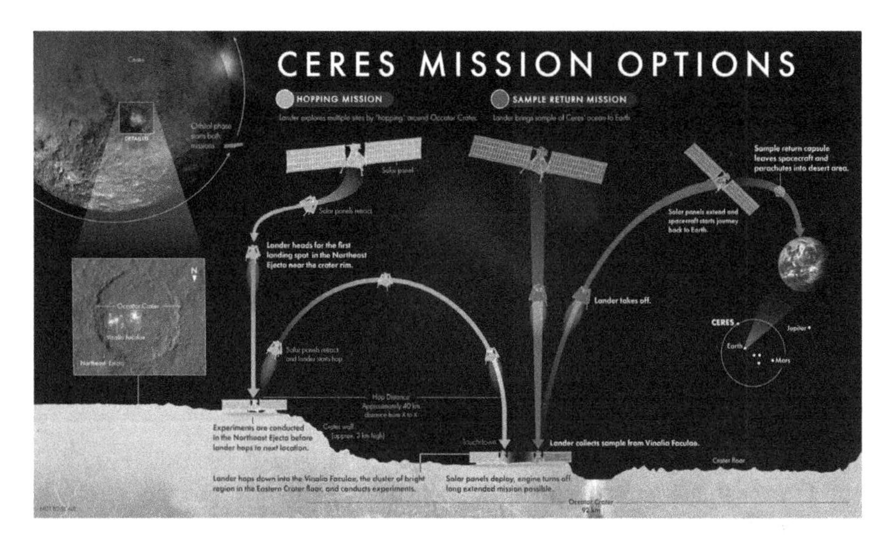

Figure 10.10: Two examples of mission scenarios for the future exploration of Ceres. Reprinted from Castillo-Rogez and Brophy (2020); Credit: Raoul Ranoa.

(2020) show that a simple but robust sample return mission would fall under the same cost cap as a hopper with a Raman spectrometer, APXS, and tunable laser spectrometer. Ceres's gravity is too high for sampling via a touch-and-go maneuver, like achieved by OSIRIS-REx, to be possible. Hence, sample collection has to be performed by a landed platform. The aforementioned studies looked at a variety of sampling techniques. Burbine and Greenwood (2020) and Gassot *et al.* (2021) assumed sampling via coring based on techniques developed for the Mars rovers. Castillo-Rogez and Brophy. (2020) considered sampling via use of a pneumatic vacuum system developed for NASA's Dragonfly and JAXA's Mars Moon eXplorer missions (Zacny *et al.*, 2020). These techniques currently under development would need to be adapted and tested for Ceres's conditions. Following material capture, the sample return capsule would be sealed to prevent contamination by Earth's atmospheric volatiles.

Representative examples for the two kinds of concepts described above are featured in Fig. 10.10 (from Castillo-Rogez and Brophy, 2020). Variants exist and concepts for the future exploration of Ceres are in their infancy at the time of writing.

It is realistic to expect that an in situ and/or sample return mission to Ceres could happen in the next decade for the following reasons. First, Castillo-Rogez and Brophy (2020) identified that most of the technologies required to access Ceres's surface and return material exist. Furthermore, the very strong interest demonstrated by scientists all over the world for follow-on exploration of Ceres suggests international collaboration could foster an ambitious mission. At the time of writing, the United States National Academy of Sciences, Engineering, and Medicine is considering a Planetary Mission Concept Study that features a hopping mission and a sample return mission (Castillo-Rogez and Brophy, 2020).

References

Ammannito, E., *et al.* (2016). Distribution of phyllosilicates on the surface of Ceres. *Science*, **353**, id.aaf4279.

Bahr, D. B., Hutton, E. W. H., Syvitski, J. P. M. and Pratson, L. F. (2001) Exponential approximations to compacted sediment porosity profiles. *Comput. and Geosci.*, **27**, 691–700.

Benzerara, K., *et al.* (2006). Nanoscale detection of organic signatures in carbonate microbialites. *PNAS*, **103**, 9440–9445.

Bland, P. A. and Travis, B. J. (2017). Giant convecting mud balls of the early solar system. *Sci. Adv.*, **3**, e1602514.

Bland, M. T., *et al.* (2019). Dome formation on Ceres by solid-state flow analogous to terrestrial salt tectonics. *Nat. Geosci.*, **12**, 797–801.

Bottke, W., Nesvorný, D., Grimm, R., *et al.* (2006). Iron meteorites as remnants of planetesimals formed in the terrestrial planet region. *Nature* **439**, 821–824.

Bouquet, A., Glein, C. R., Wyrick, D. and Waite, J. H. (2017). Alternative energy: Production of H_2 by radiolysis of water in the rocky cores of icy bodies. *Astrophys. J. Lett.*, **840**, L8 (7 pp).

Bowling, T. J., *et al.* (2019). Post-impact thermal structure and cooling timescales of Occator crater on asteroid 1 Ceres. *Icarus*, **320**, 110–118.

Bowling, T., Marchi, S., De Sanctis, M. C., Castillo-Rogez, J. C. and Raymond, C. A. (2020). An endogenic origin of Cerean organics. *EPSL*, **534**, id. 116069.

Buczkowski, D. L., *et al.* (2019). Tectonic analysis of fracturing associated with Occator crater. *Icarus*, **320**, 49–59.

Burbine, T. H. and Greenwood, R. C. (2020). Exploring the bimodal solar system via sample return from the main asteroid belt: The case for revisiting Ceres. *Space Sci. Rev.*, **216**, 59.

Castillo-Rogez, J. C. and McCord, T. B. (2010). Ceres' evolution and present state constrained by shape data. *Icarus*, **205**, 443–459.

Castillo-Rogez, J. C., Neveu, M., McSween, H. Y., Fu, R. R., Toplis, M. J. and Prettyman, T. H. (2018). Insights into Ceres' evolution from surface composition. *Meteorit. Planet. Sci.*, **53**, 1820–1843.

Castillo-Rogez, J. C., *et al.* (2019). Conditions for the long-term preservation of a deep brine reservoir in Ceres. *Geophys. Res. Lett.*, **46**, 1963–1972.

Castillo-Rogez, J. C. and Brophy, J. (2020). Ceres Planetary Mission Concept Study. https://science.nasa.gov/files/science-red/s3fs-public/atoms/files/Exploration%20of%20Ceres%20Habitability.pdf.

Castillo-Rogez, J. C., *et al.* (2020). Ceres: Astrobiological target and possible ocean world. *Astrobiology*, **20**, 269–291.

Castillo-Rogez, J. C., Scully, J., Neveu, M., Wyrick, D., Thangjam, G., Rivkin, A., Sori, M., Vinogradoff, V., Miller, K., Ermakov, A., Hughson, K., Quick, L., Nathues, A., De Sanctis, M. C. (2021). Science motivations for the future exploration of Ceres. Planetary Science and Astrobiology Decadal Survey 2023-2032 white paper e-id. 303; *Bulletin of the American Astronomical Society*, **53**, e-id. 303.

Chan, Q. H. S., *et al.* (2018). Organic matter in extraterrestrial water-bearing salt crystals, *Sci. Adv.*, **4**, eaao3521.

Chiang, C.-C., Kuan, Y.-J. and Chuang, Y.-L. (2019). ACA observations of Ceres' molecular exosphere. 16th Asia Oceania Geosciences Society Annual Meeting, Singapore, July 28–August 2, 2019, Abstract # PS16-A023.

Choblet, G., *et al.* (2017). Powering prolonged hydrothermal activity inside Enceladus. *Nat. Astron.*, **1**, 841–847.

Chuang, Y.-L., Kuan, Y.-J., Charnley, S., Chuang, M.-C. and Yeh, Y.-F. (2019). Submillimeter spectral observations of molecular exospheres of the Ceres icy world. 16th Asia Oceania Geosciences Society Annual Meeting, Singapore, July 28–August 2, 2019, Abstract # PS16-A025.

Combe, J.-P., *et al.* (2018). Exposed H_2O-rich areas detected on Ceres with the Dawn visible and infrared mapping spectrometer. *Icarus*, **318**, 22–41.

Davison, T. M., *et al.* (2015). Impact bombardment of Ceres. 46th Lunar and Planetary Science Conference, LPI contrib. no. 1832, p. 2116.

De Sanctis, M. C., *et al.* (2015). Ammoniated phyllosilicates with a likely outer Solar system origin on (1) Ceres. *Nature*, **528**, 241–244.

De Sanctis, M. C., *et al.* (2017). Localized aliphatic organic material on the surface of Ceres. *Science*, **355**, 719–722.

Ermakov, A. I., *et al.* (2019). Surface roughness and gravitational slope distributions of Vesta and Ceres. *J. Geophys. Res. Planet.*, **124**, 14–30.

Fu, R., *et al.* (2017). The interior structure of Ceres as revealed by surface topography. *Earth Planet. Sci. Lett.*, **476**, 153–164.

Gainey, S. R. and Ellwood Madden, E. R. (2012). Kinetics of methane clathrate formation and dissociation under Mars relevant conditions. *Icarus*, **218**, 513–524.

Gassot, O., *et al.* (2021). Calathus: A sample-return mission to Ceres. *Acta Astronaut.*, **181**, 112–129.

Grazier, K. R., Castillo-Rogez, J. C. and Sharp, P. W. (2014). Dynamical delivery of volatiles to the outer main belt. *Icarus*, **232**, 13–21.

Grimm, R., Castillo-Rogez, J. C., Raymond, C. A. and Poppe, A. (2021). Feasibility of characterizing subsurface brines on Ceres by electromagnetic sounding. *Icarus*, **362**, 114424.

Hendrix, A. R., *et al.* (2012). The lunar far-UV albedo: indicator of hydration and weathering. *J. Geophys. Res.*, **117**, E12001.

Hendrix, A. R., Vilas, F. and Li, J.-Y. (2016). Ceres: sulfur deposits and graphitized carbon. *Geophys. Res. Lett.*, **43**, 8920–8927.

Hendrix, A. R., *et al.* (2019). The NASA roadmap to ocean worlds. *Astrobiology*, **19**, 1–27.

Hesse, M. A. and Castillo-Rogez, J. C. (2019). Thermal evolution of the impact-induced cryomagma chamber beneath Occator crater on Ceres. *Geophys. Res. Lett.*, **46**, 1213–1221.

Hiesinger, H., *et al.* (2016). Cratering on Ceres: Implications for its crust and evolution. *Science,* **353**, aaf4758.

Kamata, S., *et al.* (2019). Pluto's ocean is capped and insulated by gas hydrates. *Nat. Geosci.*, **12**, 407–410.

Kaplan, H. H., Milliken, R. E. and Alexander, C. M. O'D. (2018). New constraints on the abundance and composition of organic matter on Ceres. *Geophys. Res. Lett.*, **45**, 5274–5282.

Kelley, D. S., *et al.* (2005). A serpentinite-hosted ecosystem: The Lost City hydrothermal field, *Science,* **307**, 1428–1434.

Kruijer, T. S., Burkhardt, C. and Kleine, T. (2017). Age of Jupiter inferred from the distinct genetics and formation times of meteorites. *PNAS*, **114**, 6712–6716.

Küppers, M., *et al.* (2014). Localized sources of water vapour on the dwarf planet (1) Ceres. *Nature,* **505**, 525–527.

Landis, M., *et al.* (2017). Sublimating water ice can be a source of Ceres' transient atmosphere. *J. Geophys. Res.*, **122**, 1984–1995.

Landis, M. E., *et al.* (2019). Water Vapor Contribution to Ceres' Exosphere from Observed Surface Ice and Postulated Ice-Exposing Impacts. *J. Geophys. Res.*, **124**, 61–75.

Li, J.-Y., *et al.* (2020). Disk-integrated thermal properties of Ceres measured at millimeter wavelengths. *Astron. J.*, **159**, 215 (9 pp).

Mao, X. and McKinnon, W. B. (2020). Spin evolution of Ceres and Vesta due to impacts. *Meteorit. Planet. Sci.*, **55**, 2493–2518.

Marchi, S., *et al.* (2016). The missing large impact craten Ceres. *Nat. Comm.*, **7**, 12257.

Marchi, S., *et al.* (2019). An aqueously altered carbon-rich Ceres. *Nat. Astron.*, **3**, 140–145.

McKinnon, W. B. (2008). Could Ceres be a Refugee from the Kuiper Belt? Asteroids, Comets, Meteors 2008 Proceedings, 1405.

Milam, S. N., Stansberry, J. A., Sonneborn, G. and Thomas, C. (2016). The James Webb Space Telescope's plan for operations and instrument capabilities for observations in the solar system. *Publ. Astron. Soc. Pac.*, **128**, 018001.

Mousis, O. and Alibert, Y. (2005). On the composition of ices incorporated in Ceres. *Mon. Not. R. Astron. Soc.*, **358**, 188–192.

Nathues A., *et al.* (2019). Unique Light Scattering at Occator's Faculae on (1) Ceres. *Astron. J.*, **158**, 85.

Nesnas, I. A. and Burdick, J. W. (2013). Axel Rovers for Exploring Extreme Planetary Terrains, Proc. IEEE International Conference on Robotics and Automation, Workshop on Space Robotics, May 2013. https://pdfs.semanticscholar.org/fa12/2420cc4cefae9e130201ed22fdeb329609e4.pdf.

Neveu, M. and Desch, S. J. (2015). Geochemistry, thermal evolution, and cryovolcanism on Ceres with a muddy ice mantle. *Geophys. Res. Lett.*, **42**, 10,197–10,206.

Parks, M., *et al.* (2019). Using ALMA spectra to investigate a potential transient exosphere of Ceres. 50th Lunar and Planetary Science Conference, LPI Contrib. 2132, id.2974.

Pieters, C. M., *et al.* (2018). Geologic constraints on the origin of red organic-rich material on Ceres. *Meteorit. Planet. Sci.*, **53**, 1983–1998.

Prieto-Ballesteros, O. and Kargel, J. S. (2005). Thermal state and complex geology of a heterogeneous salty crust of Jupiter's satellite, Europa. *Icarus*, **173**, 212–221.

Quick, L., *et al.* (2019). A possible brine reservoir below Occator Crater: Thermal and compositional evolution and formation of the Cerealia Dome and Vinalia Faculae. *Ceres Occator Special Issue of Icarus*, **320**, 119–135.

Raponi, A., *et al.* (2018). Variations in the amount of water ice on Ceres' surface suggest a seasonal water cycle. *Sci. Adv.*, **4**, eaao3757.

Raymond, S. N. and Izidoro, A. (2017). Origin of water in the inner Solar System: Planetesimals scattered inward during Jupiter and Saturn's rapid gas accretion. *Icarus*, **297**, 134–148.

Raymond, C. A., *et al.* (2020). Impact-driven mobilization of deep crustal brines on dwarf planet Ceres. *Nat. Astron.*, **4**, 741–747.

Rivkin, A. S., *et al.* (2016). Asteroids and the James Webb Space Telescope. *Publ. Astron. Soc. Pac.*, **128**, 018003.

Rivkin, A. S., *et al.* (2019). Infrared spectroscopy of large, low-albedo asteroids: Are Ceres and Themis archetypes or outliers? *J. Geophys. Res.*, **124**, 1393–1409.

Rousselot, P., *et al.* (2011). A search for water vaporization on Ceres. *Astron. J.*, **142**, 125.

Rousselot, P., *et al.* (2019). Search for water outgassing of (1) Ceres near perihelion. *Astron. Astrophys.*, **628**, 22.

Rubin, A. E., Zolensky, M. E. and Bodnar, R. J. (2002). The halite-bearing Zag and Monahans (1998) meteorite breccias: Shock metamorphism, thermal metamorphism and aqueous alteration on the H-chondrite parent body. *Meteorit. Planet. Sci.,* **37**, 125–141.

Ruesch, O., *et al.* (2016). Cryovolcanism on Ceres. Science, **353**, aaf4286.

Ruesch, O., *et al.* (2019a). Slurry extrusion on Ceres from a convective mud-bearing mantle. *Nat. Geosci.*, **12**, 505–509.

Ruesch, O., *et al.* (2019b). Bright carbonate surfaces on Ceres as remnants of salt-rich water fountains. *Icarus*, **320**, 39–48.

Schenk, P., *et al.* (2020). Impact heat driven volatile redistribution at Occator crater on Ceres as a comparative planetary process. *Nat. Commun.*, **11**, 3679.

Schenk, P., *et al.* (2021). Compositional control on impact crater formation on mid-sized planetary bodies: Dawn at Ceres and Vesta, Cassini at Saturn. *Icarus.*, **359**, 114343.

Schmidt, B. E., *et al.* (2020). Post-impact cryo-hydrologic formation of small mounds and hills on Ceres's Occator crater. *Nat. Geosci.*, **13**, 605–610.

Scully, J. E. C., *et al.* (2019). Synthesis of the special issue: The formation and evolution of Ceres' Occator crater. *Icarus,* **320**, 213–225.

Scully, J. E. C., *et al.* (2020). The varied sources of faculae-forming brines in Ceres' Occator crater emplaced via hydrothermal brine effusion. *Nat. Comm.*, **11**, 3680.

Scully, J. E. C., Baker, S., Castillo-Rogez, J. C. and Buczkowski, D. (2021). The In-Situ exploration of a relict ocean world: An assessment of potential landing and sampling sites for a future mission to the surface of Ceres. *Planet. Sci. J.*, **2**, 94.

Shi, X., *et al.* (2020). GAUSS — Genesis of asteroids and evolution of the solar system. Experimental astronomy, ESA Voyage 2050 White Paper, arXiv:1908.07731.

Sori, M. M., *et al.* (2017). The vanishing cryovolcanoes of Ceres. *Geophys. Res. Lett.*, **44**, 1243–1250.

Tosi, F., *et al.* (2018). Mineralogy and temperature of crater Haulani on Ceres. *Meteorit. Planet. Sci.*, **53**, 1902–1924.

Travis, B. J., Bland, P. A., Feldman, W. C. and Sykes, M. V. (2018). Hydrothermal dynamics in a CM-based model of Ceres. *Meteorit. Planet. Sci.*, **53**, 2008–2032.

Turner, N. J., Choukroun, M., Castillo-Rogez, J. and Bryden, G. (2012). A Hot Gap around Jupiter's Orbit in the Solar Nebula. *Astrophys. J.*, **748**, 92.

Villarreal, M. N., *et al.* (2017). The dependence of the Cerean exosphere on solar energetic particle events. *Astrophys. J. Lett.*, **838**, L8.

Vernazza, P., *et al.* (2017). Different origins or different evolutions? Decoding the spectral diversity among C-type asteroids. *Astron. J.*, **153**, 72 (10 pp).

Warren, P. H. (2011). Stable-isotopic anomalies and the accretionary assemblage of the Earth and Mars: A subordinate role for carbonaceous chondrites, *Earth Planet. Sci. Lett.*, **311**, 93–100.

Young, E. D., Zhang, K. K. and Schuber, G. (2003). Conditions for water pore convection within carbonaceous chondrite parent bodies—implications for planetesimal size and heat production, *Earth Planet. Sci. Lett.*, **213**, 249–259.

Zacny K., *et al.* (2020). Pneumatic Sampler (P-Sampler) for the Martian Moons eXploration (MMX) Mission, IEEE Aerospace Conference, 7–14 March 2020, Big Sky, MT.

Zambon, F., *et al.* (2017). Spectral analysis of Ahuna Mons from Dawn mission's visible-infrared spectrometer. *Geophys. Res. Lett.*, **44**, 97–104.

Zolensky, M. E., *et al.* (2015). The mineralogy of Ceres (Or something an awful lot like it). 78th Annual Meeting of the Meteoritical Society, LPI contrib. no. 1856, p. 5270.

Zolotov, M. Yu. (2020). The composition and structure of Ceres' interior. *Icarus*, **335**, 113404.

Index

O

P

R

S

T

CPSIA information can be obtained
at www.ICGtesting.com
Printed in the USA
JSHW020226070222
22607JS00001BB/5